SCIENCE CONNECTIONS

Author Team

Ralph M. Feather, Jr.
Earth Science Instructor
Derry Area School District
Derry, PA

Edward P. Ortleb
Science Lead Supervisor
St. Louis Public Schools
St. Louis, MO

Stephen C. Blume
Elementary Science Curriculum Specialist
Tammany Parish Schools
Slidell, LA

Gordon J. Aubrecht, II, Ph.D.
Physics Professor
The Ohio State University at Marion
Columbus, OH

Anne F. Barefoot
Physics and Chemistry Instructor
Whiteville High School
Whiteville, NC

MERRILL
PUBLISHING COMPANY
Columbus, Ohio

A Merrill Science Program

Science Connections (Blue): *Student Edition*
Science Connections (Blue): *Teacher Edition*
Science Connections (Blue): *Teacher Resource Package*
Science Connections (Blue): *Chapter Review Software*
Science Connections (Blue): *Test Generator Software*
Safety Card Package
Science Fair Handbook
Science Connections (Red) Program

Reading Consultant
Barbara S. Pettegrew, Ph.D.
Director of Reading/Study Center
Assistant Professor of Education
Otterbein College
Westerville, OH

Content Consultants
Robert T. Brown, M.D.
Director of Adolescent Medicine
Children's Hospital
Columbus, OH

Lucy Daniel
Biology Instructor
Rutherford County Schools
Spindale, NC

Anne E. Fry, Ph.D.
Department of Biological Sciences
Ohio Wesleyan University
Delaware, OH

J. Murray Mitchell, Jr., Ph.D.
Consulting Climatologist
National Oceanic and Atmospheric
   Administration, Retired
McLean, VA

George Moore, Ph.D.
Department of Geology
The Ohio State University
Columbus, OH

Robert Neff
Physics Instructor
Suffern High School
Suffern, NY

G.H. Newsom, Ph.D.
Department of Astronomy
The Ohio State University
Columbus, OH

John Norman, Ph.D.
Department of Education
Wayne State University
Detroit, MI

Susan Palmer
Department of Chemistry
Otterbein College
Westerville, OH

Susan E. Verhoek, Ph.D.
Department of Biology
Lebanon Valley College
Annville, PA

Steven Williams, Ph.D.
Department of Plant Biology
Cornell University
Ithaca, NY

Jay Yett
Department of Geology
Orange Coast College
Costa Mesa, CA

Reviewers
Sr. Johanna Danko
Science Instructor
Most Blessed Sacrament School
Franklin Lakes, NJ

John R. Grube
Science Coordinator
East Side Union High School District
San Jose, CA

Chris Hasegawa
College of Education
University of Oregon
Eugene, OR

Series Editor: Joyce T. Spangler; *Project Editor:* Angela E. Priestley, Ph.D.; *Editors:* Jane L. Parker, Ellen P. Geisler, Greg Shannon, Karen S. Brumley, Shannon Moore, Mary Dylewski; *Book Designer:* Larry W. Collins; *Project Artist:* Katie Bookwalter White; *Artist:* Joan Shaull; *Illustrators:* Lisy Boren, David Dennis, Peg Dougherty, Nancy Heim, Intergraphics, Publishers Graphics, Bill Robison, Don Robison, Jim Shough, Dennis Tasa; *Photo Editor:* Barbara Buchholz; *Production Editors:* Helen C. Mischka, Jillian Yerkey; *Editorial Assistant:* Patricia A. Evans

Cover Photograph: Float Plane: Earth Scenes/Leonard Lee Rue, III; Swan: Nancy M. Hamilton/Photo Researchers

ISBN 0-675-06618-2

Published by
MERRILL PUBLISHING COMPANY
Columbus, OH 43216

3 4 5 6 7 8 9 10 11 12 13 14 15 A—HAW 00 99 98 97 96 95 94 93 92 91

TABLE OF CONTENTS

UNIT 2
FORCES AT WORK 90

CHAPTER 5

CHAPTER 6

CHAPTER 7

CHAPTER 8

UNIT 4
EARTH'S AIR AND WATER **254**

APPENDICES

TEXT ACTIVITIES

Activities

1–1	Lab Safety Equipment
1–2	Problem Solving
2–1	Measuring Volume
2–2	Finding Mass
3–1	Making Models of Atoms
3–2	Separating a Mixture
4–1	Changes in State
4–2	Rate of Reactions
5–1	Balancing Forces
5–2	Energy Transfer
6–1	Measuring Power
6–2	Friction on Surfaces
7–1	Measuring Speed
7–2	Constructing a Rocket
8–1	Measuring Density
8–2	Bernoulli's Principle
9–1	The Moving Earth
9–2	Observing Light
10–1	Identifying Minerals
10–2	Classifying Rocks
11–1	Soil Erosion
11–2	A "Perc" Test
12–1	Measuring Runoff
12–2	Observing Sediments
13–1	Properties of Air
13–2	Thermal Energy Transfer
14–1	"Cloud" Formation
14–2	Recording Weather Data
15–1	Density Currents
15–2	Observing Wave Height

16–1	Mapping Ocean Floors
16–2	Observing Currents
17–1	Behavior of Mealworms
17–2	Osmosis in Eggs
18–1	Classifying Protists
18–2	Growing Yeast
19–1	Gravitropism
19–2	Feeding Plants
20–1	Earthworm Dissection
20–2	Frog Metamorphosis
21–1	Observing a Skeleton
21–2	Dissecting Muscles
22–1	Skin Sensitivity
22–2	Effects of Caffeine
23–1	Pulse and Breath Rates
23–2	Skin Medications
24–1	Fat and Starch
24–2	Vitamin C Content

Skill Builders

Chapter 1:	Observing and Inferring
Chapter 2:	Measuring in SI
Chapter 3:	Classifying
Chapter 4:	Using Tables
Chapter 5:	Classifying
Chapter 6:	Using Tables
Chapter 7:	Outlining
Chapter 8:	Observing and Inferring
Chapter 9:	Observing and Inferring
Chapter 10:	Graphing

UNIT 1

Matter: Its Properties

When the baker makes bread, he mixes exact volumes of ingredients. Bread dough is a mixture of different compounds that is heated in a hot oven. This changes the physical and chemical properties of the compounds. How are chemical reactions in a lab similar to those involved in the bread making process? How does bread dough differ from bread?

What Is Science?

Career: Coroner

Joe, Fred, and Steve were at Randy Evans's house playing basketball. Joe jumped up to shoot a basket, came down on the side of his foot, fell, and scraped his leg badly. The boys helped Joe into the house, and Randy called upstairs to his dad. Mr. Evans was a coroner. Randy explained that because his dad was also a medical doctor he would be able to take care of Joe's leg.

While Dr. Evans cleaned Joe's leg and bandaged it, he explained that as a coroner he doesn't have a chance to do much "doctoring." Most of his time is spent as a medical detective. He told the boys that a coroner is a specialist who studies the tissues and fluids of persons who have died. Using this information, he can find out how death occurred. It may be that death was not from natural causes. Sometimes a coroner has to identify a person who has died. This is done by studying dental work and any signs of past injuries. Dr. Evans explained that tiny bits of fiber, metal, or dirt found on a body can be evidence of a person's activities, just as the bits of tar and stone in Joe's leg showed that he had fallen on the driveway.

A coroner is a scientist who observes, gathers evidence, and uses many methods to solve problems. In this chapter you will learn more about scientific methods and problem solving.

F.Y.I. National Health Information Center, PO Box 1133 Washington, DC 20013-1133

GOALS

You will study . . .

1. some characteristics of science.
2. methods of science.
3. the importance of safety in science.

How are science topics grouped?

What is earth science?

F.Y.I. . . . Science is nothing more than a refinement of everyday thinking.—Albert Einstein

1:1 The Nature of Science

What will you do when you are older? Would you like to be a medical doctor like the coroner on page 5? Or do you want to be a dietitian, an auto mechanic, or a hair stylist? It may surprise you to find out that all of these jobs require a knowledge of science. In fact, no matter what occupation you choose, it will be related to science. How is that possible? Doesn't science deal with plants and animals and rocks? Doesn't all scientific work take place in labs with all sorts of special equipment? In this textbook, you will learn that science may use some special techniques, but first it is about you and everything you experience. Science explains how you breathe air and what happens when you push down on a bike pedal. Science is also a method that helps you find out what you are allergic to or how air is moved through the slide trombone you play in the band. What is science then? **Science** is the knowledge of all the facts that are known about the world and the methods or processes used to learn or explain these facts.

The science topics in this textbook are grouped into three main areas: earth science, life science, and physical science. Table 1–1 lists some topics in each of these three groups and some related careers.

You are probably familiar with some activities in each of these sciences. Earth science is the study of Earth and its place in space. If you have collected

FIGURE 1–1. Scientific principles are part of everyday activity.

Table 1–1

Major Topics in Science			
Science	**Topic**	**The study of**	**Related careers**
Earth	Geology	how Earth forms and changes	astronaut weather person fisherman pilot
	Astronomy	stars, planets, and other objects in space	
	Meteorology	weather and its causes	
Life	Botany	plants	veterinarian florist pharmacist food technician
	Zoology	animals	
	Taxonomy	classifying organisms	
Physical	Chemistry	the structure and properties of matter	hair stylist chemist astronaut auto mechanic
	Physics	how matter and energy work together	

rocks or tried to name stars at night, then you have an idea of some of the topics studied in earth science. Life science is the study of living or once living things called organisms and how they relate to each other and to everything around them. Knowing why a balanced diet is important means you are aware of the needs of living organisms. Physical science is the study of matter, forces, and energy. Each time you flip a light switch, pour milk into a glass, or wash your hands, you are dealing with matter, forces, and energy.

Are earth, life, and physical science connected in some way? Yes, they are. Your life and health are affected by the quality of Earth's atmosphere. Your body uses food as energy. In your body, this energy acts according to the laws of physical science. You may study each topic separately, but they are all related.

Scientists are people who study the relationships among these topics. Are scientists different from other people? Not really. But, they have learned to look at problems differently. Many people look at problems as being difficult to figure out. Scientists have learned to use special problem-solving skills. Because of this, they see problems as opportunities. It may be an opportunity to build a safer skateboard or an opportunity to find the cure for a deadly disease. Will you be a scientist? You can learn to see opportunities in problems and develop skills to solve them.

What is life science?

FIGURE 1–2. Physical science and life science are closely related in swimming.

FIGURE 1–3. Observation is an important step in learning.

1:2 Scientific Methods

Scientists use planned, orderly methods to learn new information. How do you learn new things? Have you ever watched a baby learn something new? Babies show great skill as investigators. A baby may take a small piece of cereal and push it around, shake it, turn it over and over, and maybe even bite it. The baby is learning by practicing an important skill called observation. **Observation** is the act of gathering information using the senses. Later in life, people ask questions because they want to know how something works, what it is made of, or why it works the way it does. Some of these people become scientists. A newspaper reporter once asked a famous scientist whether he knew all the answers. "No," he replied, "but I do know how to ask good questions." Observing and asking questions are the first steps in the process of scientific investigation.

In addition to observing and questioning, scientists often use models to learn how the world works. A **model** is anything that helps you understand how a

How do scientists learn new information?

FIGURE 1–4. Some models are produced on computers (a). Others are built for testing (b).

a

b

real object looks or works. There are many kinds of models. Before a car is built, an engineer has an idea or a mental model of what the car might be like. A designer will then draw a picture of the idea and build a physical model of the car. Finally, a computer model may be used to show details of the inside of the new car.

A full size model may be built to show how the real car will work. The engineer may ask if the car will work safely at different speeds. Then a possible answer or hypothesis will be given for this question. A **hypothesis** is a statement that suggests or predicts an answer to a question. The hypothesis then must be tested in an experiment. An **experiment** is a series of carefully planned steps that tests a hypothesis.

An experiment has several important steps. Each is a scientific method. These steps are listed below.

State a problem	Make an observation and ask a question about what you see. Will this car ride safely at 40 kilometers per hour?
Form a hypothesis	Suggest an answer to your problem question. Your hypothesis is that this car will ride safely at 40 km/h.
Design an experiment	How will you test the hypothesis? A **procedure** describes how an experiment will be carried out.
	What special equipment will you need for your procedure? You may need a full-size working model, a track, and equipment to time the test.
Record data	What information will your experiment give you? **Data** are the recorded facts or measurements from an experiment. You describe what you observe in a sentence or take measurements and list the data in a table.
Draw a conclusion	Think about what the data means and draw a conclusion. A **conclusion** is a logical answer to your problem question based on data. When you draw a conclusion, you analyze or think about the data to see what they mean. Using your data as evidence, can you say that your hypothesis is supported or not?

How do you draw a conclusion?

PROBLEM SOLVING

Hector's Experiment

Early in the summer, Hector had a small garden with two rows of tomato plants. As the plants grew, he tied the main stem of each plant to a stake with strips of old cloth. Hector watered the rows of tomatoes every day. He spread hay between the rows to prevent water loss and to cut down on the growth of weeds. Hector also cut off the side branches of the plants when they grew too long. But, Hector was disappointed. His plants just did not produce many tomatoes.

Hector decided to use fertilizer on one row of the tomato plants. After a week he noticed more new tomatoes on the plants in the row that had been fertilized. What was Hector's original problem? What hypothesis did he form that lead him to use fertilizer on one row of plants? What scientific methods did Hector use to test his hypothesis?

Once an experiment is finished and you have drawn a conclusion, you can compare the new information you have collected to your hypothesis. If the hypothesis is supported, then you can accept it. Yes, this car design rides safely at 40 km/h. But how safe would you feel traveling in a car that had undergone only one safety test? Even if an experiment shows that a hypothesis works the first time, the same hypothesis must be tested again by other scientists. If all tests show the car to be safe, then you can say that this car is safe for passengers.

A hypothesis that is found to work over and over might become the basis for a statement called a theory. A **theory** is an explanation of how nature works. A theory may be a hypothesis that has been tested many times with the same results. A **law** is a statement that describes nature. Laws are based on repeated observations. One law of motion states that objects tend to keep doing what they are already doing until something makes them change. What happens if new evidence shows that something about your law or theory is wrong? Then you would have to look carefully at the new evidence and be willing to change the statement.

What is a theory?

1:3 Using Scientific Methods

Amina had learned about scientific methods at school. However, she had never had to use them. When the yearly science fair was announced, the teacher explained that all projects were to use scientific methods that had been discussed in class. Amina first had to decide on a problem to investigate. She had observed that, when it was very dry during the summer, some plants around her home stopped flowering. She also observed that her father's geranium plants bloomed well even when there had been no rain. She asked the question, "How does water affect the number of flowers a geranium will produce?" Then she suggested a possible answer or hypothesis. Her hypothesis stated that geranium plants produce more flowers if they are watered only once a week.

Amina designed her experiment. She planted 12 geranium plants, each in the same-sized pot. None of the plants had flowers. Then she made three groups of four plants. She labeled these Groups A, B, and C. The plants were placed on the same table in the classroom. All plants were given the same amount of water each time they were watered. Each plant in Group A was watered every day for six weeks. Plants in Group B were watered only twice a week. Plants in Group C were watered only once a week. Group A was the control group for the experiment. A **control** is a standard for comparison. Amina would compare the result of Group A with the results from Groups B and C.

F.Y.I. Galileo pioneered the steps of the scientific method.

What is a control?

FIGURE 1–5. An experiment is designed to test a hypothesis.

Table 1-2

Experimental data		
Group	When watered	Flower total
A	every day	4
B	twice a week	7
C	once a week	13

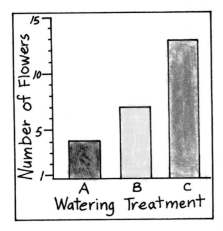

FIGURE 1-6. Bar graphs help interpret data.

Table 1-2 shows the data Amina collected. She recorded the total number of flowers each group produced. At the end of six weeks, she analyzed her data. Figure 1-6 shows the bar graph Amina made from her data. From this she concluded that geranium plants produce more flowers when watered only once a week. She compared her conclusion with her hypothesis. Her hypothesis was supported.

Amina's project had all the steps needed for an experiment. It had a problem, a hypothesis, materials, and a procedure. She recorded data and drew a conclusion from the data. Amina's experiment also had constants and variables. A **constant** is a factor that does not change during an experiment. The constants in the experiment were the type of plant, the pot size, and the amount of water given to each plant each time they were watered. A **variable** is anything that changes in an experiment. An independent variable is one that the experimenter changes. In Amina's experiment, the number of times a week the geranium plants were watered was the independent variable. A dependent variable is the change that occurs as a result of the independent variable. The number of flowers each group of plants produced was the dependent variable. The number of flowers produced depended on how often the plants were watered. When her friend Greg performed the same experiment and had similar results, Amina knew that she could be more certain that her hypothesis was supported. An experiment must be repeated with similar results for a hypothesis to be accepted.

SKILL BUILDER

Observing and Inferring

When Amina first decided on the topic for her science fair project, she made an observation in her father's garden. She also interpreted this observation. Answer the questions below. If you need help, refer to Observing and Inferring on page 535.

Questions

1. What was Amina's observation in the garden?
2. What was the inference she made?

FIGURE 1–7. Correct equipment and clean up procedures make lab work safer.

1:4 Safety in Science Class

When you were young, you were taught to stop, look, and listen when crossing streets. People were interested in your safety. This is still true. In this textbook, you will have a chance to perform science activities. You will use science tools and methods. Knowing how to prevent accidents in the science classroom and in the lab is important. Safety starts with you.

Think about the safety of yourself and your classmates at all times. Most injuries in the science lab are due to heated objects, splatters, spills, and broken glass. The safety rules that follow will keep you and others from being hurt.

What is the cause of most injuries in the science lab?

1. Always obtain your teacher's permission before starting an activity.
2. Use the safety equipment provided for you. Goggles and an apron should be worn when an activity calls for heating, using chemicals, or breaking up rocks.
3. When heating materials in test tubes, always slant the tubes away from yourself and others.
4. Never eat or drink in the lab, and never use lab glassware as food or drink containers. Never inhale chemicals. Do not taste any substance or draw any material into a tube with your mouth.
5. Read the activity all the way through before you begin to work. If you have questions, ask your teacher. Be sure you understand any safety symbols or caution statements shown before you begin.

FIGURE 1–8. A fire extinguisher should be within easy reach.

What Is Science All About?   13

A **safety symbol** in this textbook is a sign that alerts you to a particular danger within an activity. These symbols are explained in Table 1–3. Be sure you understand each symbol before you begin.

Table 1–3

Safety Symbols

DISPOSAL ALERT
This symbol appears when care must be taken to dispose of materials properly.

ANIMAL SAFETY
This symbol appears whenever live animals are studied and the safety of the animals and the students must be ensured.

BIOLOGICAL SAFETY
This symbol appears when there is danger involving bacteria, fungi, or protists.

RADIOACTIVE SAFETY
This symbol appears when radioactive materials are used.

OPEN FLAME ALERT
This symbol appears when use of an open flame could cause a fire or an explosion.

CLOTHING PROTECTION SAFETY
This symbol appears when substances used could stain or burn clothing.

THERMAL SAFETY
This symbol appears as a reminder to use caution when handling hot objects.

FIRE SAFETY
This symbol appears when care should be taken around open flames.

SHARP OBJECT SAFETY
This symbol appears when a danger of cuts or punctures caused by the use of sharp objects exists.

EXPLOSION SAFETY
This symbol appears when the misuse of chemicals could cause an explosion.

FUME SAFETY
This symbol appears when chemicals or chemical reactions could cause dangerous fumes.

EYE SAFETY
This symbol appears when a danger to the eyes exists. Safety goggles should be worn when this symbol appears.

ELECTRICAL SAFETY
This symbol appears when care should be taken when using electrical equipment.

POISON SAFETY
This symbol appears when poisonous substances are used.

PLANT SAFETY
This symbol appears when poisonous plants or plants with thorns are handled.

CHEMICAL SAFETY
This symbol appears when chemicals used can cause burns or are poisonous if absorbed through the skin.

6. If you spill any chemical on yourself or the counter, wash it off immediately with water. Report any spill to your teacher and your lab partner.

7. Know the location and proper use of the fire extinguisher, eyewash station, safety shower, fire blanket, first aid kit, and fire alarm. This equipment is to be used for emergencies only.

8. Keep all materials away from open flames. Roll up sleeves. Keep long hair and loose clothing tied back. Do not comb hair in the lab or use aerosol sprays. Hairspray contains alcohol and other flammable ingredients. Remove scarves and jewelry.

9. If a fire should break out in the classroom, or if your clothing should catch fire, smother it with the fire blanket or get under a safety shower. A fire extinguisher should be used on objects, not people. NEVER RUN.

10. Report ANY accident or injury, no matter how small, to your teacher. If first aid is needed, it should be given by your teacher or school nurse. First aid is the emergency care given to an ill or injured person until medical help is available.

Cleaning up after an activity is also very important. Follow these procedures as you clean up your work area.

1. Turn off the water and gas. Turn off electrical devices before unplugging them.

2. Return all materials to their proper places.

3. Dispose of chemicals and other materials as directed by your teacher. Place broken glass and solid substances in the proper containers. Never discard materials in the sink.

4. Clean and dry your work area thoroughly.

5. Wash your hands thoroughly with soap and water after working in the lab.

FIGURE 1–9. A fire blanket is used to extinguish a fire on a person.

What accidents or injuries should be reported to the teacher?

REVIEW

1. What is science?
2. What are the three main science topics discussed in this textbook?
3. What are the steps of an experiment?
4. How is a theory related to a hypothesis?
5. What are three safety rules used in the lab?

Problem: How can you use the classroom lab safely?

Materials

graph paper   white paper
metric ruler   colored pencils
Section 1:4 of your textbook

Procedure

1. Use graph paper to draw a diagram of the classroom lab. Include all furniture, windows, and doors.
2. Use a red pencil to label the location of safety equipment.
3. Mark the location of *your* lab station.
4. Use a green pencil to draw exit routes.
5. Make a data table like the one shown.
6. Write a purpose for each piece of safety equipment listed in the table.

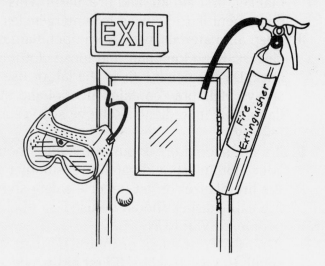

Questions and Conclusions

1. How many doors are there in the lab?
2. Where is the fire extinguisher located?
3. When are safety goggles worn?
4. What should you do if you spill a chemical on yourself?

5. What would you do if your clothing were to catch fire?
6. What should you do if you see a student injured?
7. How do you know what cautions there are for an activity?
8. What should you do with loose clothing or long hair when using a heat source or working with chemicals?
9. How can you use the classroom lab safely?

Data and Observations

Safety Equipment	Purpose
Goggles	
Apron	
First aid kit	
Fire blanket	
Fire extinguisher	
Eyewash station	
Running water	

1:5 What Is a Problem?

How good are you at solving puzzles? You need a good vocabulary to solve a crossword puzzle. Getting a puzzle cube to come out right may require time and other kinds of skills. You might have to picture how the pieces fit together and try different methods before one will work. Each method that you use to solve a problem is called a problem-solving skill. You have seen that there are methods or skills in science that are used to solve problems. The scientific methods used in Section 1:3 are skills that are helpful because they have been shown to work well.

All problems involve a certain amount of uncertainty and newness. It is perfectly normal for you to face a problem and not know how to begin to solve it. You've had homework assignments that made you stop and think. If you have all the information you need to solve something, it is an **exercise.** Problems are different from exercises. A **problem** is a situation that needs thought, planning, and skills to solve. There are many approaches to solving both science and non-science problems. You use many of these every day to conquer all kinds of problems. No one method is ever going to work well all the time.

GOALS
You will study . . .
1. problem-solving skills.
2. the role of technology in scientific-problem solving.
3. what risks are.

What is a problem-solving skill?

What skills have you studied that are helpful in solving problems?

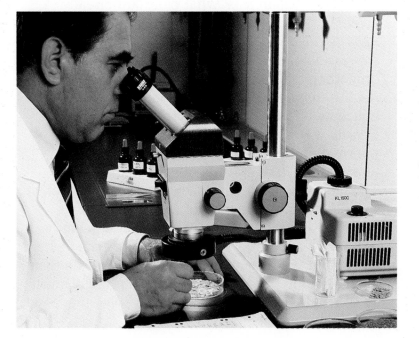

F.Y.I. The important thing in science is not to find new facts but to discover new ways of thinking about them.—W.L. Bragg

FIGURE 1–10. Scientists make use of skills and instruments to solve problems.

FIGURE 1–11. Different problems require practicing different skills.

1:6 Problem-Solving Skills

When you have a problem, your goal is to solve it. Since each problem you face is different, the skills you use to solve each one will differ. Some problem-solving skills you already use are given below.

Guess and check. Think of a logical solution and try it out. Guess again if the first one does not work.

Find a pattern. Is this problem similar to one you have already worked out?

Draw a picture. Models, tables, graphs, or drawings make information easier to understand.

Eliminate possibilities. Thousands of materials were tested to find a filament for the light bulb before one finally worked.

Identify what is wanted, needed, and given. What does the problem ask? What clues are already given?

Rewrite a word problem as a mathematical expression. Some word problems will become clear only when expressed in numbers.

Read something aloud or act it out. Difficult concepts often become clear when read aloud.

Consult a resource. Libraries are full of useful information that may save you time. Someone already may have solved your problem.

The most important approach to solving a problem in science or any other part of life is to *begin*. Homework doesn't get finished unless you begin. Diseases are not cured and stronger types of steel are not invented unless someone begins to work on them. The information needed to solve these problems will only come about if someone wants to solve them and makes use of problem-solving skills.

What is the most important approach in solving a problem?

Problem: How do you use scientific problem solving?

Materials

clear 1-L soft drink bottle
large balloon
deep heavy sauce pans (2)
goggles

rubber band
hot water
ice water
scissors

Procedure

1. Cut a piece of the balloon large enough to stretch across the mouth of the bottle and secure it firmly with a rubber band.
2. **CAUTION:** *Put on goggles. Always handle heated materials with care.* Fill one pan with hot water and the other pan with ice water.
3. Write a hypothesis stating what you think will happen to the stretched balloon when the bottle is placed in hot water and then in ice water.
4. Make a data table like the one shown. Describe the condition of the balloon at room temperature.

5. Place the bottle in the pan with hot water. Record your observations at the end of 10 minutes.
6. Now place the bottle in the pan with ice water. Record your observations at the end of 10 minutes.

Data and Observations

Bottle temperature	Condition of stretched balloon
at room temperature	
in hot water	
in ice water	

Questions and Conclusions

1. What hypothesis did you write for this experiment?
2. How did you test your hypothesis?
3. If your hypothesis was not supported, what can you do?
4. What did you observe after the bottle was in hot water for 10 minutes? Give some suggestions for your observation.
5. What did you observe after the bottle was placed in ice water for 10 minutes? Explain this observation.
6. What was the independent variable in your experiment?
7. What conclusions about the contents of the bottle did you draw from this test?
8. How do you use scientific problem solving to determine what happens to air when it is heated and cooled?

1:7 Science and Technology

How does science use the information it gathers through experiments? Frequently it seems that scientific information has little to do with our everyday lives. However, many of the facts found by the use of scientific methods have been put to practical use in the form of technology. **Technology** is the application of scientific discoveries. Have you ever eaten freeze-dried ice cream or used a solar powered calculator? Did you know that the laser is used in the operating room, to ring up groceries, and play music on a compact disc? These are all applications of facts discovered with the use of scientific methods. In this text, you will be introduced to technologies that are based on the science principles discussed in each chapter.

How are the results of scientific methods put to practical use?

TECHNOLOGY

Computer Uses

Computers are a technology that have become an important feature in our lives. They price groceries, perform calculations, relate different pieces of information, and send out bills automatically at the end of the month.

Electronic computers were not always so talented or small. Early computers performed calculations but had no ability to store this data for future use. They were very large. The first computer that was sold to a business was UNIVAC 1. It filled an entire building. The equipment that processed data for UNIVAC 1 was the vacuum tube. It was a large component that produced a lot of heat. Today's personal computer (PC) sits neatly on a desk. Many PCs are portable. They no longer contain large vacuum tubes, but tiny microprocessors. Each year new PC models are designed to perform more tasks faster and more accurately than ever before.

ADVANCE

Many new PCs can be used with modems. A modem is an instrument that uses the telephone to connect one computer with another. Using a computer modem, bank accounts are kept up to date and mail is sent electronically. PC modems connect data networks around the world. They also allow some people to work at home instead of reporting to the office every day.

a

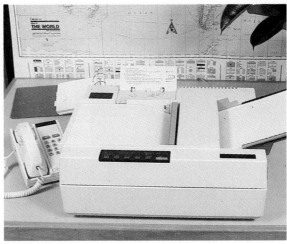

b

The antibiotic penicillin was discovered and tested by a scientist named Edward Fleming. But it was the ability to produce large quantities of this medicine through technology that has saved thousands of lives from disease. The discovery of certain properties of metals has allowed people to develop new surgical instruments and to work safely in space.

Are all technologies helpful? Certain chemicals known as fertilizers have helped produce more food for increasing world populations. However, using too much fertilizer has been found to pollute streams and water supplies. While this technology solved some problems, it has also brought about some new problems. It is not always easy to predict what effect discoveries in science will have on our lives.

FIGURE 1-12. Technology has developed a Calorie-free fat substitute (a) and machines that send letters and photographs by phone (b).

SCIENCE AND SOCIETY

1:8 What Are the Risks?

Modern technology has filled your world with many interesting and helpful things. But sometimes these new conveniences also produce unwanted effects. How do you know when a new product will produce something harmful or put you in a risk situation? A **risk** is any situation that might be a threat to health or well-being. There are two kinds of risks. First, there are those risks that clearly will harm you, such as abusing drugs. The other kinds of risks are those such as fertilizers and nuclear power that not only help people but also may have other effects that cause problems.

What is a risk?

FIGURE 1–13. Smoking on airline flights is a risk to nonsmokers as well.

What risk is involved in finding a cure for AIDS?

When you use a product or process, you make a choice about whether you can put up with the possible harmful effects. No one can avoid making choices about risk situations. Passengers on airplanes are required to wear seat belts during take-off and landing. People seem very willing to follow this rule. On the other hand, some studies have shown that only one person out of seven regularly wears a seat belt when riding in a car. Do people think that riding in a car is safer or less of a risk than flying in an airplane? Actually, there are many more accidents with cars than with airplanes. Do you always use your seat belt? Are you choosing to take a risk when you don't wear a seat belt?

Sometimes you are placed in a risk situation that is not easy for you to control. Smoking cigarettes clearly has been shown to increase the risks of heart disease and cancer. However, many people still smoke. What happens when you are in a room where people are smoking? They are exposing you to the same health risks that they choose for themselves. Should public places ban all smoking for the sake of health?

Scientists work with risk situations in many areas. The person who is working to find a cure for AIDS may be in danger of getting the disease. An astronaut is aware that he or she is taking part in a highly risky experiment. Why do these people take risks? How do they protect themselves from risk? First, they must think that some good will come from their efforts. People's lives may be saved or improved in some way. Second, they have made themselves aware of the risks involved. Third, they work carefully and thoughtfully knowing that risks exist. Does this mean that the risks are taken away? No, but it does mean that they have worked to reduce risks in their jobs. Have any important discoveries been made that didn't involve some risk? Do risks need to be taken to learn about or improve the quality of life?

REVIEW

6. How is an exercise different from a problem?
7. Give three problem-solving skills.
8. How are science and technology related?
9. Name two products of technology.
10. Why do some scientists take risks?

CHAPTER 1 REVIEW

SUMMARY

1. Science is everything that is known about the universe and the methods or processes used to obtain this knowledge. 1:1
2. The parts of a scientific experiment include: problem, hypothesis, procedure, materials, data, and conclusion. Laws describe nature. Theories explain how nature works. 1:2
3. A scientific experiment should include constants, variables, and a control for the results to be useful. Results must be reproducible for a hypothesis to be accepted. 1:3
4. Using safety procedures in the lab can prevent accidents. Safety symbols point out dangers. 1:4
5. A problem is a situation that requires thought and skill to solve. 1:5
6. There are many problem-solving skills that can be used to solve science and nonscience related problems. 1:6
7. Technology is the application of scientific discoveries. It is not easy to predict the effect of new technologies. 1:7
8. A risk is a situation that may cause harm as well as good. 1:8

VOCABULARY

a. conclusion
b. constant
c. control
d. data
e. exercise
f. experiment

g. hypothesis
h. law
i. model
j. observation
k. problem
l. procedure

m. risk
n. safety symbol
o. science
p. technology
q. theory
r. variable

Match each description with the correct vocabulary word from the list above.

1. a situation that requires thought and skills to solve
2. a standard for comparison
3. application of scientific discoveries
4. information obtained through the eyes or other senses
5. a situation that might be a threat to health
6. the part of an experiment that is not changed
7. a sign used to alert you to hazards in an activity
8. an explanation of how nature works
9. something that changes in an experiment
10. the way an experiment is carried out

CHAPTER 1 REVIEW

MAIN IDEAS

A. Reviewing Concepts

Choose the word or phrase that correctly completes each of the following sentences.

1. _____ is a process in which planned methods are used to find new information or to explain known facts.
   - **a.** Technology
   - **b.** A model
   - **c.** Science
   - **d.** Data

2. Something that changes in an experiment is a _____.
   - **a.** variable
   - **b.** constant
   - **c.** control
   - **d.** skill

3. The study of how organisms relate to each other and everything around them is part of _____.
   - **a.** earth science
   - **b.** life science
   - **c.** physical science
   - **d.** technology

4. Recorded facts or measurements from an experiment are _____.
   - **a.** materials
   - **b.** data
   - **c.** variables
   - **d.** conclusions

5. A _____ explains how nature works.
   - **a.** variable
   - **b.** procedure
   - **c.** theory
   - **d.** law

6. The use of lasers in a compact disc player is an example of a _____.
   - **a.** technology
   - **b.** risk
   - **c.** skill
   - **d.** variable

7. A logical answer to the problem question in an experiment is the _____.
   - **a.** observation
   - **b.** theory
   - **c.** procedure
   - **d.** hypothesis

8. _____ help you understand what real objects will look like or how they will work.
   - **a.** Hypotheses
   - **b.** Models
   - **c.** Controls
   - **d.** Variables

9. Observations can be made by _____.
   - **a.** hearing
   - **b.** tasting
   - **c.** seeing
   - **d.** all of these

10. A series of planned steps that tests a hypothesis is a(n) _____.
    - **a.** conclusion
    - **b.** hypothesis
    - **c.** experiment
    - **d.** observation

11. Most injuries in the science laboratory are caused by _____.
    - **a.** splatters
    - **b.** spills
    - **c.** broken glass
    - **d.** all of these

12. Always obtain your teacher's permission _____ in an activity.
    - **a.** before you begin to work
    - **b.** to use safety equipment
    - **c.** to clean up spilled water
    - **d.** to put on goggles

13. Something you know how to solve immediately is a(n) _____.
    - **a.** exercise
    - **b.** problem
    - **c.** skill
    - **d.** procedure

14. _____ are factors that do not change throughout an experiment.
    - **a.** Conclusions
    - **b.** Data
    - **c.** Constants
    - **d.** Variables

15. A hypothesis that has been tested often and still holds true might become the basis for a(n) _____.
    - **a.** theory
    - **b.** observation
    - **c.** conclusion
    - **d.** procedure

B. Understanding Concepts

Answer the following questions using complete sentences.

16. What is the difference between an independent and a dependent variable?
17. What do you study in earth science?
18. Why do scientists use models?
19. What safety equipment should you wear during an activity if you have to heat, pour, or use chemicals?
20. Why must you sometimes use different skills each time you solve a problem?
21. What are the two kinds of risks?

22. What is observation and why is it important?

23. What happens when evidence shows a theory to be incorrect?

24. How do science and technology differ?

25. List the parts of an experiment.

C. Applying Concepts

Answer the following questions using complete sentences.

26. What happens if the data of an experiment disagree with the hypothesis?

27. You decide to reorganize your room. What problem-solving skills would you use to help you accomplish this?

28. What safety symbols should you see on an activity that requires you to heat water in a beaker over an open flame?

29. How can technology help science?

30. Identify risks involved in riding a skateboard, and explain steps you can take to reduce these risks. Explain why you might continue to use a skateboard.

SKILL REVIEW

If you need help, refer to the Skill Handbook, pages 526 to 537.

1. Sit quietly in one place for 15 minutes. How many observations can you collect? Infer and record the source of each observation.

2. Classify the observations you made in Question 1 by the sense you used. You should have at least one observation in each sense category.

3. Your school has a rain gauge in the school yard. This instrument measures rainfall. Your principal asks you to keep track of the rainfall for one week. Make a data table to record the number of millimeters of rain that fall each day for that week.

4. You place a lima bean plant under a green light, another lima bean plant under a red light, and a third lima bean plant under a blue light. You measure their growth for 3 weeks to determine which color is most favorable to the plants. What are the independent and dependent variables in this experiment?

5. What is one constant you used in the experiment described in Question 4?

PROJECTS

1. Set up an experiment to find out what colors of light are most favorable to plant growth. Be sure you state a hypothesis, record data, and state a conclusion.

2. Make a list of careers in science that interest you. Consult your school or local library to find out what type of educational preparation or experiences you will need for these careers. Report your findings to the class.

READINGS

1. Cohen, Daniel. *Carl Sagan: Superstar Scientist.* New York, NY: Dodd, Mead, and Co., 1986.

2. Goldberg, Joan Rachel. "The Eureka Moment: Paul Kohl." *Science Digest,* February, 1986, pp. 34–35, 75.

3. Wicks, Keith. *Science Can Be Fun.* Minneapolis, MN: Lerner Publications, 1987.

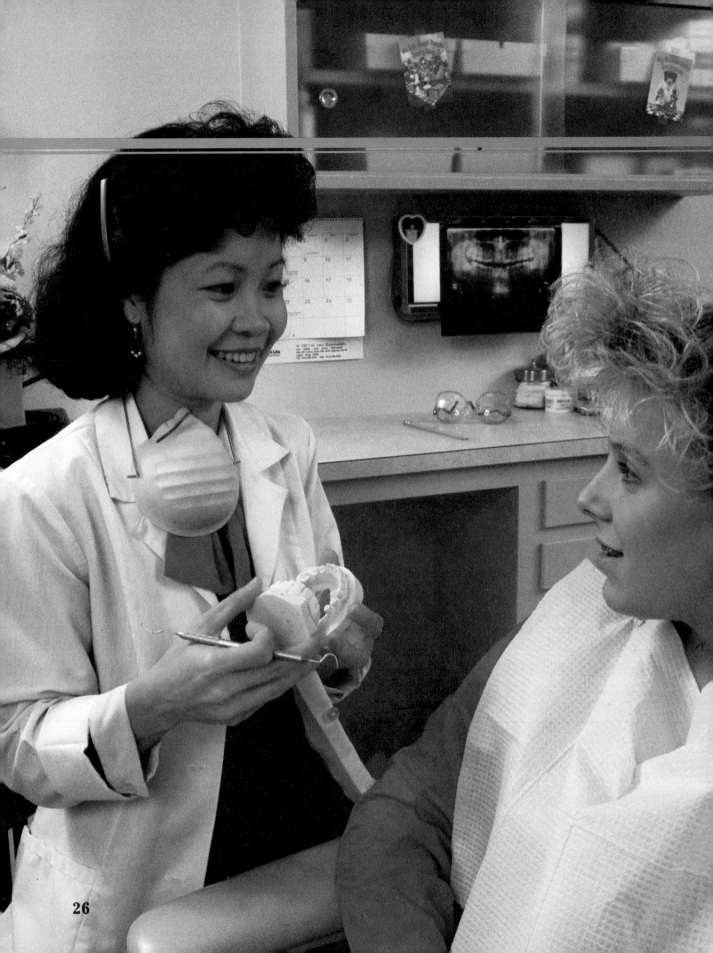

Science Skills

Career: Orthodontist

One day Mary went to the dentist. When she came out, she was very upset. Her mother asked her what was wrong. Mary told her mother that the dentist wanted her to make an appointment with an orthodontist because she might need braces. Mary's mother smiled and told Mary not to worry. She said that wearing braces wasn't the end of the world. Mother told Mary that she had worn braces for two years before Mary was born to correct jaw and bite problems. Mary looked at her mother in disbelief. Perhaps it would be worth wearing braces if she could have teeth and a smile as nice as her mother's.

Mary was very interested in all of the equipment she saw in the orthodontist's office. She asked the doctor about all of the instruments and the procedures that were to be done. The doctor told Mary that careful measuremets of her jaws would be taken and a model of her teeth and jaws would be made. The doctor would determine the procedure that would be followed to gently force Mary's teeth and jaws into proper alignment. In a few months, Mary wouldn't recognize her teeth and smile and her health also would be improved.

Orthodontists use scientific processes, measurement, and data analysis in their work. These processes are important in all of life. In this chapter, you will study more about these areas, how you use them, and how you can use them more effectively.

F.Y.I. American Dental Association, Council on Dental Education, 211 E. Chicago Ave., Chicago, IL 60611

How Is Matter Measured?

GOALS
You will study . . .
1. the reasons for standards.
2. measurable properties of matter.
3. SI units.

2:1 The Language of Measurement

Can you imagine a world in which there were no measurements? If you think about that for a while, you will realize how many times a day you use measurements. You may be asked how tall you are, how much you weigh, whether you want a small, medium, or large soft drink, or what size shoe you wear.

When you were first learning about measurement, you may have used a paper clip chain to measure objects. Perhaps your science book was seven paper clips long, while your pencil was only five clips long. However, using a paper clip chain for measuring the length and width of objects wasn't very useful. Why not? Suppose you wrote to a friend in California and gave your shoe length in paper clips. Would your friend be able to send you a pair of shoes based on your measurement? Explain your answer.

To avoid the problems of using different units of measurement, standard instruments and units were developed. When you measure, you compare the size of an object with that of a known standard. A **standard** is an exact quantity against which comparisons can be made. By using the same standards worldwide, measurements made in the United States, Argentina, France, and all other countries have the same meaning. Think how useful a standard is to a scientist in one country who wants to repeat an experiment carried out by another scientist. The results can be compared accurately.

What is a standard?

FIGURE 2–1. Measurement is important in many areas of our daily lives.

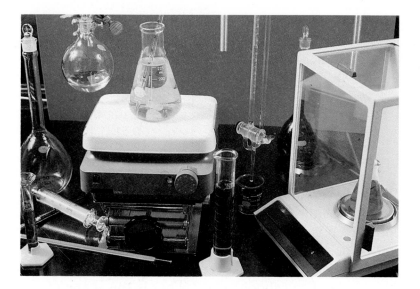

FIGURE 2-2. Measuring instruments are used to measure weight, mass, length, volume, time, and temperature.

Different systems of measurement were once used in different countries. These differences made it difficult when trading occurred or one country needed to communicate with another about measurements. In 1795, a group of scientists developed a uniform system of measurement called the metric system. Many countries adopted the metric system as did all scientists. In 1960, a modern form of the metric system was adopted for international use. This system is known as *Le Système International d'Unités,* or SI. This textbook will use metric units in all its measurements.

Table 2-1

Often Used Metric Units		
Length	**Mass**	**Volume**
meter (m)	kilogram (kg)	liter (L)
centimeter (cm)	gram (g)	milliliter (mL)
millimeter (mm)	milligram (mg)	cubic meter (m³)
kilometer (km)		cubic centimeter (cm³)

Since SI is based on the metric system, you may already know many of the units you will be using. Remember that the metric system is based on decimals. Changing from larger units to smaller, or from smaller units to larger, is done by multiplying or dividing by ten. Metric units, such as the meter, gram, and liter, are units used to measure length, mass, and volume. Prefixes are used to name larger and smaller units. Study Table 2-2 to become familiar with common metric prefixes and their meanings.

On what is SI based?

F.Y.I. In English, *Le Système International d'Unités* is the International System of Units.

Table 2-2

Some Metric Prefixes		
Prefix	Symbol	Meaning
kilo-	k	1000
deci-	d	0.1 (1/10)
centi-	c	0.01 (1/100)
milli-	m	0.001 (1/1000)

You have learned in your earlier science classes that you and everything around you is made of matter. The air you breathe is matter, your desk is matter, and your lunch is matter. All matter has properties that can be observed and described. There are physical and chemical properties of matter. What color shoes did you wear to school today? What is the shape of your textbook? Why can't you push a nail into a board with your bare hand? Color, shape, and hardness are some physical properties of matter. Different kinds of matter have different sets of properties, although some individual properties may be alike. Red shoes and a red bicycle have the same color, but they have many other properties that are different.

One good way to observe some physical properties of matter is to measure them. In doing science activities, it is extremely important to make careful

FIGURE 2-3. Physical properties of matter include hardness, color, mass, volume, weight, and the state in which matter exists.

measurements of physical properties. The following sections will describe some physical properties of matter and how they are measured using SI units.

2:2 Length, Area, and Volume

Size is a physical property of matter that can be measured. How long is your classroom? How many desks can fit in the room? How much liquid can a pail hold? Length is a physical property of many kinds of matter. You can measure length by using a metric ruler or a meter stick. A **meter** (m) is the SI unit used for measuring length. Take the meter stick in your classroom and measure from the floor to the top of a desk or table. Is that distance close to one meter? What objects in your classroom are 1 m apart? For larger distances, think of your high school football field. It is just over 90 m long. A basketball hoop is between 3 and 4 m from the floor.

You may find a meter to be too long a unit for some of your measurements. A meter can be divided into 100 equal parts called centimeters (cm). Look at Figure 2–4. Notice the slightly longer lines at the centimeter marks. One meter equals one hundred centimeters. *Centi-* means 0.01. Therefore, one centimeter equals 0.01 of one meter. Still smaller units are sometimes useful, so a meter can be divided into 1000 equal parts called millimeters (mm). Look at Figure 2–4 again. If the meter stick were extended to its full length, you could see that

$$10 \text{ mm} = 1 \text{ cm}$$
$$100 \text{ cm} = 1 \text{ m}$$
$$\text{and } 1000 \text{ mm} = 1 \text{ m.}$$

One more useful unit for measuring longer distances is a kilometer (KIHL uh meet ur) (km). One kilometer equals 1000 m. Remember that the larger the unit you are using, the fewer of these units you will have. It is easier to tell someone you rode your bicycle 10 km than that you rode 10 000 m. Do you see how useful that prefix *kilo-*, meaning 1000, is to you?

What is a meter?

F.Y.I. Metric system originators defined the meter by setting the distance from one pole to the equator as ten thousand kilometers. Later measurements showed this distance to be off by about two kilometers.

How long is a kilometer?

FIGURE 2–4. A metric ruler or meter stick is used to measure length, width, and height.

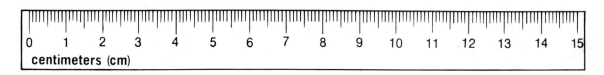

A second size measurement that you often need to use is area. **Area** is the amount of space on the surface of an object. The standard SI unit for area is the **square meter** (m²). What is the area of your desktop? Units for area are derived or obtained from the units for length. To find the area of your desktop, measure its length and width. Suppose you find these measurements to be 75 cm long by 50 cm wide. The area would be equal to the length times the width.

$$area = l \times w$$
$$area = 50 \text{ cm} \times 75 \text{ cm}$$
$$area = 3750 \text{ cm}^2$$

This means that you could cover the desktop with 3750 squares of paper that measure 1 cm wide by 1 cm long.

Volume is the amount of space occupied by an object. As with area, the SI units for volume are obtained from units of length. The standard SI unit for volume is the **cubic meter** (m³). A box that measures

PROBLEM SOLVING

Out of Wrapping Paper?

Carlita had been invited to Jane's birthday party. Carlita had no trouble finding gifts for her friend. Since Jane's favorite subject was science, Carlita bought her an astronomy book. She also found a magnifying lens at the bookstore. She was sure Jane would like the gifts.

Since the party was the next day, Carlita thought she had better wrap the gifts. Carlita looked through the drawer where her mother kept wrapping paper and ribbons. There was only one piece of wrapping paper left in the drawer. Carlita wondered if the piece of wrapping paper was large enough to wrap the gifts. The package stated that the wrapping paper was 40 cm on each side.

Carlita measured her gifts. The astronomy book measured 20 × 15 × 2 cm, and the box containing the magnifying lens measured 15 × 4 × 2 cm. How can Carlita find out if she has enough wrapping paper to wrap the gifts? Will there be any paper left? If so, how much?

1 m by 1 m by 1 m has a volume of 1 m^3. If smaller units are used to measure objects, those same units would also be used for their areas and volumes.

Suppose you have a container with sides that each measure 10 cm. The volume of this container would be 1000 cm^3. It could hold 1000 cm^3 of a material. Think about pouring a liquid into this container. The volumes of liquids are usually measured in liters (L). Liters are not SI units. One L has the same volume as 1000 cm^3. One L of apple juice takes up the same space as 1000 cm^3 of apple juice.

F.Y.I. *Volume = l × w × h*

SKILL BUILDER

Measuring in SI

Use a metric ruler to measure each side of a box of tissues and a box of paper clips. Round your measurements to the nearest whole number of units. Record all measurements for each object. Calculate the area of each side of each object and record your data. Calculate the volume of each object. If you need help, refer to Measuring in SI on pages 526–537.

Questions
1. What units did you use in your measurements?
2. How did you find the areas and volumes?

Problem: How can you measure the volumes of regular and irregular objects?

Materials

1-L beaker	small wooden block
250-mL beaker	small rock
metric ruler	thread
graduated cylinder	pencil
water	

Procedure

Part A

1. Copy the data table on your paper.
2. Use the metric ruler to measure the length, width, and height of the wooden block. Record in your table.
3. Calculate and record the areas of the top, side, and end of the wooden block.
4. Calculate and record the volume of the block.

Part B

5. Place the 250-mL beaker inside the 1-L beaker. Fill the smaller beaker to the top with water.
6. Carefully place the wooden block in the water. Then, push the block under the water with the point of a pencil.
7. Remove the 250-mL beaker from the larger beaker.
8. State a hypothesis as to how the volume of displaced water in the large beaker will compare with the calculated volume of the block.
9. Pour the displaced water from the 1-L beaker into the graduated cylinder. Record this volume in your table.
10. Tie a piece of thread around the rock and repeat steps 5–9.

Questions and Conclusions

1. In Part A, how did you determine the volume of the wooden block?
2. In Part B, how did you determine the volume of the wooden block?
3. In Part B, how does the calculated volume of the block compare with the volume of the displaced water? Explain.
4. Was your hypothesis supported? Explain.
5. How can you measure the volumes of regular and irregular objects?

Data and Observations

Object	Length (cm)	Width (cm)	Height (cm)	Area (cm²)	Calculated volume (cm³)	Overflow volume (mL)
Block						
Rock						

2:3 Mass, Weight, and Density

Other physical properties of matter that can be measured include mass, density, and weight. **Mass** is the amount of matter in an object. All matter has mass. In science, a pan balance often is used to measure mass. The standard SI unit used in mass measurement is the **kilogram** (kg). Smaller masses are measured in grams (g) or milligrams (mg). Look at a large paper clip and a nickel. The mass of the paper clip is about 1 g and the mass of the nickel is about 5 g. One L of pure water has a mass of 1 kg. What is the mass of 12 L of pure water? Density is another measurable property of matter. **Density** is the amount of mass a material has for its volume. Which would you rather carry, a grocery bag filled with cotton balls or the same size bag filled with rocks? Although the volume of the two bags is the same, the mass of the contents is different. Therefore, the bag of rocks is more dense than the bag of cotton. The SI units for density are derived from the units for volume and mass. Density is found by measuring the mass of an object and dividing by its volume. Density units are usually written as grams per cubic centimeter (g/cm³). Suppose you have an object with a mass of 60 g. It occupies a volume of 10 cm³. You would calculate its density by using an equation.

$$density = \frac{mass}{volume}$$
$$density = \frac{60 \text{ g}}{10 \text{ cm}^3}$$
$$density = 6 \text{ g/cm}^3$$

How do you find the density of an object?

FIGURE 2−6. Density depends on the mass per unit volume. The rocks are more dense than the cotton balls.

Table 2-3

Densities of Some Substances			
Substance	Density (g/cm³)	Substance	Density (g/cm³)
hydrogen	0.000 09	aluminum	2.7
oxygen	0.0013	iron	7.9
water	1.0	copper	8.9
sugar	1.6	lead	11.3
table salt	2.2	mercury	13.6
quartz	2.6	gold	19.3

What is weight?

FIGURE 2-7. Weight and mass can be measured using a spring scale (a) and a pan balance (b).

a

The density of a material is often compared with the density of water. Items less dense than water will float in it, while items that are more dense than water will sink. The density of a material is often used to identify it. If you had two pieces of metal that looked similar, you could try to identify them by comparing their densities with those of materials listed in a density table, such as Table 2-3.

A force is a push or a pull. Forces can vary in strength and can be measured. **Weight** is the measure of the force of gravity acting on an object. If you throw a ball into the air, the force of gravity pulls it back to Earth. Gravitational forces exist between all objects. The strength of a gravitational force depends on the mass of the objects and their distance apart. The moon's gravitational force on a baseball is less than Earth's, because the moon has less mass than Earth.

The SI unit of force is the **newton** (N). Since weight is a measure of gravitational force, it is measured in newtons. A 1-kg mass weighs 9.8 N on Earth. Since the moon's gravitational force is less than Earth's, the same 1-kg mass would weigh about 1.6 N on the moon.

b

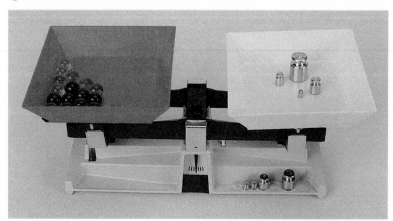

Problem: How can you estimate an unknown number of paper clips?

Materials

pan balance
empty paper clip box
paper clips (10, 20, 100)
boxes (4) of paper clips labeled
   Full, A, B, and C
graph paper

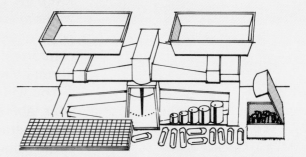

Procedure

Part A

1. Copy the data table on your paper.
2. Find the mass of the empty paper clip box and record.
3. Find the mass of 10 paper clips and record.
4. Find the mass of the full box of paper clips. Subtract the mass of the empty box. Record the mass of the paper clips under the heading "Full box."
5. Use the mass measurements to estimate the number of paper clips in the full box. Record the estimate.
6. Count the paper clips in the box. Record the number in your table.

Part B

7. Find the mass of 20 paper clips. Repeat with 100 paper clips. Record these data.
8. Construct a graph of the masses of 10, 20, and 100 paper clips. Show the number of paper clips on the horizontal axis and the mass in grams on the vertical axis. Plot the points and connect them.
9. Repeat step 4 using Boxes A-C. Use the graph to estimate the number of paper clips in each box. Count to see how close your estimate was.

Data and Observations

Items	Mass (g)	Estimate	Actual Number
Empty box			
10 clips			
20 clips			
100 clips			
Full box			
Box A			
Box B			
Box C			

Questions and Conclusions

1. How close was your estimate to the number of paper clips in the full box?
2. How did you estimate the number of paper clips in the full box?
3. Describe the line connecting the points you plotted on the graph.
4. How close were your estimates to the actual number of paper clips in Boxes A, B, and C?
5. How did you estimate the number of paper clips in Boxes A, B, and C?
6. How can you estimate an unknown number of paper clips?

2:4 Temperature and Time

Temperature is a property of matter that can be measured using a thermometer. There are two temperature scales that are used in science—the Celsius scale and the Kelvin scale. If measured at sea level, the Celsius scale records the freezing point of water at zero degrees Celsius (0°C) and the boiling point of water at 100 degrees Celsius (100°C). A comfortable room temperature is about 25°C, and the normal temperature of the human body is 37°C.

What is absolute zero?

You will probably use the Celsius scale in most of your laboratory work in this science course. However, SI temperature units use the Kelvin scale. Zero kelvin is the same as absolute zero. **Absolute zero** is the point at which almost all movement of the atoms in a material stops. You will learn more about absolute zero in a later chapter. Absolute zero is 273 degrees below the freezing point of water on the Celsius scale. Therefore, 0°C equals 273 K. What is the boiling point of water on the Kelvin scale?

Time is a measurement of the period between two events. It is not a property of matter, but it is an extremely important measurement in science. The SI unit for time measurement is the **second** (s). Scientists have agreed on the standard for the second, and all other time units are based on it. In one second, light can travel about seven and one-half times around Earth at the equator. Other familiar time units are minutes, hours, days, weeks, months, and years.

FIGURE 2–8. A timekeeper uses a stopwatch to measure the time between the start and finish of a race.

TECHNOLOGY

The Timepiece

A watch or clock measures the passing of time. A coiled mainspring or a battery supplies the power to turn a series of toothed or geared wheels. Each wheel turns faster than the one turning it. One wheel turns the minute hand and another in the series turns the second hand.

There is a built-in control, or escapement mechanism, that allows movement in only one direction. A roller on the balance wheel pushes the first part of a two-pronged lever, called a pallet, into a tooth on an escape wheel. A rocking motion of the roller lifts out the first prong as the second prong moves into the next tooth on the wheel, preventing any backward movement. The balance wheel vibrates, or rocks, at equal intervals to keep accurate time.

ADVANCE

The newest and most accurate timepiece is the atomic clock. Energy changes within an atom produce regular electromagnetic waves. The atomic clock is so accurate that it loses less than one second every 1000 years.

SCIENCE AND SOCIETY

2:5 The Switch to Metric

The International System of Units is used by all countries in the world except Burma and the United States. The English system used in the United States is very familiar to all its residents. Most of the English units are quite different from SI units. However, in 1893, the foot was defined in terms of a meter. Most U.S. citizens would prefer to continue using English-system units because they have used them all of their lives. Changes are happening, however. In 1975, Congress passed the Metric Conversion Act. This act requires that the United States change from using English-system units to using SI units. A Metric Board was appointed to aid in making the change.

Large parts of the population in the United States have resisted the switch to metric. They prefer to continue measuring weight in pounds instead of newtons, height in inches instead of centimeters, and temperature in degrees Fahrenheit instead of degrees Celsius.

F.Y.I. The National Bureau of Standards in Washington, DC was created by Congress in 1901. Its job is to establish accurate measurement standards for U.S. science, industry, and commerce.

a

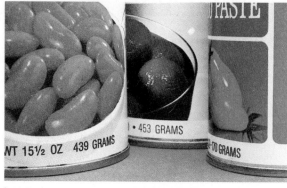
b

FIGURE 2–9. In the United States, the switch to metric is happening on the highways (a) and in the supermarkets (b).

Industries, importers, and hospitals, on the other hand, have found the switch in units to be helpful to them. Industries that sell goods in other countries must use SI units to compete in those countries. General Motors Corporation has been using SI units for its car parts since 1985. Chrysler Corporation and Ford Motor Company are also converting to SI units. Currently, mechanics have to keep two sets of tools, one metric and one English, in order to work on both American and foreign cars.

Students in school are taught SI units in their textbooks. Road signs and car speedometers have both SI and English-system units. Look at food packages and soft drink bottles. Do you find SI units given? Think about the problems that would emerge if the United States suddenly switched to SI tomorrow. What would be the advantages? The disadvantages? What are the advantages and disadvantages of a slow conversion to SI? With better communication and transportation, Earth is becoming a global village. What do you think this means? How will the United States be affected if the general population refuses to "make the switch"?

Why is it an advantage for U.S. industries to use SI units?

REVIEW

1. Why are standards necessary in making and using measurements?
2. What is SI?
3. What are derived units? Give examples.
4. What are some properties of matter that can be measured?
5. You throw an object into a pool of water and it sinks. What do you know about the object's density?

2:6 Accuracy, Estimation, and Precision

We have discussed the tools and units used in making measurements. The accuracy of your measurements depends on how close your value is to the actual or accepted value. What is an actual or accepted value? It may be the value determined by the National Bureau of Standards in Washington, DC. It may, however, be a value that is determined by your teacher. Any value can be a standard as long as it is agreed that it will be so. For instance, if your teacher gives you a piece of wooden dowel as a standard, you can measure other objects using it. Your desk may be two dowels long. The accuracy of your measurements will depend on how close you come to the standard value. Your accuracy will improve as you continue to use measuring instruments.

How could you measure the length of a book without using a metric ruler or other measuring device? You could estimate or determine the book's approximate size. If you compared it with a book you had already measured, you could say the new book was a little shorter or a little longer than the first book. If the measured book was 14 cm in length, the new book will be close to 14 cm also.

GOALS

You will study . . .
1. accuracy, estimation, and precision.
2. the uses of scientific notation.

What is accuracy?

F.Y.I. Many traditional measurement units were based on common objects as standards. An inch was the length of three barleycorns laid end-to-end. A yard was the distance from a king's nose to his fingertips.

FIGURE 2–10. Accuracy in measurements can be improved with practice.

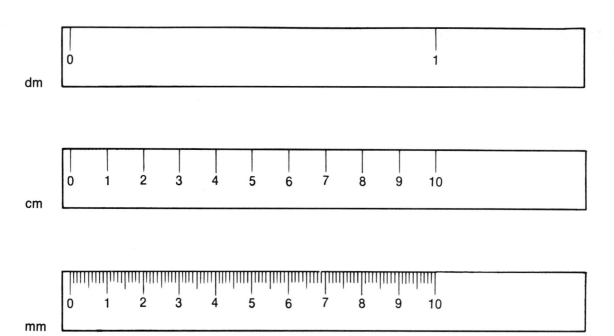

FIGURE 2-11. A more precise instrument will give more precise measurements.

At a normal walking stride, you cover about one meter with every two steps. Suppose you wanted to estimate the width of your classroom. How could you estimate it? If you paced the width of the room and then divided by two, you would find the approximate width in meters. How could you check your accuracy?

When you use a metric ruler to measure part of a line, you may use estimation in your answer. Perhaps the end of the line segment is between two millimeter marks. You must estimate which millimeter mark is closer. Estimation saves time. Estimation is a valuable skill and can be improved with practice.

What is precision?

The **precision** of a measurement is the degree of exactness with which the object is measured. Precision depends on the measuring instrument. You may measure the mass of an object by using a balance that is marked in grams, tenths of grams, or hundredths of grams. A balance that is marked in hundredths of grams would give a more precise value than a balance marked in grams or tenths of grams. Suppose you are asked to use a metric ruler to measure a box. If you measure the box in decimeters, you will not get a very precise value. However, if you measure in centimeters, you will be more precise. Using millimeter units will give an even more precise answer. You can't improve precision with practice. A measurement can only be as precise as the measuring instrument will allow it to be. Precision does not guarantee accuracy.

2:7 Scientific Notation

Sometimes measurements or calculations involve very large numbers or very small numbers. The mass of Earth is about 6 000 000 000 000 000 000 000 000 kg. The speed of light is 300 000 000 m/s. Numbers like these are difficult to work with, and it is easy to make mistakes because of the many zeros. A more efficient way of writing these numbers is to express them in scientific notation.

Scientific notation is a system in which a number is expressed as the product of a factor and a power of ten. The factor must be 1 or greater, but less than 10.

What is scientific notation?

standard notation   scientific notation

$$1\ 600\ 000 = 1.6 \times 1\ 000\ 000 = 1.6 \times 10^6$$

The mass of Earth, 6 000 000 000 000 000 000 000 000.0 kg, is written as 6×10^{24} kg. Six is multiplied by ten, 24 times. To convert a whole number from standard notation to scientific notation, you move the decimal point to the left until you have a factor between 1 and 10. The number of places you moved

How do you convert a whole number from standard to scientific notation?

FIGURE 2–12. Scientific notation is a useful shorthand method for writing large or small numbers.

the decimal point is the power of 10. How would you write 70 000 in scientific notation? The speed of light, 300 000 000 m/s, is written 3×10^8 m/s.

If you have a number less than one, the power of 10 is written as a negative number. The number 0.000 03 is written as 3×10^{-5}. This shows that the number three is divided by 10 five times. To convert a decimal fraction to scientific notation, you move the decimal point to the right until you have a factor between 1 and 10. The number of places you moved the decimal is expressed as the negative power of 10. How would you write 0.000 000 6 in scientific notation?

Example 1

Write 2.3×10^{10} in standard notation. You must move the decimal point 10 places to the right.

$$2.3 \times 10^{10} = 23\ 000\ 000\ 000$$

Example 2

Write 93 000 000 000 000 000 in scientific notation. You must move the decimal point 16 places to the left.

$$93\ 000\ 000\ 000\ 000\ 000 = 9.3 \times 10^{16}$$

Example 3

Write 7×10^{-6} in standard notation. You must move the decimal point 6 places to the left.

$$7 \times 10^{-6} = 0.000\ 007$$

Example 4

Write 0.000 000 000 002 in scientific notation. You must move the decimal point 12 places to the right.

$$0.000\ 000\ 000\ 002 = 2 \times 10^{-12}$$

REVIEW

6. How do accuracy and precision differ?
7. How can accuracy be improved?
8. What does estimation determine?
9. Express 3×10^6 in standard notation.
10. What is scientific notation and why is it useful?

CHAPTER 2 REVIEW

SUMMARY

1. The International System of Units is known as SI. SI is based on the metric system. 2:1
2. A meter is the basic SI unit used for measuring length. Volume is the amount of space occupied by an object. SI units for area and volume are derived from the basic units for length. 2:2
3. Mass is the amount of matter in an object. Density is the amount of mass for an object's volume. Weight is a measure of the force of gravity acting on an object. The SI unit of force is the newton. 2:3
4. Temperature is measured both in degrees Celsius and kelvin, and time is measured in seconds. 2:4
5. The United States is slowly making the switch to SI. It will make it easier for importers and exporters once the switch is complete. 2:5
6. Accuracy in measuring depends on the measurement's closeness to a standard. Estimation can be used to determine approximate size. Precision depends on divisions of the measuring instrument. Accuracy improves with practice but precision doesn't. 2:6
7. Scientific notation makes it easier to work with very small and very large numbers. 2:7

VOCABULARY

a. absolute zero   **f.** mass   **k.** second
b. area   **g.** meter   **l.** square meter
c. cubic meter   **h.** newton   **m.** standard
d. density   **i.** precision   **n.** volume
e. kilogram   **j.** scientific notation   **o.** weight

Match each description with the correct vocabulary word from the list above.
 1. SI unit for time measurement
 2. is measured in liters
 3. efficient way of writing very large or very small numbers
 4. SI unit for measuring length
 5. mass per volume
 6. measure of the force of gravity on an object
 7. SI unit of force measurement
 8. amount of matter in an object
 9. SI unit for mass measurement
 10. describes amount of space on the surface of an object

MAIN IDEAS

A. Reviewing Concepts

Choose the word or phrase that correctly completes each of the following sentences.

1. An instrument used to measure length is the _____.
   - **a.** meter stick
   - **b.** graduate
   - **c.** pan balance
   - **d.** beaker

2. _____ is measured in square meters.
   - **a.** Area
   - **b.** Volume
   - **c.** Length
   - **d.** Mass

3. The point at which almost all movement of atoms in a material stops is called _____.
   - **a.** zero K
   - **b.** −273°C
   - **c.** absolute zero
   - **d.** all of these

4. The basic SI unit for mass is the _____.
   - **a.** liter
   - **b.** cubic centimeter
   - **c.** gram
   - **d.** kilogram

5. The basic SI unit for temperature is the _____.
   - **a.** degree Celsius
   - **b.** kelvin
   - **c.** Boyle
   - **d.** Charles

6. A L of pure water has a mass of _____.
   - **a.** 1 gram
   - **b.** 1 kilogram
   - **c.** 1 milligram
   - **d.** 1 decigram

7. The prefix in SI that means one-hundredth is _____.
   - **a.** *kilo-*
   - **b.** *milli-*
   - **c.** *deci-*
   - **d.** *centi-*

8. Liters, cubic centimeters, and milliliters are units for _____.
   - **a.** volume
   - **b.** mass
   - **c.** area
   - **d.** time

9. Thermometers in school labs usually use the _____ scale.
   - **a.** Celsius
   - **b.** Kelvin
   - **c.** Fahrenheit
   - **d.** none of these

10. Writing a number as a factor and a power of ten is called _____.
    - **a.** estimation
    - **b.** scientific notation
    - **c.** International System
    - **d.** none of these

11. Determining approximate size is called _____.
    - **a.** estimation
    - **b.** massing
    - **c.** speculation
    - **d.** none of these

12. An exact quantity that people agree to use for comparison is called a(n) _____.
    - **a.** unit
    - **b.** unit fraction
    - **c.** estimate
    - **d.** standard

13. Four centimeters equals _____ millimeters.
    - **a.** 0.40
    - **b.** 40
    - **c.** 400
    - **d.** none of these

14. Two kilograms of water have a volume of _____ liters.
    - **a.** 2
    - **b.** 20
    - **c.** 0.2
    - **d.** none of these

15. Scientific notation for 0.0063 would be written as _____.
    - **a.** 63×10^{-2}
    - **b.** 63×10^{-4}
    - **c.** 6.3×10^{3}
    - **d.** 6.3×10^{-3}

B. Understanding Concepts

Answer the following questions using complete sentences.

16. What is the area of a table that is 4 m long and 2 m wide?
17. Convert 500 g to kg.
18. How many milliliters are there in 15 cm^3?
19. How are SI units like the United States money system?
20. Which can improve with practice, accuracy or precision?
21. Why are prefixes used in SI?
22. From what are the SI units for area and volume derived?

CHAPTER 2 REVIEW

23. Two grams of water have a volume of 2 cm³. What is the density of water?

24. How many degrees are between the boiling point and freezing point of water on the Celsius scale?

25. Which countries do not use SI?

C. Applying Concepts

Answer the following questions using complete sentences.

26. Why would the use of SI units help in trade?

27. Why is estimation of measurements helpful?

28. What is the difference between mass and weight?

29. Convert 15 m/s to km/h.

30. How could you use the concept of density to see whether a sample of milk was skim milk or whole milk?

SKILL REVIEW

If you need help, refer to the Skill Handbook, pages 526 to 537.

1. Classify each of the following as a tool for measuring volume, length, or mass.
metric ruler   100-mL beaker
graduated cylinder   pan balance
meter stick

2. You are given a glass marble and told to find its volume. List the tools and materials you will need. What additional tool would you need to find the marble's density?

3. Use a metric ruler to find the area of one side of a sheet of notebook paper. Your answer will be in square centimeters (cm²). If you cut the paper into squares 1 cm wide by 1 cm long, how many squares will you have?

4. On one day the outside temperature was measured every two hours from 8:00 A.M. to 8:00 P.M. and recorded in the table shown below. Plot these data on a graph.

Time	Temp (°C)	Time	Temp (°C)
8:00 A.M.	17	2:00 P.M.	24
10:00 A.M.	20	4:00 P.M.	23
Noon	23	6:00 P.M.	21
		8:00 P.M.	19

5. What are the independent and dependent variables in Question 4? Which variable appears on the vertical axis?

PROJECTS

1. Keep a diary of quantities for one week. Every time you notice a quantity that is measured, write the name of the item and the unit with which it is measured. At the end of the week, make a table of your findings. Classify all the items as SI or English measurements.

2. Calculate and compare the densities of ten liquids other than water. Make a display for the classroom.

READINGS

1. Fraser, J.T. *Time: The Familiar Stranger.* Amherst, MA: University of Massachusetts Press, 1987.

2. Lemonick, M.D. "Whatever Happened to Metric? Despite Some Changes, The U.S. Hardly Gave an Inch." *Time.* July 6, 1987, pp. 80–81.

3. Marson, Ron. *More Metrics Thirty-Six.* Canby, OR: Tops Learning, 1985.

48

Matter

Career: Electroplater

Bill had helped his parents clean out the attic and found his baby shoes. Bill wanted to throw them away, but his parents wanted to have them plated with a metal to preserve them. Bill thought the whole idea was silly, but he was interested in how it could be done.

Bill and his parents went to an electroplater who specialized in plating small items. They were shown examples of gold, silver, and bronze plating. Bill decided on the silver and asked about the process that would be used. First, the shoes would be thoroughly cleaned, and the laces would be tied and pinned. The shoes would then be wetted with a silver nitrate solution. A wire would be attached to the shoes and to a copper anode. Both would then be placed into a warm copper acid bath. The copper ions would settle on the shoes. The shoes would need two electroplating baths. The process would then be repeated using a warm silver cyanide bath and a silver anode until the shoes were covered with silver. The shoes would be carefully shaped, dried, and polished.

In electroplating, metal salt compounds are dissolved in water to form a plating solution. In this chapter, you will study elements and their uses. You will also study solutions, compounds, and mixtures.

F.Y.I. American Electroplaters and Surface Finishers Society, 12644 Research Parkway, Orlando, FL 32826

What Is Matter?

GOALS
You will study . . .
1. matter and its properties.
2. atoms and the parts that compose them.
3. elements and their properties.

3:1 Matter

The universe is composed of matter. Your body, this book, and your house are matter. The ancient Greeks believed that all matter was a combination of four items: fire, Earth, air, and water. Today, we define matter as anything that has mass and takes up space.

Pure water always has a certain composition. It is made of two parts hydrogen and one part oxygen. Water is a substance. A **substance** is a kind of matter that is always the same in composition.

All matter has properties. A property is a quality or characteristic of matter. A property can be physical or chemical in nature. A **physical property** is a characteristic that may be observed without changing the chemical composition of the material. A black color is a physical property of coal. You do not have to break down coal to observe that it is black. A **chemical property** determines how a substance reacts to form other substances. Is the ability of paper to burn in air a chemical or physical property? What properties of glass make it different from a rubber band? No two substances have the same set of properties. Why?

What is a physical property?

What is a chemical property?

FIGURE 3–1. Water, in the form of snow and clouds, is a substance.

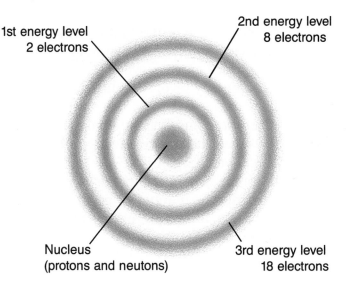

1st energy level
2 electrons

2nd energy level
8 electrons

Nucleus
(protons and neutons)

3rd energy level
18 electrons

FIGURE 3–2. Atoms are made of protons, neutrons, and electrons.

3:2 Atoms

All matter is made of tiny particles called **atoms.** Atoms are the building blocks of matter in much the same way that bricks are the building blocks of a house. All atoms are alike in some ways. All atoms have a core called a **nucleus** (NEW klee us). The nucleus contains protons and neutrons. A **proton** (PROH tahn) is a particle that has a positive electric charge and is located in the nucleus of an atom. A **neutron** (NEW trahn) is a particle that has no electric charge and is also located in the nucleus of an atom. Protons and neutrons have similar masses, and together they make up most of the mass of an atom.

A third particle in an atom is an electron. An **electron** has a negative electric charge and a very small mass. Because electrons move so fast, it is hard to pinpoint the exact location of an electron at any given time. This is why a model of electrons shows them as creating a cloud around the nucleus. Think about the moving blades of a fan. Just as you can't see the individual blades of a fan, you can't see the electrons in an atom. Electrons can be anywhere in the cloud. However, scientists have calculated that they are located close to the nucleus most of the time.

Not all electrons that make up an electron cloud have the same energy. In atoms, electrons are at certain fixed energies. Electrons with the lowest amount of energy are in the first energy level. The first energy level is closest to the nucleus.

What does the nucleus contain?

What is a neutron?

F.Y.I. Protons and neutrons are made up of smaller particles called quarks. Scientists believe that there are at least six different kinds of quarks and other particles called gluons.

Only two electrons can be in the first energy level. The second energy level in an atom can hold up to eight electrons. The third energy level can hold up to 18 electrons. Higher energy levels can hold 32 or more electrons.

The mass of a proton is much greater than the mass of an electron. However, the positive charge of the proton and the negative charge of the electron are equal in strength. In an atom, the number of positively charged protons equals the number of negatively charged electrons. Thus, atoms are electrically neutral. Recall that neutrons have no charge.

How do the masses of electrons and protons compare?

TECHNOLOGY

Atomic Structure

Early scientists did not know much about atoms. Two Greek philosophers in the fifth century B.C. first talked about atoms. In the 1600s and 1700s, Isaac Newton and John Dalton explained the nature of matter based on the behavior of atoms.

In the late 1800s, J.J. Thomson did experiments that led to the identification of the electron. In 1910, Ernest Rutherford and his coworkers performed an experiment that led to the theory of a positive nucleus with electrons around it.

ADVANCE

Since the early 1930s, scientists have discovered or predicted the existence of more than 200 subatomic particles. Nuclear scientists divide the particles into two broad classes, leptons and hadrons. Leptons ("light" particles) are considered to be elementary particles. An electron is an example. A neutrino, a neutral particle given off when an electron is emitted from the nucleus, is also a lepton. Hadrons are divided into two groups, mesons and baryons. Protons and neutrons are examples of baryons. Mesons and baryons are made of even smaller particles called quarks and gluons. It is believed that every particle has an antiparticle. They are identical except for opposite electric charges. New technologies will allow further exploration.

3:3 Elements

A substance made of just one type of atom is an **element.** Carbon is a common element. Carbon is made of only carbon atoms. Lead is an element made of only lead atoms. Presently, there are 109 known elements. Of these, 90 are found in nature. Other elements are made in nuclear physics labs.

The number of protons in an atom is called the **atomic number.** For example, hydrogen has one proton in its nucleus. Its atomic number is 1. Carbon has an atomic number of 6. How many protons are in a carbon atom? The number of protons plus the number of neutrons is the **mass number.** If you know the mass number and the atomic number of an element, can you figure out how many neutrons it has? How?

Scientists organize elements into a table called the **periodic table.** Elements are listed in the table in order of atomic number. Look at the periodic table on pages 542–543. Notice that each element is represented by a symbol. A symbol may be one, two, or three letters. The first letter is always a capital letter. The second and third letters are lowercase. What is the symbol for carbon? How does the symbol for carbon differ from the symbol for chlorine?

You probably recognize some of the elements listed. Copper (Cu) and aluminum (Al) are used in some cookware. Gold (Au) and silver (Ag) are used in the jewelry industry and in dentistry. Substances containing calcium (Ca) and phosphorus (P) are essential for strong bones and teeth. Hydrogen (H) and oxygen (O) make up water.

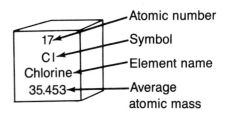

FIGURE 3–3. Reading the periodic table is easy when you know the shorthand.

F.Y.I. Californium was named for California, europium for Europe, and americium for America.

FIGURE 3–4. Copper, aluminum, calcium, and phosphorus are common elements found in household items, bones, and teeth.

Problem: How can you make models of atoms?

Materials

paper dots   glue
  (red, blue, green)   drawing compass
white paper   periodic table

Procedure

1. On a piece of paper, draw a circle about 2 cm in diameter to represent the nucleus of an atom.
2. Refer to the periodic table. In the circle, glue 6 red dots to represent the number of protons in a carbon atom.
3. Glue blue dots to represent the number of neutrons in a carbon atom in the circle with the protons.
4. Draw a 3-cm circle around the first circle. On this circle, glue 2 green dots to represent electrons in the first energy level of the carbon atom.
5. Draw a 4-cm circle around the second circle. Glue 4 green dots to represent the number of electrons in the second energy level of the carbon atom.

6. Keep adding circles if necessary until all the electrons are in place.
7. Using steps 1 through 6, make diagrams for each atom listed in the data table.
8. Write the chemical symbol, mass number, and number of protons, neutrons, and electrons for the elements in the data table.

Questions and Conclusions

1. Which part of your model atom represents the nucleus?
2. Which particles are found in the nucleus of an atom?
3. Which part of your model atom represents the electron cloud?
4. What is the maximum number of electrons found in the first energy level? The second energy level?
5. Study the data table. How does the number of protons compare with the number of electrons in an atom?
6. How are electrons distributed in a sodium atom?

Data and Observations

Element	Symbol	Mass number	Number of protons	Number of neutrons	Number of electrons
Carbon					
Oxygen					
Helium					
Lithium					
Boron					
Neon					
Nitrogen					
Sodium					

21 **Sc** Scandium 44.95591	22 **Ti** Titanium 47.88	23 **V** Vanadium 50.9415	24 **Cr** Chromium 51.9961	25 **Mn** Manganese 54.9380
39 **Y** Yttrium 88.9059	40 **Zr** Zirconium 91.224	41 **Nb** Niobium 92.9064	42 **Mo** Molybdenum 95.94	43 **Tc** Technetium 97.9072*

FIGURE 3–5. Elements are organized into a table called the periodic table.

The elements in the periodic table can be classified in many ways. One way to classify elements is by atomic structure. Elements with similar arrangements of electrons in their atoms have similar properties.

Elements with similar electron arrangements are grouped together in families or groups. The elements in a group are in columns in the periodic table. All of the elements in a column have similar properties. The elements with the lightest atoms are at the top of each column. The more massive elements are at the bottom.

Another way to classify elements is to group them into metals and nonmetals. Metals are usually shiny. Look at the periodic table on pages 542–543 again. About 75 percent of the elements are metals. Nonmetals, except for hydrogen, are found toward the right side of the periodic table. Nonmetal solids usually have dull surfaces and are brittle.

F.Y.I. The human body is composed mainly of four elements: carbon, hydrogen, oxygen, and nitrogen.

SKILL BUILDER

Classifying

Use the periodic table on pages 542–543. Find the elements with atomic numbers 1 through 18. Classify each of these as a metal or nonmetal. If you need help, refer to Classifying on page 534.

Questions

1. How does the stair-step line in the periodic table help you classify the elements?
2. Why is hydrogen an exception when classifying elements?
3. Find potassium in the table. Would you expect potassium to be solid and shiny? Why or why not?

Physicist Paul Chu discovered a superconducting material in 1986. Superconductors are able to transmit electric current efficiently. The first superconductors worked at very cold temperatures. Chu's material works at higher temperatures.

FIGURE 3–6. The SSC is a type of particle accelerator.

SCIENCE AND SOCIETY

3:4 Super Colliders

The Superconducting Super Collider, or SSC, is a new type of particle accelerator. The SSC will consist of an 84-km circular underground tunnel. Two streams of protons will travel around the tunnel in opposite directions. The tunnel will be surrounded by thousands of powerful electromagnets that will force the protons to change direction each time they pass a magnet until they are made to collide. The results of the collisions will be carefully monitored with computers and other equipment. The collisions allow scientists to study the particles that make up protons and the unique forces that bind them. The magnets needed to change the direction of the protons get their strength from electric current carried by a superconducting wire.

The possibilities for research offered by the SSC are great, but so is the cost, which has been estimated between four and eight billion dollars. Texas was chosen from more than 40 states competing for the SSC site. There was fierce competition because the construction will provide thousands of jobs. However, there is some concern about how the SSC will affect the environment.

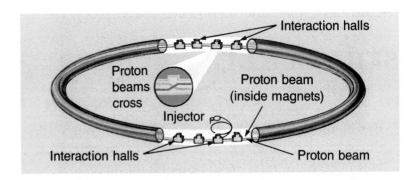

REVIEW

1. What are atoms?
2. Define the three particles that make up an atom.
3. What is a chemical group?
4. What is mercury's atomic number?
5. What is the symbol for zirconium? Atomic number?

How Does Matter Combine?

3:5 Compounds

You have learned that every substance is always the same in composition. A **compound** is a substance made of two or more elements whose atoms are chemically combined. Look around your kitchen. What compounds can you name? Compounds form when atoms share electrons or when they exchange electrons. A **molecule** is a particle that forms when atoms of some elements share electrons. Water is a compound composed of molecules. Each molecule of water (H_2O) is formed of two atoms of hydrogen (H_2) and one atom of oxygen (O). An **ion** (ı ahn) is an atom or group of atoms that has gained or lost an electron. An ion has either a positive charge or a negative charge. Table salt (NaCl) is a compound composed of ions of sodium (Na) and chlorine (Cl). Some common compounds are listed in Table 3–1.

GOALS

You will study . . .
1. how matter combines to form compounds.
2. homogeneous and heterogeneous mixtures.

What is the charge on an ion?

Table 3–1

Common Compounds		
Common Name	**Chemical Name**	**Chemical Formula**
water	hydrogen oxide	H_2O
table salt	sodium chloride	NaCl
table sugar	sucrose	$C_{12}H_{22}O_{11}$
baking soda	sodium hydrogen carbonate	$NaHCO_3$
carbonated water	carbonic acid	H_2CO_3
carbon dioxide	carbon dioxide	CO_2
ammonia	ammonia	NH_3
calcite	calcium carbonate	$CaCO_3$

FIGURE 3–7. Water, salt, and sugar are compounds.

How Does Matter Combine? 57

Compounds can be represented by chemical formulas. A **formula** lists the elements that make up a compound in their exact ratios. Table sugar (sucrose) is made of 12 atoms of carbon (C), 22 atoms of hydrogen (H), and 11 atoms of oxygen (O). The chemical formula for table sugar is $C_{12}H_{22}O_{11}$.

Based on their composition, compounds can be classified into two groups: organic and inorganic. Generally, an organic compound is one that contains carbon. Most organic compounds also contain hydrogen. Vitamins, petroleum, soaps, and plastics are made up of organic compounds.

Inorganic compounds are all compounds that are not classified as organic. Inorganic compounds are further classified into four groups: oxides, acids, bases, and salts. Oxygen combined with one other element makes an oxide. An example of an oxide is aluminum oxide. Aluminum oxide forms when oxygen combines with aluminum. This oxide, Al_2O_3, forms a dull looking coating on the outside of aluminum metal. Silicon can combine with oxygen to form silicon dioxide, SiO_2. Perhaps you have walked barefoot on silicon dioxide at a beach. What is another name for silicon dioxide?

An acid is a substance that forms hydrogen ions as it dissolves in water. Lemon, for example, owes its sour taste to citric acid. When acids dissolve in water, hydrogen atoms lose electrons to water molecules and form hydrogen ions. Soft drinks often contain carbonic acid. You may like acetic acid on your salad. What common liquid contains acetic acid? Some acids, however, are poisonous. Some cause burns on skin and destroy other materials. **CAUTION:** *NEVER taste or touch a substance to find out if it is an acid. Always wear safety goggles when working with acids.*

FIGURE 3–8. Many common products are acidic.

a

b

c

d

A base is a substance that dissolves in water to form hydroxide (hi DRAHK side) ions. A hydroxide ion is a unit of hydrogen and oxygen. Many household chemicals are bases. Baking soda dissolved in water is a base. Antacids are bases. Ammonia is a base used for cleaning floors and windows. Lye, sodium hydroxide, is a strong base in many drain cleaners and is used to make some soaps. **CAUTION:** *NEVER taste or touch a substance to find out if it is a base. Always wear safety goggles when working with bases.*

If an acid is added to a base, a chemical reaction occurs. One of the products of this reaction is water; the second product is a salt. Most salts are composed of ions of a metal and a nonmetal. Some salts are common in your home. The most common salt is table salt or sodium chloride (NaCl). Sodium chloride is often used to flavor food. Some "salt substitutes" used to flavor food are made of the salt potassium chloride (KCl). Both sodium chloride and calcium chloride ($CaCl_2$) can be used to melt snow and ice on streets and sidewalks.

FIGURE 3–9. Oxides (a), acids (b), bases (c), and salts (d) are inorganic compounds.

What are the products of an acid-base reaction?

3:6 Mixtures

Peter sleepily made his way to the kitchen one Saturday morning. He poured some cereal into a bowl. He added milk and fruit. As he ate, he thought of the different forms of matter he had learned about in science. What type of matter is the cereal? What kind of matter is milk? How can the bowl of cereal with milk be classified?

FIGURE 3–10. Mixtures play an important role in daily life.

PROBLEM SOLVING

What Happened to the Drawing?

Even though it was almost time for dinner, David was in the kitchen eating a snack. His mother was also in the kitchen preparing a salad. They were talking about David joining the science club when his younger brother Frank ran into the room.

Frank had a drawing in his hand. He had just created it with a black marker. He showed it to David who told him the drawing looked nice. Frank then showed his picture to his mother.

Frank expected the drawing to be hung on the refrigerator door. His mother told him to place the paper on the counter, and she would hang it as soon as she had time. Frank threw the paper on the counter and ran out.

The drawing landed in a puddle of water. By the time Frank's mother had finished the salad, the paper had absorbed

much of the water. The marker had dissolved in the water and moved with it as it was absorbed. The black lines were now blue surrounded with faded black. The faded black then turned into green with a yellow edge. Frank's mother was surprised at what had happened to the ink. David, however, knew what had happened. How might David explain the different colors to his mother?

Peter's breakfast is a mixture. A **mixture** is a combination of substances that is formed without a chemical reaction. The parts of a mixture usually can be separated more easily than the elements in a compound. Recall that the chemical properties of elements change when they form compounds. All matter in a mixture, however, keeps its own properties and keeps its own identity. In Peter's bowl, the fruit is still fruit, the milk is still wet, and the cereal is still cereal. None of the properties of the individual parts has changed. Much of the matter around you is in the form of mixtures.

What is the definition of a mixture?

How are compounds and mixtures different?

3:7 Heterogeneous Mixtures

Have you ever noticed that the number of chocolate chips may vary among cookies in a batch or that you can pick out the raisins from a bowl of cereal? Cookie dough and cereals are heterogeneous (het uh ruh JEE nee us) mixtures. A heterogeneous mixture is a mixture in which the substances are not evenly distributed. Its composition varies from one sample to another, and you can pick out its individual parts. Bottled Italian salad dressing is a heterogeneous mixture of solids and liquids.

How are substances distributed in a heterogeneous mixture?

A **suspension** (suh SPEN chun) is a heterogeneous mixture in which the particles of one material are supported in a liquid. In time, larger particles will settle out of the mixture. Waves on a beach can form a suspension of sand and water. Pearly nail polish also is a suspension.

Give two examples of a suspension.

FIGURE 3–11. A heterogeneous mixture is one in which the substances are not evenly distributed.

In a solution, what are the solute and solvent?

3:8 Homogeneous Mixtures

A homogeneous (hoh muh JEE nee us) mixture is one in which the particles of substances are spread evenly throughout the mixture. Particles will not settle out. A **solution** is a homogeneous mixture. Solutions can be mixtures of gases, solids, liquids, or any one of these in another. Air is a solution of gases. Brass is a solid solution formed from zinc and copper. Many common solutions are aqueous solutions; that is, solutions in which the particles are dissolved in water. Seawater is an aqueous solution.

In a solution, the **solute** (SAHL yewt) is the substance being dissolved. The **solvent** (SAHL vunt) is the substance in which a solute is dissolved. The substance present in the largest amount is the solvent. When you dissolve sugar in iced tea, the sugar is the solute, and water is the solvent.

Some solutions may be stronger or weaker than other solutions. One spoonful of sugar in a glass of iced tea might be too sweet for one person but not sweet enough for another. More sugar could be placed

FIGURE 3–12. Brass is a homogeneous mixture of zinc and copper (a). Seawater is an aqueous solution (b).

a

b

FIGURE 3–13. The temperature of a material affects its solubility.

in the glass. The tea will become sweeter as more sugar is added until, eventually, no more sugar will dissolve. The amount of solute a solvent can dissolve at a given temperature is known as the solubility. If no more solute will dissolve at a particular temperature, the solution is said to be saturated.

The rate at which a solute will dissolve varies. If you stir tea after adding sugar, the sugar will dissolve faster. If you crush the sugar into a fine powder before adding it to the tea, it will dissolve faster. If you increase the temperature of the tea, the sugar will dissolve faster. Also, raising the temperature of a solvent usually increases the amount of a solid solute that will dissolve in the solvent. You can dissolve a certain amount of sugar in iced tea before it becomes saturated. If you heat the tea, more sugar can be dissolved before the solution becomes saturated.

REVIEW

6. How is a mixture different from a compound?
7. What is a heterogeneous mixture?
8. How would you classify a mixture of marbles, sand, and buttons?
9. What is a saturated solution?
10. How can you change a saturated solution to an unsaturated solution?

Problem: How can you separate materials in a mixture?

Materials

prepared mixture
magnet
filter paper
ring stand
thermal mitt
graduated cylinder
plastic cup
screen (12 cm²)

clear plastic bag
water
funnel
stirring rod
hot plate
250-mL beakers (2)
permanent marker
typing paper (2)

Procedure

1. Copy the data table.
2. Spread a small amount of the prepared mixture in the middle of a piece of typing paper. Observe the different substances that make up the mixture.
3. Use the wire screen to filter large particles from the remaining mixture. Place the filtered materials in the plastic cup, and label it "Material A." Observe the physical properties and record.
4. Put the material from the typing paper into the plastic bag, and label it "Material B." Put the magnet in the plastic bag, and move it around in Material B. Remove the magnet and attached particles. Observe their properties and record.

5. Label the dry filter paper "Material C," and place it in the funnel. Place the funnel in the ring stand with a 250-mL beaker under the funnel.
6. Place the remaining Material B mixture into the other 250-mL beaker. Add 30 mL of water to the beaker, stir, and pour through the filter paper. Allow the filter paper to dry. Observe and record the physical properties of Material C.
7. Place the beaker on a hot plate set on medium heat. **CAUTION:** *Do not touch the hot plate or beaker.* Allow most of the liquid to evaporate. Turn off the hot plate. Allow the rest of the liquid to evaporate while the beaker cools. The beaker's contents are "Material D." Observe the properties and record.

Questions and Conclusions

1. What properties did you use to separate different materials?
2. How can you separate materials in a mixture?
3. Was the original mixture heterogeneous or homogeneous? Explain your answer.
4. What property allowed you to separate C and D?

Data and Observations

Material	Physical properties	How separated from mixture
A		
B		
C		
D		

CHAPTER 3 REVIEW

SUMMARY

1. A substance is always the same in composition. A property is a quality or characteristic of matter and can be physical or chemical in nature.   3:1
2. Atoms are the building blocks of matter. All atoms are made of protons, neutrons, and electrons.   3:2
3. An element is a substance made of just one type of atom. Elements are arranged by atomic number in the periodic table. Elements can be classified by atomic structure or as metals or nonmetals.   3:3
4. The Superconducting Super Collider is a giant particle accelerator that will allow scientists to study the particles that make up protons and the forces that bind them.   3:4
5. Compounds can be organic or inorganic and are represented by chemical formulas.   3:5
6. A mixture is a combination of substances that forms without a chemical reaction.   3:6
7. A heterogeneous mixture contains unevenly distributed substances. In a suspension, particles are suspended in a liquid.   3:7
8. In a solution, a solute is dissolved and evenly distributed in a solvent.   3:8

VOCABULARY

a. atomic number
b. atoms
c. chemical property
d. compound
e. electron
f. element
g. formula

h. ion
i. mass number
j. mixture
k. molecule
l. neutron
m. nucleus
n. periodic table

o. physical property
p. proton
q. substance
r. solute
s. solution
t. solvent
u. suspension

Match each description with the correct vocabulary word from the list above.

1. determines how a substance reacts to form other substances
2. the number of protons in an atom
3. in a solution, the substance being dissolved
4. building blocks of matter
5. a particle in an atom with a positive charge
6. elements listed according to atomic number
7. a substance composed of two or more elements whose atoms are chemically combined
8. combination of substances that forms without a chemical reaction
9. a homogeneous mixture
10. the core of an atom

CHAPTER 3 REVIEW

MAIN IDEAS

A. Reviewing Concepts

Choose the word or phrase that correctly completes each of the following sentences.

1. Matter is anything that takes up space and has _____.
   - **a.** color
   - **b.** oxygen
   - **c.** mass
   - **d.** chemicals

2. A substance of just one type of atom is a(n) _____.
   - **a.** equation
   - **b.** compound
   - **c.** symbol
   - **d.** element

3. _____ list the elements that make up compounds.
   - **a.** Equations
   - **b.** Formulas
   - **c.** Atoms
   - **d.** Signs

4. The first letter of a symbol is _____.
   - **a.** always a capital letter
   - **b.** sometimes a small letter
   - **c.** never a capital letter
   - **d.** always a small letter

5. Two elements essential for strong bones and teeth are _____.
   - **a.** oxygen and hydrogen
   - **b.** calcium and phosphorus
   - **c.** silicon and oxygen
   - **d.** lithium and sodium

6. Elements are listed in the periodic table in order of _____.
   - **a.** mass number
   - **b.** chemical formulas
   - **c.** atomic number
   - **d.** acidity

7. Oxygen combined with one other element is a(n) _____.
   - **a.** acid
   - **b.** base
   - **c.** oxide
   - **d.** mixture

8. The number of protons plus the number of neutrons in an atom is the _____.
   - **a.** mass number
   - **b.** atomic number
   - **c.** charge
   - **d.** none of these

9. Table salt contains _____.
   - **a.** silicon and oxygen
   - **b.** carbon and oxygen
   - **c.** sulfur and oxygen
   - **d.** sodium and chlorine

10. The symbol for lead is _____.
    - **a.** L
    - **b.** Le
    - **c.** P
    - **d.** Pb

11. An atomic particle with no electric charge is a(n) _____.
    - **a.** neutron
    - **b.** proton
    - **c.** electron
    - **d.** nucleus

12. A quality or characteristic of matter is a _____.
    - **a.** formula
    - **b.** suspension
    - **c.** symbol
    - **d.** property

13. Water is a(n) _____.
    - **a.** compound
    - **b.** element
    - **c.** metal
    - **d.** salt

14. Elements are made up of _____.
    - **a.** atoms
    - **b.** compounds
    - **c.** mixtures
    - **d.** all of these

15. All atoms are _____.
    - **a.** positively charged
    - **b.** neutral
    - **c.** negatively charged
    - **d.** none of these

B. Understanding Concepts

Answer the following questions using complete sentences.

16. What is the atomic number of gold?
17. Is a solution a mixture or a compound? Explain.
18. Differentiate among protons, neutrons, and electrons.
19. How are heterogeneous mixtures different from homogeneous mixtures?
20. Contrast solvent and solute.
21. Explain how elements are arranged in the periodic table.
22. Compare and contrast organic and inorganic compounds.

23. Compare and contrast suspensions and solutions.

24. Describe a saturated solution.

25. If atoms are neutrally charged, how can you account for the positive charges in the nucleus?

C. Applying Concepts

Answer the following questions using complete sentences.

26. What is the purpose of the Superconducting Super Collider?

27. Which elements would you expect to have properties similar to those of potassium (K)? Why?

28. Which of the following elements are metals: Ca, As, Zr, Na, C, Mn? How do you know they are metals?

29. How could you dissolve more sugar in a glass of iced tea if it were saturated?

30. How are many salts formed? What is another product of the reaction?

SKILL REVIEW

If you need help, refer to the Skill Handbook, pages 526 to 537.

1. Classify each of the following mixtures as heterogeneous or homogeneous.
salad dressing   beach sand   cereal
seawater   apple juice   brass
concrete

2. Suppose you heat 50 mL of water to 98°C and 50 mL of water to 65°C. You cool 50 mL of water to 10°C. You measure the amount of sugar that dissolves in each of the three containers of water. Make a data table that could be used to record the results of this experiment.

3. What is the independent variable in the experiment described in Question 3? What is the dependent variable?

4. Complete the table below on paper. The first one has been done for you.

Cause	Effect
an acid is added to a base	water and a salt are produced
oxygen combines with aluminum	
	silicon dioxide is formed
an acid is dissolved in water	

5. Make a pie graph to show the percentage of elements that are metals. Refer to Section 3:3 if you need help.

PROJECTS

1. Determine how temperature affects the amount of sugar that can be dissolved in a certain amount of water. Make a data table and graph your results. Determine the relationship between amount of sugar dissolved and temperature.

2. Select 20 household items, such as over-the-counter drugs, cleaners, foods, or soaps. Read the labels. Determine whether they are compounds, elements, or mixtures. If they are mixtures, classify them and record your findings in a table.

READINGS

1. Bains, Rae. *Molecules and Atoms.* Mahwah, NJ: Troll Associates, 1985.

2. Berger, Melvin. *Atoms, Molecules and Quarks.* New York: Putnam, 1986.

3. Ruben, Samuel. *Handbook of the Elements.* LaSalle, IL: Open Court, 1985.

Changes in Matter

CHAPTER 4

Career: Glassblower

Ellen and Susan had just left the midway at the state fair when they stopped to watch a glassblower. The glassblower held the end of a glass tube over the flame of a small gas burner until it softened into a small, glowing ball of jelly. He began to twirl the tube with his thumb and forefinger and to blow gently into the other end of the tube until the ball was nearly the size of a small rubber ball. Then he began to turn the tube rapidly and continued to blow into the open end. Suddenly, the ball began to flare out and became larger. The glassblower took the glass away from the flame and used long tweezers to pull and twist the melted glass. Before it could cool and harden, he held it over the flame again. Then he pulled and twisted with the tweezers and even snipped off a bit of the soft glass. When he finished, he had an amazingly delicate swan that he added to a collection of glass figures.

Ellen decided to buy the swan, and Susan chose a pretty glass rose that rested on its stem. The girls asked the man how he came to be a glassblower. He told them he had learned the trade by taking classes and working with a glassblower.

The glassblower was able to shape the heated glass. In this chapter, you will learn more about the different forms of matter and how matter changes physically and chemically.

F.Y.I. Toledo Museum of Art, P.O. Box 1013, Toledo, OH 43697

How Does Matter Change Physically?

You will study . . .
1. the four states of matter.
2. how matter changes state.
3. other physical properties of matter.

Name the four states of matter.

F.Y.I. Materials that appear to be solids but don't have a crystalline structure are amorphous (uh MOR fus) materials.

FIGURE 4–1. A rock is in a solid state (a). Salt crystals have a cubic shape (b).

4:1 States of Matter

Describe the shoes you are wearing. Perhaps they are white with laces or maybe they are brown loafers. Remember that your shoes are matter and that they have physical and chemical properties. A physical property is a characteristic of matter that can be observed without changing the makeup of the matter. One physical property you know is state. Matter is found in four states—solid, liquid, gas, and plasma.

Matter is composed of particles, and the particles are always in motion. A **solid** is matter that is a crystalline material with a definite volume and shape. A rock is in a solid state. The particles in a solid are in motion but simply vibrate in place. All the particles are packed closely together. In solids, the particles are always found in the same repeating pattern called a **crystal.** The crystals forming a particular solid are all alike. For example, the patterns or shapes of all table salt crystals are identical. The particles of crystals are held together by an attraction. The attraction between particles is stronger in some solids than in others. The strength of the attraction affects how easily the solid changes to another state. Materials with weak attraction will melt at a lower temperature than materials with strong attraction. Think about holding an ice cube and a paper clip in your hands. Which would melt from the heat of your body? In which solid is the attraction between particles stronger?

a

b

FIGURE 4–2. The particles in syrup have stronger attractive forces than the particles in milk. Therefore, syrup is more viscous than milk.

A **liquid** is matter that has a definite volume and takes the shape of its container. The particles in a liquid are packed almost as closely together as they are in a solid. However, the particles in a liquid can move more freely than those in a solid. They are not held in fixed positions but can move over and around one another. This allows liquids to flow from one container to another when they are poured.

What is a liquid?

Some liquids, such as oil or syrup, have strong attractive forces. These attractive forces prevent the liquids from flowing easily and are responsible for viscosity. **Viscosity** is the resistance of a liquid to flow. Syrup has a high viscosity compared with that of milk. Imagine pouring syrup and pouring milk on pancakes. Which liquid would hit the pancakes first?

F.Y.I. The curved surface of a liquid, noticeable in a narrow container, is called the meniscus.

A **gas** is matter that has no definite shape or volume. The particles move very freely and are spread apart so that there is very little attractive force among the particles. The particles move all over the inside of a container. The particles are in rapid motion, moving in straight lines until "bumped" by other gas particles or the walls of the container. Gas particles do not lose energy when they hit each other. They just go flying off in another direction. You may have observed this property of a gas if you have ever sprayed an air freshener. A small spray in one area will carry particles throughout the room until the odor is everywhere.

What is a gas?

F.Y.I. Over 99 percent of the matter in the universe is in the plasma state.

What is plasma?

F.Y.I. Stars are plasma.

What does the kinetic theory state?

FIGURE 4–3. Particles in a solid state (a) form a regular repeating pattern and are constantly vibrating. Particles of the same matter in a liquid state (b) move more freely. Particles in the gas state (c) move rapidly and freely.

Oxygen is an important gas for maintaining life on Earth. Several gaseous elements are found in nature as molecules. Hydrogen, nitrogen, oxygen, fluorine, and chlorine are gaseous elements found as molecules. Other gases include carbon dioxide, a product of respiration and combustion, and carbon monoxide, a product of incomplete burning of carbon fuels.

The fourth state of matter is plasma. **Plasma** is matter that consists of charged particles. Plasma occurs where temperatures are very high and where matter consists of positive and negative particles. Most of the matter in the universe is plasma. Plasma will conduct electricity. The matter in fluorescent tubes is plasma. The outer layer of the atmosphere that surrounds Earth is in a plasma state. This layer aids in communication.

How do scientists explain the differences in the states of matter? Many experiments have led scientists to an explanation called the kinetic theory. It states:
1. All matter is made of particles.
2. The particles are in constant motion.
3. The particles collide without losing energy.

The four states of matter consist of particles in motion. The particles of a solid substance are vibrating around a fixed position. They remain close together and therefore, the solid has a definite shape and volume. The particles in the liquid state of the same substance do not hold a fixed position but can move over each other. In the gas state of the same substance, particles have enough energy to overcome the attractive forces that hold them together. As you observe and study solids, liquids, and gases, recall that the amount of motion of the particles and the strength of the forces among the particles make the difference between steam, a block of ice, and a pool of water.

| a | solid | b | liquid | c | gas |

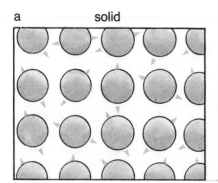
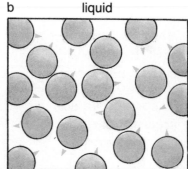
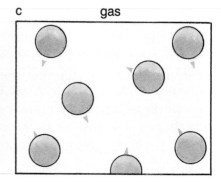

SKILL BUILDER

Using Tables

Make a table to classify the following substances as solids, liquids, or gases: ice, milk, oxygen, gold, water, helium, carbonated drink, sugar, mercury, and steam. If you need help, refer to Using Tables on page 530.

Questions

1. How many columns are there in your table?
2. What substance is represented in all three states in your table?
3. What substance could you classify in two columns of the table?

4:2 Changing States

You see matter change states every day. Liquid water changes to a solid when it freezes into ice. Melting ice is an example of a solid changing to a liquid. The steam over a kettle of boiling water is an example of a liquid changing to a gas. In all of these changes, thermal energy is added to or removed from matter to cause a change in state.

A solid material has less energy than the same material in a liquid state. Matter in a gaseous state has more energy than the same matter in a liquid state. Since all particles are in motion, adding thermal energy causes the particles to move even faster. When the particles move fast enough, attractive forces can no longer hold them together. As more thermal energy is added, the crystal pattern of a solid is broken and the solid melts. The **melting point** of a material is the temperature at which it changes from a solid state to a liquid state. The reverse of melting is freezing. The **freezing point** of a material is the temperature at which it changes from a liquid to a solid.

In a liquid, some particles have enough energy to become a gas. If these particles are at the surface of the liquid, they can break free of attractive forces and become a gas. This process is evaporation. **Evaporation** is the change from the liquid to the gaseous state at the liquid's surface. Where have you observed evaporation? How can the rate of evaporation be increased?

F.Y.I. Ice melts at a lower temperature than normal when it's under pressure. Ice skaters exert pressure on ice, and the skater skates on a thin film of water.

Define melting point and freezing point.

What is evaporation?

F.Y.I. Evaporation of water from the skin is a cooling process. The particles leaving the surface remove thermal energy and leave the body feeling cooler.

What is condensation?

It will take many hours for water in a pan to evaporate, but if you add heat to the pan, the water will evaporate more quickly. At the **boiling point** of a liquid, particles have gained enough energy to form a gas within the liquid. Boiling occurs throughout the entire liquid. The gas travels to the top of the liquid and into the air.

The opposite of evaporation is condensation. **Condensation** is the process in which a gas changes to a liquid. As the gas cools, the particles move more slowly. The attraction among the particles increases as they move closer together. Heat is transferred from the gas to its surroundings during condensation. Think about a cold soft drink can after it has been in a warm room for a while. What do you see on the outside of the can? How did the water droplets form?

Some solids can change directly into a gas or vice versa. The change from a solid to a gas or a gas to a solid without becoming a liquid is **sublimation.** Ice and snow can sublime. The ice in frozen foods sublimes. Sublimation dries out the food and changes the taste. We say that the food is freezer burned. Dry ice is an example of a material that sublimes. Dry ice is solid carbon dioxide. If you have ever seen a mystery movie, you may have been aware of the misty, foglike clouds. These may have been caused by dry ice.

PROBLEM SOLVING

The Haunted House

Eugene and a group of friends were making plans to prepare a haunted house. The children in the neighborhood had really enjoyed the one they had made last year in Eugene's garage. The boys were discussing what they had done and how they could make it different this year. Frank suggested that they include a pile of bones. The boys liked the idea. Tom thought that there was too much light last year. He said the kids weren't scared enough. The boys agreed and decided to use only two lights instead of four. Then, Eugene suggested that they make fake

fog. He said fog would make the haunted house seem really haunted. The boys thought that was a great idea. How could the boys make fake fog for the haunted house? Explain how fake fog works.

Problem: How does water change state?

Materials

hot plate	wooden dowel rods (2)
400-mL beaker	rubber bands (2)
ice cubes	clock or watch
water	Celsius thermometer
thermal mitt	graph paper

Procedure

1. Copy the data table.
2. Place 100 mL of water into the beaker. Add ice cubes until the ice cubes and water are about even. Put the beaker on the hot plate, but DO NOT turn on.
3. Attach the thermometer to the dowel rod by fastening it in two places with rubber bands so that you can read the temperature easily. Place the thermometer in the ice water and adjust the position of the thermometer up or down so that the bulb is near one end of the rod but is not touching the beaker's bottom.
4. Wait several minutes. Record the temperature of the ice water.
5. Write a hypothesis stating the effect of heat on ice water.
6. Turn the hot plate on a medium setting. **CAUTION:** *The hot plate, beaker, and thermometer will get very hot.*

DO NOT TOUCH. Be careful of rising steam.

7. Use a dowel rod to stir the ice water slowly and constantly. Record the water temperature after each minute until the water boils. Record any changes you observe.
8. Continue to record data for 5 minutes after the water has started to boil.
9. Turn off the hot plate.
10. Use the data from the table to make a graph. Put the time on the *x*-axis, and the temperature on the *y*-axis. Plot and connect the points.

Questions and Conclusions

1. What happens to the temperature during the activity?
2. When did the ice melt completely?
3. How long did it take the water to begin to boil?
4. What happened to the temperature of the water after it began to boil?
5. What was the maximum temperature reached by the water?
6. How does the water change state?
7. How would the results of the activity change if the hot plate were on a hotter setting?

Data and Observations

Time (min)	Temperature (°C)	Observations	Time (min)	Temperature (°C)	Observations
0			6		
1			7		
2			8		
3			9		
4			10		
5					

FIGURE 4–4. Cooking pans are good conductors. Their handles are made of insulators.

What are insulators?

4:3 Other Physical Properties

In this chapter and the last, you have studied physical properties of matter such as density, volume, shape, boiling point, freezing point, and solubility. Some other unique physical properties are ductility (duk TIHL ut ee), malleability (mal yuh BIHL ut ee), and conductivity. Conductivity is the ability of a material to transmit heat or electricity. What type of material makes up a cooking pan? Many metals, such as iron, copper, and aluminum, are good conductors of heat. Some materials are not good conductors. Materials through which heat and electricity flow poorly are **insulators.** Think about the handle of the cooking pan. What material covers the handle? The covers are usually made of wood or hard plastics. Are these conductors or insulators?

Malleability is the ability of a material to be hammered, pressed, or rolled into a thin sheet. Steel is malleable. It can be formed into sheets that are molded to form car bodies. Likewise, aluminum, tin, and gold can be rolled into thin foil. Ductility is the ability of a material to be drawn into thin wires. Copper and platinum are ductile and are useful in making electrical wiring.

REVIEW

1. What is a crystal?
2. How do solids, liquids, and gases differ?
3. What can you say about the freezing and melting points of a material?
4. Define sublimation.
5. Why is the property of malleability important?

4:4 Chemical Properties

You have been studying physical properties of matter. Physical properties are those that can be observed without changing the chemical makeup of a material. You can observe color or shape. You can measure volume or density. Suppose you observe two containers of milk. In one container, the milk is smooth and white, and you want to drink a glass with your sandwich. The second container, however, is clumpy and yellow. You do not want to drink it. You have observed physical properties of the milk. The containers of milk also have chemical properties. A chemical property relates to how one substance changes to a new one. The second container smelled sour, indicating that the milk had changed.

Under certain conditions, some materials will decompose and change to other materials. A chemical property of such matter is that it is unstable under those conditions. Hydrogen and oxygen combine to form water. Water can be broken down into hydrogen and oxygen by passing an electric current through the water. It is often necessary to add energy to enable a chemical reaction to occur. Most chemical and physical changes involve either the addition or the release of energy.

Other materials react with one another when placed together. Their chemical property is that they are reactive toward one another. Reactivity is the chemical property of a material that describes its general tendency to react with other materials. Some metals are highly reactive and form compounds easily. Corrosion is the result of the reactivity of some metals. Iron and oxygen react to form rust.

GOALS
You will study . . .
1. chemical properties.
2. how to balance a simple equation.
3. four types of chemical reactions.

What is reactivity?

FIGURE 4–5. Rust is the result of the reactivity of iron and oxygen.

What happens when you touch a lighted match to a piece of paper? The appearance of the paper changes. Light, smoke, hot gases, and thermal energy are released, and a small pile of ashes is left. A chemical change has occurred. A **chemical change** is any change or reaction in which a new substance is formed. The new substance has different chemical properties from the original. Hydrogen and oxygen are gaseous elements. In a chemical change, they form water, a substance with completely different properties from either hydrogen or oxygen. In the reaction of the burning paper, the paper and oxygen are reactants and the light, ashes, smoke, gases, and thermal energy are products of the reaction.

TECHNOLOGY

Rusting

Rusting is a chemical reaction. Iron combines with oxygen in the presence of water to form iron(III) oxide or rust. Rusting of machinery and other iron products costs consumers over $50 billion per year. Iron does not rust in dry air. Automobiles and bicycles last longer in the dry Southwest than along the humid East Coast. Other chemicals, such as salt, increase the rate of rusting.

Paint, oil, or grease may be used as a protective coating on iron products. If the paint chips or the surface is exposed, rusting will occur and continue underneath the coating. Metal plating is an-other means of protecting iron. Some bright automobile trim is made of steel coated with the metal chromium. Tin is plated onto thin steel to make "tin" cans. In a process called galvanizing, zinc is used to cover steel. Metal buckets and tubs are often made of galvanized steel.

ADVANCE

In 1985, work began on the process of replacing the iron supports in the Statue of Liberty. Salt water, salt air, wind, and pollution had caused severe corrosion or destruction of parts of the statue. The iron supports were replaced with a stainless steel alloy made of iron, nickel, chromium, and molybdenum.

Some seams and gaps in the statue's skin were sealed. However, nothing was done to the outer copper covering. The greenish surface is an external layer of copper carbonate that protects the copper from further corrosion.

4:5 Balancing Equations

In your math classes, you have learned that an equation is a shorthand way of stating relationships between numbers. If you want to say three plus two equals five, you can write it $3 + 2 = 5$. A **chemical equation** is a shorthand way of writing the changes that occur during a chemical reaction. You can use word equations, such as carbon combines with oxygen to yield carbon dioxide. However, it is easier to write the shorthand form.

$$C + O_2 \rightarrow CO_2$$

Combining substances is like making a cake. You combine flour, sugar, eggs, butter, milk, and flavoring and bake them to make a cake. What happens to the flour and sugar? The eggs and butter? They are not destroyed but are changed into the cake. There is the same total amount of material you started with, but the properties are different. The **law of conservation of mass** states that matter is neither created nor destroyed in a chemical reaction. The mass of the reactants before a reaction is present in the products of the reaction. This applies to all chemical reactions.

State the law of conservation of mass.

Because matter is never lost in a chemical change, it is necessary that chemical equations be balanced. A balanced equation shows that the same number of atoms present at the beginning of a chemical reaction are present at the end of the reaction. An equation is balanced by placing numbers called coefficients (koh uh FIHSH unts) in front of symbols and formulas. When writing a chemical equation, you first write the formula for each reactant and for the product. Then you look at each side of the arrow to be sure the numbers of each kind of atom on each side of the arrow balance. If they don't, you add coefficients to balance the equation.

What does a balanced equation show?

What are the four categories of reactions?

Follow these steps to write balanced equations.

1. Write the word equation for the burning of hydrogen. Hydrogen reacts with oxygen to yield water.
2. Write the formulas.
$$H_2 + O_2 \rightarrow H_2O$$
3. Check the numbers of atoms on each side of the arrow to see if the equation is balanced.
   - 2 atoms of hydrogen yield 2 atoms of hydrogen
   - 2 atoms of oxygen yield 1 atom of oxygen

   The equation is not balanced.
4. Add coefficients to balance the equation. If you add a coefficient of 2 before the H_2O on the right, you will balance the number of oxygen atoms— $H_2 + O_2 \rightarrow 2H_2O$. However, then there will be four atoms of hydrogen to the right of the arrow. If you then add a coefficient of 2 before the H_2, you will have four atoms of hydrogen to the left of the arrow and four atoms of hydrogen to the right of the arrow. Then the equation is balanced— $2H_2 + O_2 \rightarrow 2H_2O$.

4:6 Types of Chemical Reactions

Most chemical reactions can be placed in four general categories. The four categories are synthesis (SIHN thuh sus), decomposition, single displacement, and double displacement reactions.

Burning sulfur in oxygen is an example of a synthesis reaction. Synthesis means putting together. A **synthesis reaction** occurs when two or more substances combine to form one new substance.

sulfur + oxygen yields sulfur dioxide

$$S \quad + \quad O_2 \quad \rightarrow \quad SO_2$$

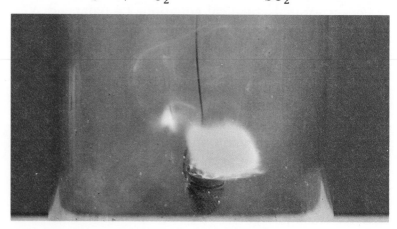

FIGURE 4–7. Sulfur burning in oxygen yields sulfur dioxide and is an example of a synthesis reaction.

FIGURE 4–8. Hydrogen and oxygen can be obtained from water through electrolysis, passing an electric current through the water. This is a decomposition reaction.

One sulfur atom combines with one oxygen molecule to form a sulfur dioxide molecule. Notice that the equation is balanced. There are one sulfur atom and two oxygen atoms on each side of the arrow. This is the same reaction that occurs when the tip of a match containing sulfur is struck.

Something decomposes when it breaks down into two or more simpler substances. Therefore, a **decomposition reaction** occurs when one substance breaks down into two or more products. Hydrogen peroxide, H_2O_2, can be broken down into the gases hydrogen and oxygen—$H_2O_2 \rightarrow H_2 + O_2$. This is an example of a decomposition reaction. In a decomposition reaction, one reactant yields two or more products.

Give the formula for the decomposition of H_2O_2.

Another type of reaction is a single displacement reaction. In a **single displacement reaction,** one element displaces another from a compound. For example, if you place a piece of copper wire in a solution of silver nitrate, copper will displace the silver in the silver nitrate solution. Silver crystals will form, and a new substance, copper nitrate, will be left in the solution. Copper wire and silver nitrate solution yield silver crystals plus copper nitrate solution.

$$Cu + 2AgNO_3 \rightarrow 2Ag + Cu(NO_3)_2$$

Another example of a single displacement reaction is when chlorine displaces bromine in the following reaction. Sodium bromide and chlorine yield sodium chloride plus bromine.

$$2NaBr + Cl_2 \rightarrow 2NaCl + Br_2$$

Give an example of a single displacement reaction.

How Does Matter Change Chemically? 81

Problem: What is the effect of temperature on the reaction time of an effervescent tablet?

Materials

250-mL beakers (3)
effervescent tablets (3)
Celsius thermometer
ice water
room-temperature water

warm water
clock or watch
   with second
   hand
masking tape

Procedure

1. Copy the data table.
2. Use the masking tape to label the beakers A, B, and C.
3. Write a hypothesis stating the effect of temperature on the decomposition of an effervescent tablet.
4. Pour exactly 150 mL of ice water into beaker A. Measure the temperature of the water. Record the temperature in the data table.
5. Carefully drop one effervescent tablet into the beaker. Measure and record the number of seconds needed for the tablet to completely decompose.
6. Pour 150 mL of room-temperature water into beaker B. Measure and record the temperature of the water.
7. Repeat step 5 using the room-temperature water.
8. Pour 150 mL of warm water into beaker C. Measure and record the temperature of the water.
9. Repeat step 5 using the warm water.

Questions and Conclusions

1. In which beaker did the reaction occur most rapidly?
2. In which beaker was the reaction slowest?
3. What evidence of chemical change did you observe when the effervescent tablet was placed in water?
4. What is the type of reaction you observed?
5. What is the effect of temperature on the reaction time of an effervescent tablet?
6. What was the independent variable in the activity?
7. What was the dependent variable?
8. Why did each beaker contain exactly 150 mL of water?
9. How does your hypothesis compare with the results of the activity?

Data and Observations

Beaker	Temperature (°C)	Reaction time (seconds)
A		
B		
C		

The fourth category of reaction is a double displacement reaction. In a **double displacement reaction,** the atoms or groups of atoms in two compounds switch places. An example of this reaction is zinc bromide and silver nitrate yield zinc nitrate and silver bromide.

What happens in a double displacement reaction?

$$ZnBr_2 + 2AgNO_3 \rightarrow Zn(NO_3)_2 + 2AgBr$$

The silver combines with the bromine, and zinc nitrate is a second product. Nitric acid (HNO_3) can be produced by the following double replacement reaction.

$$H_2SO_4 + 2NaNO_3 \rightarrow 2HNO_3 + Na_2SO_4$$

SCIENCE AND SOCIETY

4:7 Over-the-Counter Drugs

One time in your life when your knowledge of compounds may come in handy is in the purchase of over-the-counter (OTC) drugs. OTC drugs are medications that can be bought without a doctor's prescription. OTC drugs usually are used to relieve symptoms of minor illnesses. OTC drugs include pain relievers, antacids, vitamins, decongestants, skin medications, antiperspirants, and allergy medications.

Have you ever stood in front of a drug display and wondered which product you should purchase? Perhaps you recall seeing various brands advertised on TV or in magazines. One thing you may notice is that the prices of the products vary a great deal. How do you choose the product you will buy?

F.Y.I. Aspirin overdose can cause death. The first symptom of aspirin overdose is ringing in the ears. Stop taking aspirin immediately if this occurs. Read all labels and closely follow the directions given for all medications.

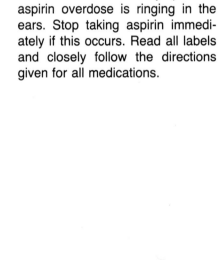

FIGURE 4–9. Over-the-counter drugs are chemical compounds that can be purchased without a doctor's prescription.

COLD MEDICATION	Caplets are easy to swallow because they are specially coated and sha
EACH CAPLET CONTAINS THESE ACTIVE INGREDIENTS:	FOR THE TEMPORARY RELIEF OF:
ANTIHISTAMINE (Chlorpheniramine Maleate 2 mg)	RUNNY NOSE, SNEEZING, WATERY AND ITC
NASAL DECONGESTANT (Pseudoephedrine HCl 30 mg)	NASAL CONGESTION
COUGH SUPPRESSANT (Dextromethorphan HBr 15 mg)	COUGHING
ANALGESIC/ANTIPYRETIC (Acetaminophen 325 mg)	ACHES, PAINS AND FEVER

DOSAGE: Adults: Two caplets every 6 hours, not to exceed 8 caplets in 24 hours. Children (6-12): One caplet every 6 hours, not to exceed 4 caplets in 24 hours for 5 days.

WARNING: Do not administer to children under 6 or exceed the recommended dosage because nervousness, dizziness or sleeplessness may occur. May cause excitability especially in children. A persistent cough may be a sign of a serious condition. If fever persists for more than three days, or if symptoms do not improve or new ones occur within five days or are accompanied by high fever, rash, excessive mucus, persistent cough or headache, consult a physician before continuing use. This preparation may cause drowsiness; alcohol may increase the drowsiness effect. Avoid alcoholic beverages when taking this product. Use caution when driving a motor vehicle or operating machinery. Do not take this product if you have heart disease, high blood pressure, thyroid disease, diabetes, asthma, glaucoma, emphysema, chronic pulmonary disease, shortness

of breath, difficulty in breathing or difficulty in due to enlargement of prostate gland or are prescription drug for high blood pressure o sion unless directed by a doctor.

DO NOT USE IF CARTON IS OPENED BLISTER UNIT IS BROKEN. KEEP THIS A MEDICATION OUT OF THE REACH C DREN. AS WITH ANY DRUG, IF YOU AR NANT OR NURSING A BABY, SEEK THE OF A HEALTH PROFESSIONAL BEFORE THIS PRODUCT. IN THE CASE OF ACCI OVERDOSAGE, CONTACT A PHYSIC POISON CONTROL CENTER IMMEDIATE

See side panel for expiration date. Store at room temperature.

INACTIVE INGREDIENTS: Cellulose, Gly acetate, Hydroxypropyl Methylcellulose, Ma Stearate, Sodium Starch Glycolate, Starch, Dioxide, Blue #1 and Yellow #6 & #10. ©

FIGURE 4–10. Compare the chemical compounds in over-the-counter drug products in order to make informed and wise choices in your purchases.

One method for making your choice should be to compare the ingredients listed on the packages. If two or more brands have identical ingredients, the choice will depend on the prices of the products. Sometimes the major ingredient of several brands will be the same, but there may be different additives. For example, one brand of cough syrup may be cherry flavored while another is lemon flavored. You must then decide if one additive or another is worth the extra cost of the product.

Table 4–1

Aspirin Comparison		
Type of aspirin	Amount of aspirin per tablet	Cost per tablet
Name Brand	325 mg	$ 0.10
Generic brand	325 mg	$ 0.008
Coated generic	325 mg	$ 0.07
Buffered	325 mg	$ 0.14

Aspirin is a compound that relieves fever and minor pain. It is possible to buy aspirin compounds packaged by different companies. Use Table 4–1 to compare four brands of aspirin. You must decide how important coating or buffering is to you before you make your choice of brands. Coated tablets may be easier to swallow. Buffered aspirin is supposed to help prevent stomach irritation that may be caused by plain aspirin. As you can see from the table, the main ingredient is 325 mg of aspirin. The cost per tablet varies. How will you make your choice? Remember to read the labels on all OTC drugs you buy. Be a wise consumer when you purchase OTC drugs.

REVIEW

6. What is a chemical property? Name one.
7. How does a chemical property differ from a physical property?
8. State the law of conservation of mass. Give an example.
9. What kind of chemical reaction is $2Na + Cl_2 \rightarrow 2NaCl$?
10. Balance this equation.
   $4Fe + 3O_2 \rightarrow \_\_ Fe_2O_3$

CHAPTER 4 REVIEW

SUMMARY

1. The four states of matter are solid, liquid, gas, and plasma. 4:1
2. Changes of state occur because thermal energy is added to or removed from matter. 4:2
3. Ductility, malleability, and conductivity are physical properties. Insulators are materials through which heat and electricity flow poorly. 4:3
4. A chemical property relates to how one substance changes to a new one in a chemical reaction. 4:4
5. A balanced chemical equation contains the same number of each kind of atom on each side of the arrow. 4:5
6. Four general categories of chemical reactions are: synthesis, decomposition, single displacement, and double displacement. 4:6
7. Comparing lables on OTC drug packages is a good way to make informed choices among products. 4:7

VOCABULARY

a. boiling point
b. chemical change
c. chemical equation
d. condensation
e. crystal
f. decomposition reaction
g. double displacement\ reaction
h. evaporation
i. freezing point
j. gas
k. insulators
l. law of conservation of mass
m. liquid
n. melting point
o. plasma
p. single displacement reaction
q. solid
r. sublimation
s. synthesis reaction
t. viscosity

Match each description with the correct vocabulary word from the list above.
1. process in which a gas changes to a liquid
2. shorthand way of writing the changes that occur during a chemical reaction
3. a chemical reaction with two or more reactants yielding one product
4. temperature at which a solid changes to a liquid
5. materials through which heat and electricity flow poorly
6. the resistance of a liquid to flow
7. changing from a gas to a solid or from a solid to a gas without a liquid state
8. having definite shape and volume
9. having no definite shape or volume
10. point at which a liquid becomes a solid.

MAIN IDEAS

A. Reviewing Concepts

Choose the word or phrase that correctly completes each of the following sentences.

1. _____ are examples of OTC drugs.
   a. Antacids   c. Antiperspirants
   b. Vitamins   d. All of these
2. Physical properties of gold include the fact that gold is _____.
   a. shiny   c. dull
   b. malleable   d. both a and b
3. The ability of a material to be drawn into a thin wire is _____.
   a. malleability   c. conductivity
   b. ductility   d. flexibility
4. Properties that depend on how materials change to new ones are _____.
   a. physical properties
   b. electrical properties
   c. chemical properties
   d. happy properties
5. Changes in state occur because of the addition or removal of _____.
   a. matter   c. chemical energy
   b. thermal energy d. all of these
6. The particle motion in a gas is _____.
   a. more than in a liquid
   b. less than in a liquid
   c. same as in a solid
   d. none of these
7. An example of the plasma state is _____.
   a. sugar   c. glowing matter in a fluorescent tube
   b. salt   d. water
8. Ice is matter in a _____ state.
   a. solid   c. gas
   b. liquid   d. plasma
9. _____ is a high viscosity liquid.
   a. Milk   c. Water
   b. Syrup   d. Tea

10. The equation $2H_2O \rightarrow 2H_2 + O_2$ is an example of a _____ reaction.
    a. synthesis
    b. decomposition
    c. single displacement
    d. double displacement
11. The state of matter that consists of charged particles is _____.
    a. solid   c. gas
    b. liquid   d. plasma
12. Adding thermal energy to a material causes the particles to _____.
    a. move faster   c. not change
    b. move more slowly   d. all of these
13. A liquid changes to a gas state at its surface when _____ occurs.
    a. freezing   c. condensation
    b. evaporation   d. melting
14. When a material is changed to a new material, a _____ has occurred.
    a. physical change
    b. physical property
    c. chemical change
    d. chemical property
15. In a chemical reaction, the mass of the products is _____ the mass of the reactants.
    a. less than   c. equal to
    b. more than   d. unequal to

B. Understanding Concepts

Answer the following questions using complete sentences.

16. Give examples of water occurring in three ordinary states of matter.
17. Define viscosity.
18. Why will some solids change to liquids more easily than others?
19. What are insulators? Give examples.
20. Are the particles closer together in a liquid or a gas?

21. In which state of matter are particles vibrating around a fixed point?
22. What is the most common state of matter in the universe?
23. What can you do to increase the rate of evaporation of a liquid?
24. What is an OTC drug?
25. Why is it important to read labels on OTC drugs?

C. Applying Concepts

Answer the following questions using complete sentences.

26. What occurs in displacement reactions?
27. Why isn't iron used for filling teeth?
28. How are chemical properties different from physical properties?
29. Alcohol evaporates faster than water. What does this tell you about the forces between alcohol particles?
30. Balance the equation—$C + O_2 \rightarrow 2CO$. Name the reactants, the product, and the kind of reaction.

SKILL REVIEW

If you need help, refer to the Skill Handbook, pages 526 to 537.

1. You have three beakers, each containing 50 mL of water. You place beaker A in a room that is 25°C. You place beaker B in a room that is 15°C, and beaker C in a room that is 5°C. After five days, you find that 12 mL of water have evaporated from beaker A, 7 mL from beaker B, and 3 mL from beaker C. What can you infer about the relationship between evaporation and temperature?
2. In the experiment described in Question 1, what are the independent and dependent variables? The constants?

3. On a piece of paper, complete the information missing from this table.

Cause	Effect
C and O_2 chemically combine	
	SO_2 is formed
electrolysis of H_2O	

4. Classify each of the following as condensation, evaporation, or sublimation: (a) water on the outside of a cold can; (b) dry ice changing to "fog"; (c) water level dropping in an aquarium.
5. Test five brands of antacid tablets to determine which dissolves quickest in water. Make a data table. Name one constant in your experiment.

PROJECTS

1. Grow crystals. Display them with a brief description of materials used, how they were grown, and their structures.
2. Dissolve different amounts of salt in equal volumes of water and place in the freezer. Keep track of the time it takes each to freeze. Draw conclusions from the results.

READINGS

1. Cobb, Vicki. *Chemically Active: Experiments You Can Do At Home.* New York: Lippencott, 1985.
2. Spackling, Michael. *Liquids and Solids.* New York: Methuen, 1985.
3. "Superconductivity." *The World Book Encyclopedia.* Chicago: World Book Inc., 1988.

FUN WITH

Chinese make gunpowder.

1860

First 3D movies are shown.

1912

1000

Abraham Lincoln wins the presidency.

1894

Neon signs light up Paris, France.

Did you know that a piece of gold with a mass of 28 g can be stretched into a thin wire about 80 kilometers long?

Why does popcorn pop?

Corn kernels have water at their centers. When the kernels are heated, the water expands and eventually becomes steam. The pressure the steam exerts on the kernels forces them to pop open.

QUESTION AND ANSWER

What do diamonds and pencils have in common?
Diamonds and pencil "lead" (graphite) are both carbon (C). If they are the same element, why do they look so different? The carbon atoms in graphite are bonded in a way different from the way carbon atoms in diamond are bonded. Thus, graphite and diamond have very different properties. Graphite is soft. In addition to pencil "lead," graphite is used in paints, batteries, and lubricants. Diamond, on the other hand, is one of the hardest substances known. Diamonds are used in cutting tools, phonograph needles, abrasives, and jewelry.

Riddle
Q. The longer I stand, the shorter I grow. What am I? **A.** a burning candle

TEASER

FUN RECIPE

GORP (TRAIL MIX)
Use any or all of the following ingredients to make a tasty snack: nuts, carob chips, dried apricots, raisins, dried coconut, banana chips, sunflower seeds, dates, dried pineapple, and other dried fruits. Combine the ingredients in proportions to suit you. Keep in a covered container in a cool, dry place. What type of matter is gorp?

SCIENCE

Sliced bread is introduced in the U.S.

1945

Hula hoop is invented.

1960

1930

Tupperware Corporation is founded.

1958

The International System of Units (SI) is created.

QUIZ

Planet Earth has an average density of 5.52 g/cm³. Its mass is about 5 960 000 000 000 000 000 000 000 000 g. What is the volume of Earth? Hint: Use scientific notation.

Why does a cut apple turn brown? Air reacts with the apple and oxidation occurs. You can prevent this by covering cut fruit with plastic wrap. It can also be prevented by sprinkling the fruit with lemon juice. Vitamin C prevents oxidation.

Maria made herself a cup of hot tea one cold winter morning. Before she added sugar, she accidentally filled the cup to the rim with hot water. Rather than trying to pour out the hot liquid, she added a spoonful of sugar to her tea. It did not overflow. She added another spoonful to the seemingly full cup. It still did not overflow. Why?

JOKE

Q. What happened when the glassblower inhaled?
A. She got a pane in her stomach!

THE FAR SIDE

"Now that desk looks better. Everything's squared away, yessir, squaaaaaared away."

© 1985 Universal Press Syndicate

89

UNIT 2

Forces at Work

Imagine yourself as a fish swimming in the ocean. As a human, you also live in an ocean—an ocean of air. Forces act on objects in these two fluids. Pressure is pushing on the fish and the submarine. What other forces are acting on the fish and the submarine? Where do the fish get energy for their life processes?

Forces and Energy

CHAPTER 5

Career: Bike Mechanic

John was on the Tour of the Scioto River Valley, a 325-km bicycle tour. He had less than 40 km to go, and was easily pedaling his new ten-speed bicycle up a hill when he felt something give. At first his pedals seemed to slip around without turning the wheels. Then he had so much trouble pushing the pedals that he was sure that the tour was over for him. Disappointed, he stopped and waited for the repair team.

After examining the bike, the repair team told John that only minor adjustments were needed. The head mechanic said that the rear derailleur on John's ten-speed was allowing the chain to slip from the large sprocket to a smaller one. He was losing the use of his lower gears, but they weren't broken. When the chain rides on the large rear gear, the pedaling is easy, but speed is slow. When the chain is moved to a smaller sprocket, more force must be applied to the pedals to turn the wheels. However, speed is greater with the lower gear. The mechanic made some careful adjustments to repair the derailleur. When all of his gears were working, John took off to finish the tour.

John's body changes the chemical energy in food to mechanical energy when he pushes on the pedals. The force applied to the pedals of his bicycle causes the wheels to turn. In this chapter you will study forces and how forces relate to energy.

F.Y.I. Mechanics Seminars, 2755 Ore Mill Drive #14, Colorado Springs, CO 80904

What Are Forces in Your World?

GOALS

You will study . . .
1. the nature of forces that are all around you.
2. net forces and balanced forces.

F.Y.I. Gravitational force on the moon is 1/6 that on Earth.

FIGURE 5–1. A skateboarder uses forces to start moving, change direction, or stop (a). Gravitational forces cause the ball to hit the ground (b).

5:1 Forces

Suppose your skateboard is on the sidewalk. You can move it by pulling it. You can push it away from you. The push or pull that one object exerts on another is a **force.** Any time two or more objects interact, forces are the cause of the interaction. You use forces to make an object start moving, to change its direction, or to stop its motion. Without forces, you would not be able to ride the skateboard, walk, talk to your friend on the telephone, watch TV, or pour a glass of water. A volleyball goes across the net because of forces. Blood flows through your blood vessels because of forces.

Objects do not even have to be touching to exert forces on each other. If you drop your book, what happens to it? It falls to the floor, of course. A force has caused the motion. **Gravitational** (grav uh TAY shun ul) **force** is the force every object exerts on every other object. The gravitational force between objects depends on their masses. Both Earth and the book exert forces on each other. The book exerts just as much force on Earth as Earth exerts on the book. But the book has much less mass than Earth, so the book is much easier to move. Thus, the book falls toward Earth's surface. You cannot see gravitational forces, but you can see what they do.

a

b

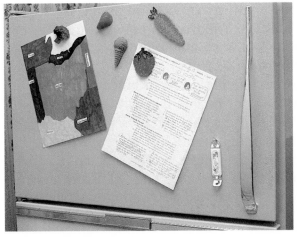

a   b

Think about magnets. Do you use magnets to hold papers on the refrigerator? A magnet exerts a force on the refrigerator. A magnet is any object that produces a magnetic field around itself. A magnetic field is where magnetic forces act. If you bring another magnet or piece of iron into this field, you can observe that the first magnet either attracts or repels it. Look at Figure 5–2b. What is happening to the magnets? Magnets are found in compasses and in some toys.

If you have taken clothes out of a dryer and found them "sticking" together, you have seen electric forces in action. Remember that all matter is made of atoms. Atoms contain positive protons and negative electrons. The clothes in the dryer became charged as they rubbed against each other. Electrons from some of the clothes were transferred to other clothes. The atoms in the clothes that lost electrons became positively charged. The atoms in clothes that gained electrons became negatively charged. Negatively charged clothes attracted positively charged clothes, and they stuck.

If you push off on your skateboard, you roll down the sidewalk. You roll along rapidly at first, but then slow and eventually stop. The force between the wheels of the skateboard and the sidewalk is friction. **Friction** is a force that opposes motion. The amount of friction depends on the types of surfaces involved and the amount of force pressing them together. A boat moving through water is slowed by the friction of the boat bottom rubbing against the water. Friction between your feet and the ground allows you to walk across a surface without falling.

FIGURE 5–2. Magnetic forces are holding up these papers (a). The magnet in the boy's hand repels the magnet on the string (b).

FIGURE 5–3. Clothes in a dryer can become charged as they rub against each other.

What happens if you try to walk on an icy sidewalk? You may slip and fall. The friction between the icy surface and your feet is so low that, as you push against the surface, your feet slip.

You have been studying different kinds of forces. One force you may not be familiar with is nuclear (NEW klee ur) force. The small particles in the nuclei of atoms are held together by nuclear forces. When the bonds between these particles are broken, large amounts of energy are released. You will learn more about these forces when you study about nuclear energy.

5:2 Forces—Balanced or Unbalanced?

Forces always exist in pairs. They can cause changes in the shape and motion of objects. But sometimes two or more forces act on an object and no change in shape or motion occurs. If all forces acting on an object are opposed by equal and opposite forces, then they are called **balanced forces.** Think about bouncing on a trampoline. When you hit the trampoline, gravitational force is pulling you downward. When you reach your lowest point, the downward force of gravity is balanced by the upward force of the trampoline. Is the force of gravity acting on you when you are sitting in a chair? Yes, the force

What are balanced forces?

PROBLEM SOLVING

A Sticky Situation

Sam was watching a gymnast perform on the uneven parallel bars. He noticed that before she began her routine, the gymnast put powder on her hands. Sam had always thought of powder as a lubricant, as it made his hands slide past each other easily when he rubbed them together. He thought it was odd that the gymnast would put a lubricant on her hands. After thinking about it for a while, Sam decided that the powder would help keep the gymnast from slipping. Why do you think Sam decided this?

TECHNOLOGY

Ball Bearings

A ball bearing is a round, smooth object that is put between two surfaces to reduce friction. Ball bearings are used in bicycles, automobile wheels, and between some other machine parts. Ball bearings range from the size of pin heads to large marbles. Some are sealed with a cover on both sides and come with grease. Some are not sealed and require the addition of grease.

ADVANCE

Perfectly round and smooth ball bearings would reduce friction better than irregularly shaped bearings. On Earth, gravitational force prevents ball bearings from being perfectly smooth and round. Instead, they are pulled slightly out of shape as the liquid steel cools and becomes a solid. In the future, a space station may provide a factory for making better ball bearings. Because gravity causes the circular motion of the space station, it does not distort the ball bearings. Hence, the ball bearings would be perfectly round and smooth.

of gravity is always present, pulling you downward. Why don't you move? The chair is pushing up on you with an equal force opposite to the force you are exerting downward. Again, the two forces are balanced, but acting in opposite directions.

When forces acting on an object are unbalanced, there is a **net force** on the object. Motion occurs only if a net force acts on an object. When you hit a baseball, a net force changes the direction of motion of the ball. When you crumple a sheet of paper or stretch a rubber band, you see the results of a net force.

What is a net force?

REVIEW

1. What is a force?
2. List three types of forces.
3. Why does a bowling ball slow down before it hits the pins?
4. How do balanced forces and net forces differ?
5. On Earth, an astronaut can jump 1 m into the air. On the moon, the same astronaut can jump six times higher. Explain.

 # ACTIVITY 5–1 **Balancing Forces**

Problem: How can you balance a force?

Materials
spring scale
rubber bands (2)
metal ring
goggles

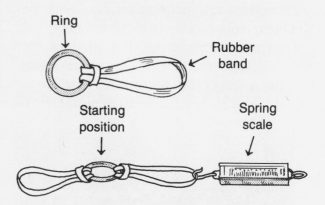

Ring — Rubber band — Starting position — Spring scale

Procedure
1. Copy the data table.
2. Slip one of the rubber bands through the ring. When the rubber band is halfway through the ring, slip one end of the rubber band back through the loop on the other side of the ring. Keep pulling until the rubber band is firmly attached to the ring.
3. Repeat with the second rubber band on the other side of the ring.
4. Attach one of the rubber bands from the loop to the hook of the spring scale.
5. Adjust the spring scale to read zero. Place the assembly on a piece of paper on a flat surface. Trace the metal ring on the paper. This is the starting position.
6. Put on your goggles. Pull on the spring scale while your partner pulls on the free rubber band. Try to keep the ring at the starting position.
7. Have your partner pull the rubber band three times, each time with increasing amounts of force. Record in your data table the amount of force needed to keep the ring in the starting position for each of the three trials.
8. Change places with your partner and repeat step 7.

Data and Observations

Student	Trial Number		
	1	2	3
A			
B			

Questions and Conclusions
1. What force is acting on the ring when it is resting on a flat surface?
2. How much pull was needed to keep the ring in the starting position in trial 1? In trial 2? In trial 3?
3. What sideways forces are acting on the ring in each of the trials?
4. What must be done to keep the ring at the starting position when the rubber band is pulled with more force?
5. How did the force you exerted compare with the force exerted by the other student to keep the ring at the starting position?
6. How did the direction of force you exerted compare with the force exerted by your partner?
7. How can you balance a force?

5:3 Energy

"I don't have enough energy to walk up the stairs."
"Would you like some raisins? They'll give you
energy." You may use the word "energy" in many
different ways. What does energy really mean?

Energy is the ability to do work. Any object has
energy if it is able to exert a force or move something.
You use energy from food when you do work or play a
game. A truck uses the energy in diesel fuel to
transport goods from one place to another. Energy, in
a way, is like money. It can be stored, put to use, and
transferred back and forth between matter.

A rock on the side of a mountain has energy due to
its position. The rock may roll down the side of the
mountain causing a rock slide or smashing the roof of
a house at the bottom of the mountain. A stretched
rubber band has energy due to its condition. Snapping
the rubber band could cause a piece of paper to fly
across the room. The energy that an object has due to
its position or condition is **potential energy.** When a
rock rolls, water spills over a dam, a car rolls down a
hill, or a rubber band snaps, the potential energy of
each object changes form. The objects are moving.
Energy of motion is **kinetic energy.** Consider a child
playing with a windup toy. As the spring is wound
tight, it gains potential energy due to its condition.
When the spring is released, the toy begins to move.
The potential energy of the spring is transferred to the
toy as kinetic energy.

GOALS

You will study . . .
1. potential energy and kinetic
   energy and their relationship.
2. different forms of energy and
   conservation of energy.
3. how dams provide energy to
   produce hydroelectric power.

What is potential energy?

F.Y.I. The unit of energy is
the joule. One joule is the amount
of energy used to lift an apple 1 m.

FIGURE 5-4. The toys on the left
have the potential energy of wound
springs (a). When the springs are
released, potential energy changes
to kinetic energy (b).

a

b

FIGURE 5-5. People or objects in motion are examples of mechanical energy.

F.Y.I. The water at the bottom of Niagara Falls is about 0.12°C warmer than the water at the top of the falls due to the kinetic energy of the falling water changing to thermal energy.

What is mechanical energy?

FIGURE 5-6. Even though their temperatures are the same, 1.0 L of boiling water has more thermal energy than 0.5 L of boiling water.

1 liter

½ liter

5:4 Forms of Energy

Kinetic energy and potential energy that cause objects to move are grouped together and called **mechanical energy.** You probably know about and often use this form of energy. When you pedal a bicycle, take a bite of food, or throw a ball, you are putting an object in motion and using mechanical energy.

All matter is made up of moving particles. These particles have kinetic energy. The temperature of an object is a measure of the average kinetic energy of the moving particles in that object. The particles in boiling water have a higher average kinetic energy than the particles in cold water. Thus, the temperature of the boiling water is higher than that of the cold water. **Thermal energy** is the total kinetic energy of the moving particles that make up an object. A liter of boiling water has more thermal energy than half a liter of boiling water. The liter and half-liter of boiling water both have the same average kinetic energy (temperature). They have different thermal energies because there is more total energy in one liter than in half a liter.

Electrical energy is the kinetic energy of moving electrons. A flow of electrons along a path or circuit is called an electric current. What happens when you flip a light switch from off to on? You complete a circuit allowing electric current to light the bulb. Electric current also allows you to operate a TV, radio, microwave oven, or a computer.

Radiant energy is a form of energy that travels in waves. You are probably most familiar with radiant energy in the form of solar energy. **Solar energy** is radiant energy from the sun that travels in waves through space. Solar energy is absorbed by objects and changes their temperature. Earth is warmed by absorbed solar energy. Plants need solar energy to make food, which is the base of most food chains on Earth. Solar energy can be used to heat homes and warm water. Would heating and cooking with solar energy be possible everywhere?

Chemical energy is potential energy that is stored in bonds between atoms. Chemical energy is released when a chemical reaction occurs. The chemical energy may be transformed into thermal, radiant, or electrical energy. It may also remain stored in the new bonds formed in the reaction. Have you ever sat around a campfire? Burning wood releases stored chemical energy as heat and light. A car battery or flashlight cell releases chemical energy in the form of electrical energy. The food you eat has chemical energy that is converted to mechanical energy and thermal energy and allows your body to function properly. The energy your body uses to run, breathe, and circulate blood comes from the chemical energy stored in food.

What is chemical energy?

FIGURE 5–7. The appliances you operate every day use electrical energy (a). Solar energy can be changed to electricity to run this telephone (b).

a

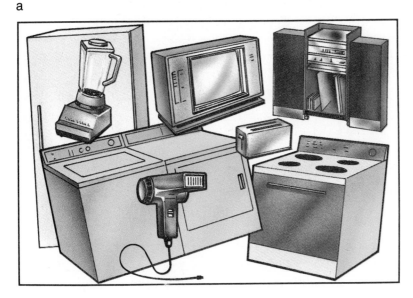

b

Nuclear energy is produced when the bonds holding the particles of the nucleus of an atom together are broken. Nuclear energy is used to produce electricity. Nuclear energy also is used to detect some major health problems and as a cure for some diseases.

5:5 Energy Transfer and Conservation of Energy

Any flow of energy from one object to another is **energy transfer.** What happens when you pull an arrow on a bowstring and then release it? The potential energy of the drawn bow is transferred to the arrow as kinetic energy. Energy is transferred in many ways. Radiant energy is transferred by waves. Thermal energy is transferred between objects of different temperatures. It always moves from an object at a higher temperature to one at a lower temperature. Electrical energy is usually transferred through conductors.

You can think of this flow of energy as an energy chain. Solar energy is transferred by waves to a plant and is converted to chemical energy. A cow eats grass and uses the chemical energy for its life processes. Milk or meat from the cow gives you chemical energy to convert to mechanical energy when you talk, run, and breathe.

FIGURE 5–8. In this energy chain, solar energy is converted to chemical energy.

Problem: What factors affect the energy transferred by a rolling ball?

Materials

balance
small rubber ball
golf ball
milk carton
wooden block (2 identical)

scissors
grooved ruler
meter stick
masking tape

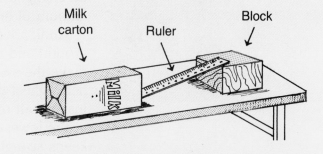

Procedure

Part A

1. Copy the data table.
2. Remove the top of the milk carton using the scissors.
3. Find and record the masses of the balls.
4. Measure and record the height of a block and place it on a table.
5. Use the grooved ruler to make a ramp against the block. Place the milk carton at the other end of the grooved ruler so that the balls can roll into it. Mark the place on the table where the carton ends with tape.
6. Hypothesize the effect of the mass of each ball on the distance the carton will travel.
7. Hold the rubber ball at the top of the ramp. Let it roll down the groove and into the carton.
8. Mark the final location of the carton. Measure and record the distance the carton moved.
9. Repeat steps 7 and 8 with the golf ball.

Part B

10. Repeat steps 4 and 5 using two blocks.
11. Hypothesize what will happen when the height of the ramp is increased.
12. Repeat steps 7 through 9.

Data and Observations

| Height of blocks | Objects | | | |
| | Rubber ball | | Golf ball | |
	Mass	Distance	Mass	Distance

Questions and Conclusions

1. In what form was the mechanical energy of the ball sitting at the top of the ramp? At the end of the ramp?
2. At what points did the transfer of energy occur?
3. How did you know energy was transferred to the carton?
4. In Part A, how did the mass of the balls affect the distance traveled by the carton?
5. In Part A, how does your hypothesis compare with your results?
6. In Part B, how did the height of the ramp affect the distance traveled by the carton?
7. In Part B, how does your hypothesis compare with your results?
8. What factors affect the energy transferred by a rolling ball?

How Do You Use Energy?   103

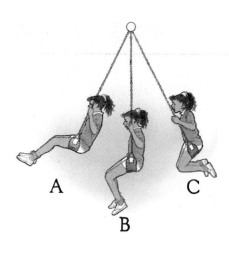

FIGURE 5–9. At points A and C, the girl on the swing has maximum potential energy and no kinetic energy. At point B, kinetic energy is greatest and potential energy is lowest.

What is the law of conservation of energy?

Energy transfers and conversions have been carefully studied by many scientists. They noted that energy never just appears or disappears during a change. The **law of conservation of energy** states that energy can't be created or destroyed. Energy may be changed from one form into another, but the total amount of energy never changes.

Think about a child on a swing. She pushes on the ground and then pumps her legs to add energy to make the swing go higher and higher. When she is at her highest point and the swing stops for just an instant, all the added energy is potential. When she is at the lowest point, all the added energy is kinetic. She keeps swinging forward, again reaching a point where all the energy is potential. Even though energy has changed from potential to kinetic and back to potential, the total amount of energy has stayed the same. Thus, energy is conserved. Why will the swing finally stop? As the swing moves, friction causes some of its energy to change to thermal energy where the swing is attached. Also, the moving swing pushes air molecules around, causing them to gain thermal energy. Eventually, the mechanical energy of the swing will all change to thermal energy, and the swing will stop.

SKILL BUILDER

Classifying

Claudia had just come back from an overnight camping trip. She had cooked food over a bottled-gas stove, eaten breakfast, lunch, and dinner, taken a 10–km hike, warmed herself at a campfire, and turned the light switches on and off in the main cabin. Since she had a test the next day on forms of energy, she decided to classify her activities by the forms of energy she used. Help Claudia classify her activities. If you need help, refer to Classifying on page 534.

Questions
1. List forms of energy Claudia used.
2. Are there different ways to classify some of the forms of energy? Explain.
3. Did the energies Claudia used change form as she used them? If so, give examples.

SCIENCE AND SOCIETY

5:6 Dams

For thousands of years, moving water has been used as an energy source. It has carried people and supplies from place to place. Water wheels have provided energy for grinding grains and running sawmills. In recent times, moving water has been used to produce electricity. Artificial waterfalls can be made by damming rivers. Water behind the dam has increased potential energy. As the water falls, potential energy is changed into kinetic energy. When falling water hits the blades of a turbine, mechanical energy is transferred to the blades. The blades turn the turbines and electricity is produced. The electric power generated by the use of moving water is called **hydroelectric power.**

Hydroelectric power has many advantages. Because water is renewable, the energy source for producing the power will not run out. Hydroelectric power is relatively inexpensive. A dam functions for many years after it is built. The production of the energy creates no air pollution and no wastes. The lake behind the dam provides recreational areas for people to enjoy.

However, there are also disadvantages to hydroelectric power. Damming of rivers causes drastic changes in the environment of the original river valley.

FIGURE 5–10. Turbines in this dam change the mechanical energy of falling water into electrical energy.

What is hydroelectric power?

a

b

FIGURE 5–11. Damming a river destroys the old river valley (a). The lakes formed by hydroelectric dams provide recreational areas (b).

People, towns, and highways often have to be relocated when a dam is built. Organisms that were adapted to the old river valley may be destroyed. Many of the lakes created by the dams have problems with silting. The silt carried by the rivers into the lakes cannot escape downstream. Instead, it settles and builds up behind the dam. Living things in a stream below a dam also can be affected. Water falling over a dam may change temperature. High water temperatures can reduce oxygen content and kill fish and other organisms.

Before any large hydroelectric project is approved, an environmental study must be done. The study must show that the environmental costs of the dam are outweighed by the benefits of expanded recreational areas and plentiful electricity. Some projects have been cancelled because of the effects they would have on the environment. As with any technology, there is a constant struggle to balance the needs of the environment and the needs of humans.

REVIEW

6. How do potential and kinetic energy differ?
7. Give an example of potential and kinetic energy.
8. What is the total kinetic energy of the moving particles in an object called?
9. List some pros and cons of hydroelectric power.
10. Describe the energy chain that results when you are riding a bicycle. Start with the food you eat.

CHAPTER 5 REVIEW

SUMMARY

1. The push or pull that one object exerts on another is called a force. 5:1
2. Forces that oppose each other with equal strength are balanced forces. A net force exists when forces are unbalanced, and motion occurs. 5:2
3. Energy due to position or condition is potential energy. Energy of motion is kinetic energy. 5:3
4. Mechanical, thermal, electrical, radiant, chemical, and nuclear energy are some of the different forms of energy. 5:4
5. Energy can be transferred from one place or object to another and changed in form, but the total amount of energy remains the same. 5:5
6. Dams change potential energy into kinetic energy to produce hydroelectric power. 5:6

VOCABULARY

a. balanced forces
b. chemical energy
c. electrical energy
d. energy transfer
e. force

f. friction
g. gravitational force
h. hydroelectric power
i. kinetic energy
j. law of conservation of energy

k. mechanical energy
l. net force
m. potential energy
n. solar energy
o. thermal energy

Match each description with the correct vocabulary word from the list above.

1. the push or pull that one object exerts on another
2. energy of motion
3. energy of position or condition
4. radiant energy from the sun
5. total energy of the moving particles in an object
6. kinetic energy of moving electrons
7. force every object exerts on every other object
8. force that opposes motion
9. forces that oppose each other with equal strength
10. energy cannot be created or destroyed, but it can be transferred

CHAPTER 5 REVIEW

MAIN IDEAS

A. Reviewing Concepts

Choose the word or phrase that correctly completes each of the following sentences.

1. A kinetic and potential energy that involves lifting, bending, and stretching is _____.
   a. electrical energy
   b. chemical energy
   c. thermal energy
   d. mechanical energy

2. Motion occurs only if the forces acting on an object are _____.
   a. balanced   c. unbalanced
   b. gravitational d. absent

3. The electricity generated by the kinetic energy of falling water is called _____.
   a. magnetic energy
   b. hydroelectric power
   c. gravitational power
   d. nuclear energy

4. The area around a magnet is called _____.
   a. a magnetic field
   b. an electrical field
   c. a gravitational field
   d. a football field

5. Clothes may cling to each other when you take them out of the dryer due to _____.
   a. a magnetic force
   b. a nuclear force
   c. a chemical force
   d. an electric force

6. One advantage of using hydroelectric power is that it _____.
   a. is inexpensive
   b. displaces people
   c. is expensive
   d. floods river valleys

7. Motion occurs when a(n) _____ force acts on an object.
   a. balanced   c. net
   b. hydroelectric d. potential

8. A falling rock has _____ energy.
   a. kinetic
   b. chemical
   c. nuclear
   d. electrical

9. One kilogram of ice at 0°C contains more thermal energy than _____.
   a. 2 kg of ice   c. 3 kg of ice
   b. 0.5 kg of ice d. a and c

10. When the potential energy of water at the top of a dam changes to kinetic energy of moving turbine blades, the energy is _____.
    a. gained   c. transferred
    b. lost   d. balanced

11. Electrical energy is the kinetic energy of moving _____.
    a. protons
    b. electrons
    c. neutrons
    d. none of these

12. Solar energy travels only in _____.
    a. waves   c. solids
    b. water   d. gases

13. The force that causes a dropped object to fall to the floor is _____ force.
    a. friction   c. nuclear
    b. gravitational d. electric

14. Energy in food is stored in the form of _____ energy.
    a. chemical   c. mechanical
    b. radiant   d. electrical

15. Flow of energy from one place or object to another is _____.
    a. equilibrium
    b. not possible
    c. nuclear energy
    d. energy transfer

B. Understanding Concepts

Answer the following questions using complete sentences.

16. What form of energy results from friction?
17. What energy changes take place after you eat a sandwich?
18. State the law of conservation of energy.
19. How is hydroelectric power produced?
20. List three advantages of dams.
21. List three disadvantages of dams.
22. Is it just Earth that has a gravitational force? Explain.
23. Why is it easier to move an object across the floor if it has wheels?
24. What forces hold the particles in the nuclei of atoms together?
25. Does a match have kinetic energy? Explain.

C. Applying Concepts

Answer the following questions using complete sentences.

26. How are magnetic and electric forces similar?
27. When does a falling object have both potential and kinetic energy?
28. Why is solar energy important?
29. Give an example that shows the law of conservation of energy.
30. Give an example of an energy chain.

SKILL REVIEW

If you need help, refer to the Skill Handbook, pages 526 to 537.

1. The damming of rivers causes changes in the original river valley. Name two effects of these changes.

2. Some households use solar collectors to convert solar radiation into another form of energy. When they turn on a television or switch on a light, they are using solar energy that has been converted. From this, you can infer that the solar energy is being converted into what other type of energy?
3. Outline Section 5:4 of this chapter.
4. You decide to classify your daily activities by the forms of energy they use: electrical energy, chemical energy, and mechanical energy. List at least three activities for each category.
5. Nuclear energy is used to produce electricity. Nuclear power plants also produce wastes. Is the waste a cause or effect of using nuclear energy?

PROJECTS

1. Organize a debate on nuclear energy. What are the advantages and disadvantages of using nuclear energy?
2. Research the effects of a depleted ozone layer on the amount of solar energy received from the sun. Include in your report how this affects the amount of solar energy that is transformed to thermal energy at Earth's surface.

READINGS

1. Conway, Lorraine. *Energy.* Carthage, IL: Good Apple, 1985.
2. DeBruin, Jerry. *Young Scientists Explore: An Encyclopedia of Energy Activities.* Carthage, IL: Good Apple, 1985.
3. Laithwaite, Eric. *Force: The Power Behind Movement.* Danbury, CT: Watts, 1986.

Work and Machines

CHAPTER 6

Career: Crane Operator

Jamie lived near the school. Early one hot summer morning, she watched a large crane arrive in the school yard. She knew that it had come to lift the large, heavy air conditioning units to the roof of the school building. After the crane was unloaded from its trailer, she watched the crane operator move the long boom forward and backward. Then, the operator moved the entire cab in a circle. On the end of the boom, there was a chain from which a large hook dangled. The chain and hook were lowered and raised. Jamie thought that the operator must be testing the machine to see if it was working properly.

Jamie moved closer to the fence around the school yard. She could hear the operator and the supervisor discussing the weight of the air conditioners. Then the operator climbed back into the cab, carefully adjusted the angle of the boom, and lowered the hook to the ropes around one of the air conditioners. The operator lifted the unit into the air, moved in closer to the school building, and lowered it onto the roof. Soon all the air conditioners were in place.

Machines perform many tasks that are necessary or that help to make life more enjoyable. In this chapter, you will study the topics of work and machines. You will discover that you use machines in almost everything you do.

F.Y.I. Crane Manufacturers Association of America, 8720 Red Oak Boulevard, Charlotte, NC 28217

What Is Work?

GOALS

You will study . . .

1. work and how to calculate the amount of work that is done.
2. how to calculate power.

6:1 Work

"Don't bother me when I'm working." "I'll come over as soon as I finish my work." "I can't play baseball with you until my work is done." How many times have you made statements like these? Work is a common word that you hear and use. However, people don't always use the word "work" in the scientific sense. Did you know you are doing work when you play a game or ride a bicycle? What does work really mean?

If you use a force to move an object, you have done work. **Work** is the result of a force moving an object through a distance. Recall that energy is the ability to do work. Potential energy is the amount of work an object can do because of its position or condition. Suppose an object falls from a higher position to a lower position. The amount of work that a falling object can do depends on the weight of the object and how far it falls. A heavy stone that falls a distance of one meter does more work on what it hits than a feather falling the same distance.

You have studied that a force is a push or pull that one object exerts on another. The work done by an object depends on the amount of force it exerts and the distance through which the force moves another object. Now do you see why the way the word work is used doesn't always fit the scientific meaning of the word?

What factors determine how much work is done?

FIGURE 6–1. Work is done whenever a force moves an object through a distance.

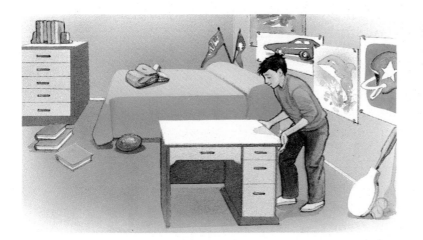

Work is always the result of an object being moved by a force. That means that work can be calculated using a mathematical formula. The formula for work is *work = force × distance.* $W = F \times d$

The SI unit of work is the **joule** (J). One joule is the work done when a force of 1 N moves an object a distance of 1 m. One joule is $1 \text{ N} \times 1 \text{ m}$ or one newton·meter (1 N·m).

What is the SI unit of work?

F.Y.I. One joule is about the amount of energy used to lift a medium apple one meter.

Example 1 Calculating Work

How much work in joules is done when you lift a 10-N object straight up for a distance of 2 m?

Step 1   Write the formula. $W = F \times d$

Step 2   Substitute the values for force and distance given in the problem.
$W = 10 \text{ N} \times 2 \text{ m}$

Step 3   Multiply to find the answer. Be sure to include the units.
$W = 20 \text{ N·m} = 20 \text{ J}$

Example 2 Calculating Work

A force of 20 N is needed to push a desk across the floor a distance of 3 m. How much work is done?

Step 1 $W = F \times d$

Step 2 $W = 20 \text{ N} \times 3 \text{ m}$

Step 3 $W = 60 \text{ N·m} = 60 \text{ J}$

Work is done only when a force is exerted and motion occurs in the direction of the force. If you pushed against a wall all day, you would become very tired. Would you have done any work on the wall? The answer in the scientific sense is no because the force did not cause the wall to move through a distance.

F.Y.I. The joule, a unit of energy or work, was named after James Prescott Joule, an English scientist.

PROBLEM SOLVING

Who Did More Work?

It was close to the end of the school day when Mrs. Sharp, the principal, walked into the classroom. She talked briefly with the teacher and then turned to face the class. Mrs. Sharp asked if anyone in the class would volunteer to stack several boxes of old textbooks in the storage room.

Pedro and Irving had gotten into some trouble in the lunchroom last week. Since they were eager to get back on the principal's good side, they quickly raised their hands to volunteer. They were selected and taken to the storage room. Mrs. Sharp showed the boys the four boxes of textbooks on the floor and the bookcase. Only the bottom shelf and the second shelf from the top had enough space for the books.

Since the four boxes were identical, Pedro and Irving each stacked two boxes of books. Pedro stacked his two boxes of books on the bottom shelf of the bookcase. Irving lifted his two boxes of books to a chair and then stacked them on the upper shelf of the bookcase. Which boy did more work? Why was the amount of work done by the boys different?

6:2 Power

Many times you are concerned with more than just the amount of work to be done. You might want to carry out your work at different rates. If you are helping unload groceries after a shopping trip, you may need to put frozen foods away quickly so that they will not thaw. Suppose you need to load a pile of dirt into a cart. You could use a shovel to load the dirt. You also could load the dirt with a spoon, one spoonful at a time. In either case, the amount of work done on the dirt would be the same. But the time it takes to do the work in the two cases will be different.

The rate at which work is done is called power. **Power** is the work done during a given unit of time. Loading the dirt with a shovel would take less time than loading the dirt with a spoon. With the shovel, you would use more power to do the same amount of work. You can calculate power by dividing the work done by the time required to do the work.

How do you calculate power?

$$power = \frac{work}{time} \quad \text{or} \quad P = \frac{W}{t}$$

The unit for power in the SI system is the watt (W). One **watt** is work being done at the rate of one joule per second. You are probably most familiar with the watt in connection with electric power. You may have a 100-watt light bulb in your lamp. The watt is such a small unit of power that kilowatts are often used instead. One kilowatt (kW) equals 1000 watts. A watt or kilowatt is used to describe any kind of power.

How many watts are in one kilowatt?

Example 3 Calculating Power

An elevator weighing 26 000 N is lifted 40 m in 80 s. Find the power in watts and kilowatts that the elevator motor must generate to do this job.

Given: $F = 26\ 000$ N; $d = 40$ m; $t = 80$ s

In order to determine power, you must first find the amount of work done.

Step 1 $W = F \times d$

Step 2 $W = 26\ 000$ N $\times$ 40 m

Step 3 $W = 1\ 040\ 000$ J

Now you can use the formula for calculating power and use the answer you just found for work.

Step 1 $P = \dfrac{W}{t}$

Step 2 $P = \dfrac{1\ 040\ 000 \text{ J}}{80 \text{ s}}$

Step 3 $P = 13\ 000$ W or 13 kW

F.Y.I. The watt is named in honor of James Watt, who improved the steam engine.

F.Y.I. A sleeping adult uses energy at a rate of about 80 watts.

REVIEW

1. Define work and give the unit for work.
2. What do you have to know to calculate work?
3. How much work is done when you lift an object weighing 20 N a distance of 2 m?
4. Define power and give the unit for power.
5. How can power be increased?

Problem: What factors determine the amount of power produced in walking up a flight of steps?

Materials

meter stick   flight of steps
watch with second hand   bathroom scale

Procedure

1. Copy the data table on your paper.
2. Use a bathroom scale to measure the weight in newtons of one volunteer in your group. If your scale reads in kilograms, compute the person's weight and record in the data table. (A mass of 1 kg weighs about 9.8 N on Earth's surface.)
3. Use the meter stick to measure the vertical height of one step. Multiply the height of one step by the number of steps. Record the total height in meters in the data table.
4. Use a watch to measure the amount of time it takes the volunteer to walk up the flight of steps. Record the time in the data table.
5. Calculate the work done in walking up the steps in joules. Record the amount of work done in the data table.
6. Calculate the power produced in walking up the steps and record in the table.

Questions and Conclusions

1. Which person exerted the greatest force?
2. Which person did the most work?
3. Which person generated the most power in walking up the steps?
4. If the person with the least amount of weight walked up the steps more quickly, what would happen to the amount of power generated?
5. If the person with the greatest amount of weight walked up the steps more slowly, what would happen to the amount of power generated?
6. What factors determine the amount of power produced in walking up the steps?
7. Which person could probably produce the most power? Explain your answer.

Data and Observations

Student's name	Force (N)	Distance (m)	Work (J)	Time (s)	Power (W)
Sally					
George					
Tim					
Jane					

6:3 Simple Machines

Think about what you have done today. Have you used any machines? Which ones? Why do you use machines? A machine is used to change the amount or direction of a force or the speed at which an object is moved. Machines make work easier, faster, more convenient, or better suited to human body structure. Suppose you wanted to tighten a bolt. You would probably use a wrench because you could not grasp the bolt tightly enough to turn it using just your fingers. Keep in mind, though, that *machines never reduce the amount of work that has to be done.* Suppose you want to raise a flag to the top of a flagpole. You pull down on one end of a cord, and the flag that is attached to the other end of the cord is raised. You have used a simple machine, a pulley, to raise the flag. Your job is made easier because you were able to lift the flag to a great height simply by pulling down on a rope while standing on the ground. There are six types of simple machines as shown in Figure 6–4. Levers, pulleys, wheels and axles, inclined planes, wedges, and screws are simple machines.

Some machines make a job seem easier because they increase the amount of force that can be exerted or they change the direction in which the force is applied. Think about lifting the lid off a can of paint. Do you think you could do it by just using your fingers? Why? Now suppose you use a screwdriver to pry off the lid. The screwdriver acts as a lever.

GOALS

You will study . . .
1. simple and compound machines.
2. the efficiency of machines.
3. the idea of perpetual motion machines.

How do some machines make a job seem easier?

FIGURE 6–4. Simple machines change the amount of force that can be exerted or the direction of the force.

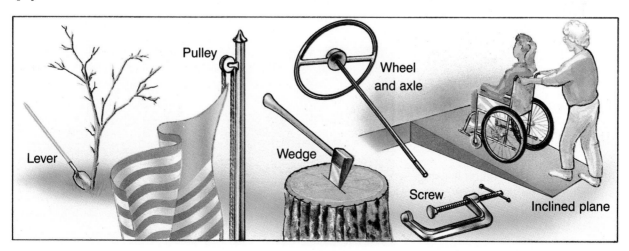

Pulley Wheel and axle Lever Wedge Screw Inclined plane

A **lever** is an arm that turns around a fixed point. The **fulcrum** of a lever is the point around which the arm turns. When a lever is used, two forces always act on it. One force is the effort force, the force you apply. The other force is the resistance force. In Figure 6–5, the effort force is being applied to the handle of the screwdriver. The resistance force is caused by the lid of the paint can at the opposite end of the lever. Where is the fulcrum? The small force you exert on the handle is increased to a large force to lift the lid.

We use three types of levers to help us in different ways. Classes of levers are identified by where the effort and resistance forces are applied in relation to the fulcrum. All classes of levers can be used to change the direction in which a force is applied or to change the force necessary to do the work.

Another simple machine is a pulley. A pulley can change the direction of force applied to an object, such as a cord on drapes. When you want the drapes open, you pull down on a cord attached to a pulley system. The drapes open and close when you pull on the cords. A pulley can also be used to change the amount of force applied. Sometimes both direction and amount of force are changed. A block and tackle is a combination of pulleys that can be used to move heavy objects. People who repair car and truck engines may use a block and tackle to lift and move the engines. With the use of pulleys, it is possible for one person to move an engine. How many persons might it take to remove an engine from a car and place it on a workbench without the aid of machines?

A doorknob is an example of a wheel and axle. Can you imagine opening a door if there were no doorknob

FIGURE 6–5. This person is using a small force on the handle of the screwdriver. The force is increased by the lever to lift the lid off the can.

FIGURE 6–6. Cars move from level to level in this parking garage via inclined planes.

for you to grasp? You would find it difficult if you had to grasp the little shaft with your fingers and turn it to open the latch. By attaching a wheel (knob) for you to grasp, opening the door becomes much easier. A wheel and axle consists of a larger wheel that is attached to a smaller axle. Anything you see that has a crank is a wheel and axle. Less force is needed to turn the axle when the larger wheel is grasped. A wheel and axle changes the amount of force needed to do work. It may also be used to increase the speed or distance of the wheel. Potter's wheels, for instance, change the speed at which the pot rotates.

How does a wheel and axle help you do work?

Have you ever climbed a flight of stairs into a building and noticed a ramp running beside the stairs? The ramps are used by people in wheelchairs or by people who need to push heavy objects into the building using wheeled carts. The ramp is an inclined plane, another type of simple machine. An inclined plane allows you to change the amount of force you use. You can use less force to move an object a longer distance up the slanted surface of the ramp gradually rather than using more force to lift it straight up to the same height.

F.Y.I. Winding roads in mountains are machines as is a wheelchair ramp.

SKILL BUILDER

Making Tables
Make three columns. Label them Simple machines, Changes direction, and Changes force. List the six simple machines. In the next two columns, write yes or no. If you need more help, refer to Using Tables on page 530.

Questions
1. Which simple machines change the direction of the applied force?
2. Which change the amount of force?

How Are Machines Useful? 119

FIGURE 6–7. A screw is a simple machine useful for pushing objects together or moving materials.

Two more examples of simple machines are the wedge and the screw. Both are closely related to inclined planes. A wedge is a simple machine made of two inclined planes placed back to back. Figure 6–4 shows an ax being used to split a tree stump. Notice that the downward force used on the ax translates to a sideways spreading of the stump. Knife blades and most cutting tools are also examples of wedges. A screw can be thought of as an inclined plane wrapped in a spiral around a cylinder. Screws are objects used for exerting forces to move materials or to push two objects together. Well and oil drilling equipment use screws to remove long columns of dirt from the ground. Screws are used to hold pieces of wood or metal together and are used in car jacks and vises.

6:4 Mechanical Advantage

Remember that work is the result of a force moving an object through a distance. A machine that moves an object through a distance does work on the object. But something must put work into the machine. If you use your muscles to apply a force on the machine, you do work on the machine. But because machines aren't perfect, the work you put into the machine is always more than the work you get from the machine. The less perfect a machine is, the more work you must put in to make it work. Machines may increase forces to make work easier but they can never reduce the amount of work that is done to less than the amount of work put in.

Do machines help to reduce the amount of work done?

FIGURE 6–8. A machine increases the effort force used on it.

Mechanical (mih kan ih kul) **advantage** (MA) of a machine is the amount that the machine can increase an effort force. Machines can increase forces by various amounts. You can use a formula to calculate the mechanical advantage of a machine. In order to find the mechanical advantage of a machine, you divide the force the machine provides by the force you used to operate the machine. The equation to calculate MA is

How do you find the MA of a machine?

$$MA = \frac{\text{force exerted by machine (resistance force)}}{\text{force applied to machine (effort force)}} = \frac{F_r}{F_e}$$

Example 4 Calculating MA

If a machine lifts an object that weighs 200 N (resistance force) using an effort force of 50 N, what is its mechanical advantage?

$$MA = \frac{F_r}{F_e}$$

$$MA = \frac{200 \text{ N}}{50 \text{ N}} = 4$$

The mechanical advantage of the machine is four. The machine increased the effort force used on the machine by four times.

Machines that only change the direction of an effort force have a mechanical advantage equal to one. The effort and resistance distances are equal. The flagpole is an example. You pull down on the rope with a force equal to the weight of the flag, and the flag goes up.

Some machines have an MA less than one. These machines change either the distance an object is moved or its speed. A tennis racket is an example. The distance moved by the racket handle is less than the distance moved by the head.

Are most machines simple or compound?

FIGURE 6–9. A pencil sharpener is a compound machine.

6:5 Compound Machines

In Section 6:3, you studied simple machines. Most of the machines in the world are not as simple as these machines. Most machines are compound machines. A **compound machine** is made of two or more simple machines. Think about a wheelbarrow. A wheelbarrow is a machine made from a wheel and a lever. Where is the wheel? What acts as a lever? Now look at Figure 6–9. The sharpener handle is a wheel and axle, and it turns a screw. Screws also are used to hold the parts of the machine together.

6:6 Efficiency

All compound machines contain moving parts. These moving parts produce some friction. Some of the work you put into a machine acts to overcome friction and is changed to thermal energy. Therefore, the useful work the machine does is lessened by the work used to overcome friction. The efficiency of a machine increases as friction is reduced or eliminated.

Machine **efficiency** is a measurement of the work put into the machine compared with the work the machine does. A machine in which much of the work put into it is changed to unwanted thermal energy has low efficiency. High efficiency means that much of the work put in is changed to useful output work. Efficiency is usually expressed as a percent.

How do you increase the efficiency of a machine?

TECHNOLOGY

Bicycles

The first bicycle had no pedals, cranks, chains, or sprockets. It was simply two wheels, a seat, and a handlebar. Riders straddled the seat and pushed along the ground with their feet. This design allowed people to travel faster than they could by walking, but it didn't have a great mechanical advantage. In the 1840s, Kirkpatrick Macmillan designed a drive system that used cranks and pedals. He rode 220 km on his machine. People began thinking of the bicycle as a practical way to travel. In the 1880s, manufacturers added chains to the drive system. Before this, the crank arms were attached to the axle of the front wheel. The added chain allowed the pedals and cranks to be placed elsewhere on the frame. Today's bicycles are much lighter than those of a few years ago. The first bicycles were constructed mostly of wood and steel. Bicycles are now being made of chrome-molybdenum, aluminum, carbon fibers, and even titanium.

ADVANCE

Many of today's bicycles have a cluster of sprockets attached to the axle of the rear wheel. The number of sprockets determines the number of "speeds" a bicycle has. You've probably heard of 10-, 12-, or even 18-speed bicycles.

A derailleur moves the chain from one sprocket to another. The rider can control the mechanical advantage of the bicycle by shifting gears.

Problem: How do different surfaces affect friction?

Materials

spring scale
piece of string
wooden block
sandpaper

waxed paper
aluminum foil
newspaper
tape

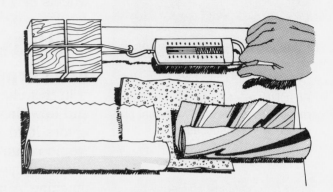

Procedure

1. Copy the data table.
2. Tie the string tightly around the wooden block. Then, tie the end of the string in a loop.
3. Place the block on the floor. Attach the hook of the spring scale to the loop of string. Pull steadily on the other end of the scale. Use just enough force to pull the block across the floor slowly.
4. Read the spring scale as you are pulling and record the amount of force in newtons required to overcome the friction of the floor.
5. Write a hypothesis stating the effect the different surfaces listed in the data table will have on friction.
6. Place the block on a table. Attach the hook of the scale to the loop of string. Pull steadily on the scale.
7. Read and record in the data table the amount of force required to overcome the friction of the table's surface.
8. Tape the waxed paper on the table. Attach the hook of the spring scale to the loop of string. Pull steadily on the other end of the scale. Read and record in the data table the amount of force required to overcome friction.
9. Repeat step 8 using aluminum foil, newspaper, and sandpaper.

Data and Observations

Surface	Force (N)
Floor	
Table	
Waxed paper	
Aluminum foil	
Newspaper	
Sandpaper	

Questions and Conclusions

1. Which surface had the most friction?
2. Which surface reduced friction the most?
3. How do different surfaces affect friction?
4. How does your hypothesis compare with the results of the activity?
5. How could you increase friction between two surfaces?
6. Why might you want to increase friction?
7. How could you decrease friction between two surfaces?
8. Why might you want to decrease friction?

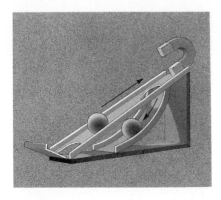

FIGURE 6–10. Many perpetual motion machines have been proposed with no success.

How can machine efficiency be increased?

All machines have efficiencies less than 100 percent because of friction. To increase the efficiency of a machine, friction must be reduced. Surfaces are sanded or waxed to reduce friction. Oil and grease are used in machines to reduce friction. Bearings in wheels or a cushion of air reduces friction.

SCIENCE AND SOCIETY

6:7 Perpetual Motion Machines

In this chapter, you have studied about machines and how they work. What must happen to a machine before it does work? Can you imagine a machine that would require no energy input? For hundreds of years, inventors have worked at creating a perpetual motion machine. A **perpetual motion machine** is a mechanical device that can produce work constantly with no net energy input. These machines violate the law of conservation of energy. The law of conservation of energy states that energy can neither be created nor destroyed. If a perpetual motion machine were invented, the law of conservation of energy would need to be altered.

Why have people worked on the idea of perpetual motion for so many years? Many people have tried to create a perpetual motion machine that will do useful work. They really want to help people with their jobs. Other people may just want to prove that an accepted scientific law is inaccurate. Suppose you are approached by an inventor wanting you to invest in a new perpetual motion machine. What questions would you want to ask? Would you be willing to invest money in the project? Why or why not? What would you like to have such a machine do for you?

REVIEW

6. How do the three classes of levers differ?
7. How is mechanical advantage calculated?
8. What is a compound machine?
9. What is the MA of a machine that lifts a 4000 N object using a force of 40 N?
10. Why do scientists believe it is impossible to build and operate a perpetual motion machine?

SUMMARY

1. Work is the result of an object being moved through a distance by a force. 6:1
2. Power is the amount of work done in a unit of time. The unit for power in SI is the watt. 6:2
3. Simple machines include the lever, pulley, inclined plane, wedge, screw, and wheel and axle. Simple machines increase the amount of force that can be exerted or change the direction of the applied force. 6:3
4. Mechanical advantage is the amount the effort force is increased by a machine. The work you put into a machine is always more than the work you get from the machine. 6:4
5. A compound machine is made by combining two or more simple machines. 6:5
6. The ratio of work output to work input is called the efficiency of a machine. Machine efficiency is lessened by the work used to overcome friction. 6:6
7. A perpetual motion machine would work continuously with no energy input. 6:7

VOCABULARY

a. compound machine
b. efficiency
c. fulcrum
d. joule

e. lever
f. mechanical advantage
g. perpetual motion
  machine

h. power
i. watt
j. work

Match each description with the correct vocabulary word from the list above.
  1. work being done at the rate of one joule per second
  2. work per unit of time
  3. made of two or more simple machines
  4. an arm that turns around a fixed point
  5. point on a lever around which the arm turns
  6. amount that a machine increases the effort force
  7. a measurement of the work put into a machine compared with the work the machine does
  8. result of a force moving an object
  9. a unit for measuring work
  10. violates the law of conservation of energy

CHAPTER 6 REVIEW

MAIN IDEAS

A. Reviewing Concepts

Choose the word or phrase that correctly completes each of the following sentences.

1. The amount of work that a falling object can do depends on the _____.
   a. weight of the object
   b. distance the object falls
   c. both a and b
   d. none of the above

2. A fulcrum is a point on a _____.
   a. lever   c. wedge
   b. pulley   d. screw

3. Work being done at one joule per second is equal to one _____.
   a. newton   c. watt
   b. kilogram   d. joule

4. Work can be calculated by _____.
   a. multiplying force and distance
   b. multiplying mass and distance
   c. dividing force by distance
   d. dividing distance by force

5. A force of 2 N is used to push a box 40 m. The work done is _____.
   a. 20 N   c. 5 J
   b. 30 N   d. 80 J

6. Work is done when motion is in the _____ direction as the applied force.
   a. same   c. both a and b
   b. opposite   d. none of these

7. _____ forces are applied to a lever.
   a. Six   c. Three
   b. Four   d. Two

8. A machine may _____.
   a. decrease the force needed
   b. change the direction of the force
   c. increase speed
   d. all of the above

9. A machine can have a MA _____ one.
   a. greater than   c. equal to
   b. less than   d. all of these

10. A _____ is a simple machine.
    a. bicycle   c. wheelbarrow
    b. can opener   d. ramp

11. A _____ is a compound machine.
    a. wheelbarrow   c. screw
    b. screwdriver   d. ramp

12. The power needed to move a force of 20 N a distance of 60 m in 10 s is _____.
    a. 1200 W   c. 30 W
    b. 120 W   d. 3 W

13. A _____ machine would run continually, do useful work, and would not require work input.
    a. compound   c. perpetual
    b. simple   motion
                      d. all of these

14. _____ machines are used today.
    a. Compound and   c. Both a and b
       simple
    b. Perpetual   d. None of these
       motion

15. All machines have efficiencies less than 100 percent because of _____.
    a. friction   c. work input
    b. MA   d. power

B. Understanding Concepts

Answer the following questions using complete sentences.

16. Why is useful work limited in a machine?

17. Which action requires more power, running up a flight of steps or walking up the steps?

18. A machine lifts a 1000 N object with an effort force of 200 N. What is the mechanical advantage?

19. List the six types of simple machines.

20. What law would change if someone made a perpetual motion machine?

21. How many kilowatts are in 6000 W?

22. Why is it useful to hit a tennis ball with a racket instead of your hand?

23. Which requires more work—lifting a 5-N object a distance of 2 m, or lifting a 3-N object 5 m?

24. Which machine would require less effort force to do the same amount of work, one with a MA of 8 or one with a MA of 2?

25. How can the efficiency of a machine be increased?

C. Applying Concepts

Answer the following questions using complete sentences.

26. Give one example of each type of simple machine.

27. What simple machine is often used when loading moving vans? Why?

28. Describe a seesaw in terms of a lever. Identify the effort, resistance, and fulcrum.

29. Are you doing work when you read a book? Explain your answer.

30. Is a perpetual motion machine an impractical goal? Explain.

SKILL REVIEW

If you need help, refer to the Skill Handbook, pages 526 to 537.

1. Classify each of the following simple machines: doorknob, knife blade, ramp, boat oar, bicycle wheel, and ax blade.

2. What two simple machines combine to make a shovel?

3. You notice your skateboard rolls much faster and farther on concrete than it does on a wood ramp. Is this an observation or an inference?

4. You correctly assume that there is more friction between your wheels and the wood than between your skateboard wheels and the concrete. Is this an observation or an inference?

5. You own a company that manufactures machines that lift heavy objects. Using the table below, make a bar graph to show the mechanical advantage of each of your machines.

Machine	Mechanical advantage
A	4
B	2
C	7

PROJECTS

1. Make a consumer report of different machines and their energy efficiency ratings. Include heaters, stoves, and all appliances generally found in a home. Compare different models of the same appliance.

2. Decorate a bulletin board for your classroom showing the kinds of simple machines, and label their parts. Try to use common objects such as a doorknob for a wheel and axle.

READINGS

1. Baines, Rae. *Simple Machines.* Mahwah, NJ: Troll Associates, 1985.

2. Echasre and Wentz. *Machines.* Hayward, CA: Janus Books, 1987.

3. Gardner, Martin. "Perpetual Motion: The Quest for Machines That Power Themselves." *Science Digest.* October 1985, pp. 68–72.

Motion

Career: Demolition Expert

Jeff read in the paper that they were finally going to tear down the old brick building on the corner of Park and High Streets. He had never seen a building being demolished, so he decided to go downtown and watch.

The building site was surrounded by a large chain-link fence. Soon water, gas, and electric company trucks pulled up. The workers began disconnecting all the utility lines. Then they took out all the electric and phone cables, the water pipes and heater, the bathroom fixtures, and the furnace and duct work. The next day, Jeff watched them remove all the windows, ceiling fixtures, and mirrors so that there was no glass left in the building. Only a shell of the building was left when the backhoe arrived. The backhoe had a special arm attached to where the shovel usually is located. The operator placed the arm of the backhoe about 60 cm below the top of the front wall. The machine applied a strong push to the wall, and most of the building collapsed. The backhoe moved to the back wall, and with another push, the entire building was down in a cloud of dust.

Objects such as the building resist a change in movement until acted on by an outside force, in this case, the backhoe. In this chapter, you will study objects in motion and their resistance to change. You will also study objects moving in circles.

F.Y.I. National Association of Demolition Contractors, 4415 West Harrison Street, Hillside, IL 60612

What Is Motion?

GOALS
You will study . . .
1. speed and inertia.
2. velocity and acceleration.
3. falling objects.

What is position?

What is motion?

7:1 Position and Speed

Where do you sit in the science classroom? Is your desk near the windows, in the front row, or near a corner? In order to describe the position of your desk, you must choose a reference point. **Position** is the place or location where an object is in relation to a reference point. If your reference point is the classroom door, you might describe your position as two rows east of the door.

If you get up and move around in the classroom, your position changes. **Motion** is the changing of position. You can describe your motion in terms of how fast you are moving, the direction you are moving, and changes in your speed and direction.

It is not always easy to tell if an object is moving. If you are in an elevator that moves slowly, do you always have the feeling of motion? Or is your feeling of motion limited to the starting and stopping of the elevator? Usually you take your clue about motion from objects around you. You ride down the road and you see the trees and buildings "flying past you." Your brain, of course, lets you know that it is you moving, not the stationary objects.

FIGURE 7–1. Motion is the changing of position.

FIGURE 7-2. The person in car A can't tell whether he is rolling backward or car B is moving forward. The observer on the corner can easily observe that car B is moving forward.

Sometimes you might be confused as to which object is moving. Have you ever been stopped in a car at a red light and been unsure if the car next to you is creeping forward or if you are rolling backward? The confusion occurs because you are not sure whether your reference point, the other car, is stationary. You are used to judging motion in relation to stationary reference points. An observer of the two cars on the street corner could easily tell which car was moving. The observer has a stationary reference point, the ground, from which to judge motion.

If you ride a bus to school each day, you experience motion. How fast does the school bus move? **Speed** is a measure of how far an object moves in a given period of time. Sometimes the speed of the bus is constant. Most of the time, however, the bus is stopping and starting. When the bus speeds up and slows down, it changes the distance it covers in a period of time. The speedometer on the bus gives a reading for the speed at any one moment, but how can you find the average speed of the bus over the entire trip? **Average speed** is total distance traveled divided by the total time of travel.

What is average speed?

$$average\ speed = \frac{total\ distance}{total\ time}; s = \frac{d}{t}$$

If the bus makes several stops along the way but travels a total of 20 km in one hour, then the average speed of the bus is 20 km divided by one hour, or 20 km/h.

Example: Calculating average speed

What is the average speed in m/s if you ride a bike a distance of 100 m in 10 s?

Unknown: average speed

Given: distance $d = 100$ m

time $t = 10$ s

Basic formula: $s = \dfrac{d}{t}$

Solution: $s = \dfrac{d}{t}$

$$s = \frac{100 \text{ m}}{10 \text{ s}}$$

$$s = 10 \text{ m/s}$$

What is the difference between speed and velocity?

Speed describes how fast an object is moving. **Velocity** (vuh LAHS ut ee) describes both the object's speed and its direction. In "everyday" terms, you probably use speed and velocity interchangeably. In science, it is important to understand the difference. Suppose your school bus travels east at 20 km/h, and your friend's bus travels west at 20 km/h. Your buses have the same speed, but different velocities. If the buses both travel east at the same speed, then their velocities are the same.

FIGURE 7–3. Even though their speeds are the same, the velocities of the buses are different because they are traveling in different directions.

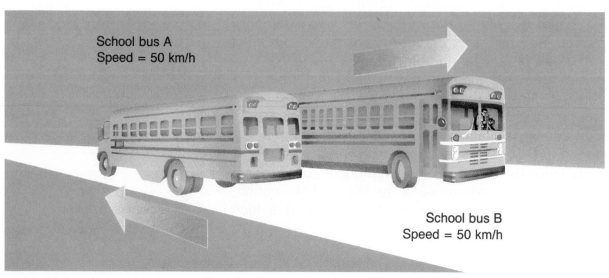

School bus A
Speed = 50 km/h

School bus B
Speed = 50 km/h

Problem: How can you determine average walking speed?

Materials

meter stick
masking tape
watch with second hand

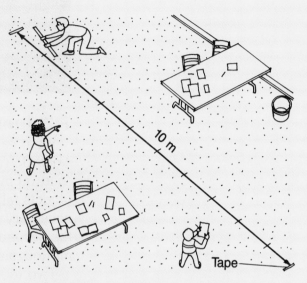

Procedure

1. Copy the data table.
2. Choose a test area on the floor in your classroom. Use the meter stick to measure a distance of 10 m on the floor. Mark the beginning and end points of the 10 m with strips of masking tape.
3. Have each person in your group walk the 10-m distance three times. Start walking several meters before the beginning of the 10-m distance. Use the watch to measure the amount of time each person takes to walk from the beginning to the end of the 10-m distance.
4. Record the total distance walked in meters and the total amount of time in seconds needed for each person to walk this distance.

5. Calculate the average speed of each person using this equation.

$$average\ speed = \frac{total\ distance}{total\ time}$$

Questions and Conclusions

1. What is your average walking speed?
2. How does your average walking speed compare with that of the other members of your group?
3. At your average walking speed, predict how far you could walk in one minute. Predict how far you could walk in one hour.
4. Why did you start walking before the beginning of the measured distance?
5. Why did you walk the 10-m distance three times?
6. How can you determine average walking speed?
7. How could you find your average biking speed?

Data and Observations

Student's Name	Total Distance (meters)	Total Time (seconds)	Velocity (m/s)

FIGURE 7–4. Seat belts stop your forward motion *before* you hit the dash or windshield.

7:2 Inertia

What causes motion? In the fourth century B.C., Aristotle recognized two kinds of motion. One was "natural motion" in the up and down direction. Heavy objects fall, and air and smoke rise. No force is necessary to produce natural motion. Aristotle called the second type of motion "violent motion." Violent motion, such as throwing a ball, requires a force.

Two thousand years later, Galileo (1564–1642) used scientific methods to study motion and forces. He hypothesized that a force is not necessary to keep an object moving. A moving object slides across ice with little change in velocity until it hits another object. A baseball moves from the pitcher toward the plate with little change in velocity until it is hit by the batter. In these cases, both the speed and direction of the objects remain constant until they hit something else. Then either the speed changes, the direction changes, or both speed and direction change. Recall that when speed or direction changes, or both change, the velocity changes.

FIGURE 7–5. The net force produced by the batter changes the velocity of the softball.

PROBLEM SOLVING

Is It Magic?

It was Saturday evening, and Dawn was having a slumber party. The girls all gathered in the family room to watch TV and listen to records. Pepper was watching a variety show. A magician was performing amazing tricks. Suddenly, Pepper had everyone watch the television. "Look," she said, "the magician is going to pull a tablecloth out from under a set of dishes." The girls all watched as the magician quickly snapped the end of the tablecloth out from under the dishes. Not a dish moved. "Wow! I wonder how he did that!" said Dawn. Only Pepper knew. Is the trick really "magic"? What did Pepper tell her friends?

The property of an object that *resists* any change in velocity is **inertia** (ihn UR shuh). What happens when the car you are riding in brakes suddenly? You move forward in the car. This is because your body resists a change in motion, stopping, and you continue to go forward until you are held back by the seatbelt. Inertia depends on the amount of mass in an object. The more mass an object has, the greater its inertia. Compare the distance needed for a car and a large, heavy truck going the same speed to stop. The truck takes a longer distance to stop because of its greater mass, and thus greater inertia. What happens when you try to accelerate a heavy box across the floor? The inertia of the box resists the change in velocity.

What is inertia?

Sir Isaac Newton (1642–1727) studied relationships between motion and forces. He expressed his findings in three laws. **Newton's first law of motion** states that an object at rest stays at rest, and an object in motion keeps moving at a constant velocity unless acted on by a net force. Simply put, objects tend to keep doing what they are already doing unless something makes them change. Recall from Chapter 5 that a net force occurs when forces acting on an object are unbalanced. Motion only occurs when a net force is present.

7:3 Velocity and Acceleration

How can you describe your motion when you go down a hill on your bike? Your direction may be constant, but your speed increases. Thus, your velocity changes. Recall that changes in velocity refer to a change in direction *or* speed. **Acceleration** describes the rate at which velocity changes. Suppose you pedaled your bike at a steady speed in a circle. Your velocity would be changing because you would be constantly changing direction. Even though speed stays the same when you go in a circle, you accelerate constantly. How could you describe your acceleration as you turn a corner on your bike? Your speed probably decreases as you make the turn. After the turn is complete, you are headed in a new direction. In this case, acceleration describes both the rate of change of speed and a directional change.

Without a net force, an object does not accelerate. The relationship between net force and acceleration is described in Newton's second law of motion. **Newton's second law of motion** states that the acceleration of an object depends on the mass of the object and the net force acting on it. Suppose you want to rearrange the furniture in your bedroom. You begin by moving your bed to the center of the room. The greater force you apply to the bed, the faster it accelerates. If your sister helps you push, the bed will reach the same velocity in a shorter time. The acceleration of the bed is in the direction of the force. If you want the bed to move forward, you push forward.

FIGURE 7–6. The acceleration of the bikers changes as they round the curve of the track.

The same amount of force will give more acceleration to a smaller mass than it will give to a larger mass. It is easier to accelerate your desk chair than your bed because of the lower mass of the chair. In Chapter 5, you studied that the unit of force is the newton. A newton is the force needed to give an object having a mass of one kilogram an acceleration of one meter per second per second.

The formula that expresses Newton's second law is usually written

$$Force = mass \times acceleration$$
$$F = m \times a$$

If you know the mass and the acceleration of an object, you can use the formula to calculate force.

What formula expresses Newton's second law?

Example: Calculating force
How much force is needed to accelerate a bike and rider with a total mass of 70 kg at 0.5 m/s^2?

Unknown: force *(F)*

Given: *mass* $m = 70$ kg
   acceleration $a = 0.5$ m/s^2

Basic Formula: $F = m \times a$

Solution: $F = m \times a$
   $F = 70$ kg $\times$ 0.5 m/s^2
   $F = 35$ kg m/s$^2 = 35$ N

FIGURE 7–8. Even though they have different sizes and masses, both objects fall at the same rate.

According to Newton's second law, when does an object accelerate?

F.Y.I. A vacuum is a space that contains no matter. There is no air resistance on a falling object in a vacuum because there are no air molecules.

What is air resistance?

7:4 Acceleration and Falling Objects

You drop a dictionary and a small paperback book at the same time. Which book hits the ground first? Does the dictionary fall faster because it has more mass? Galileo studied falling objects using balls. He found that no matter what the mass of a ball was, its acceleration when falling was the same.

Figure 7-8 shows two falling objects. You can see that one object is larger than the other. It also has a larger mass. Notice that they are the same distance from the start each time a flash picture is made. Both objects fall with the same acceleration. Scientists have calculated the acceleration of an object falling in a vacuum at Earth's surface and found it to be 9.8 m/s^2. This means that after an object is dropped, its velocity increases 9.8 m/s for each second that it falls. One second after you drop the dictionary and the paperback, they are both traveling at 9.8 m/s. At the end of two seconds, their velocities would be 2×9.8 m/s, or 19.6 m/s. If it takes four seconds for the books to hit the ground, what are their velocities on impact?

According to Newton's second law, an object accelerates only when a net force acts on it. The net force acting on a falling object near Earth's surface is Earth's gravitational force. Gravitational force between objects depends on their masses. Since gravitational force on a more massive object is greater than on a less massive object, why do they fall with the same acceleration? The more massive object also has a greater inertia, so its resistance to change in motion is greater. Thus, the objects fall at the same rate.

In Chapter 2, you studied that weight is a measure of gravitational force and is measured in newtons. Thus, on Earth, weight in newtons = mass $\times$ 9.8 m/s^2. To find the weight of an object in newtons, multiply its mass in kilograms by the acceleration due to gravitational force. If your textbook has a mass of 1 kg, its weight would equal 1 kg $\times$ 9.8 m/s^2, or 9.8 N.

Air resistance also acts on an object falling in Earth's atmosphere. **Air resistance** is the force exerted by air on a moving object. The direction of gravitational force is down. The direction of force on a falling object due to air resistance is up. Air resistance increases with speed. At some point, air resistance upward is equal to the downward gravitational force.

Aerodynamics and Cars

The rising cost of gasoline prompted manufacturers to improve their designs to improve fuel economy. As a result, today's cars are fuel efficient, high performing machines. Now, cars have smooth lines to reduce air resistance. The fastest sports cars are long and low to the ground. This design reduces the amount of energy required to overcome air resistance.

Aerodynamics is the branch of science that studies how objects in motion are affected by air resistance. The aerodynamics of a car is tested in a wind tunnel. Large fans blow trails of smoke over and around the car. By studying the way the air moves around the car's body, engineers can change the car's design to produce a smoother air flow.

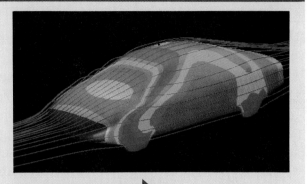

ADVANCE

Engineers develop cars using *computer aided design* (CAD) systems. CADs put car designs through computer simulated road tests to check the design's aerodynamics and performance. Using CADs, designs are improved long before the actual car is made.

At this point, the object will no longer accelerate because the net force acting on it is zero. The object will have a terminal velocity. **Terminal velocity** is the constant velocity reached by a falling object. How does a parachute change the terminal velocity of a falling person? Air resistance on the parachute is much greater than on the parachutist alone. Thus, the terminal velocity is much lower for a person using a parachute than for someone without one. The person attached to the parachute can land safely.

REVIEW

1. What two things must you know before you can calculate the average speed of an object?
2. A car travels 180 km in 2 hours. What is its average speed?
3. How does acceleration differ from speed?
4. Why did scientists use a vacuum to determine acceleration of falling objects?
5. As a sky diver falls faster and faster through the air, how does acceleration change? Explain.

F.Y.I. A satellite is launched so that it is placed in orbit at a height of more than 320 km above Earth's surface to get it above air resistance.

7:5 Newton's Third Law of Motion

If you ran into a wall it would probably hurt, not just because you hit the wall, but because the wall hit you back! You apply a force to the wall, and it applies an equal amount of force to you. The two forces have equal strength but opposite direction and are called "action-reaction" pairs. **Newton's third law of motion** states that when one object exerts a force on a second object, the second object exerts an equal and opposite force on the first. What would happen if you were on a skateboard and you ran into a wall? You would roll backwards. Your motion would be due to the equal and opposite force applied to you by the wall.

Action and reaction forces always work in pairs, and there are always two objects involved. In Figure 7–9, the space shuttle is blasting off. What are the action-reaction forces involved? Earth's gravitational force pulls down on the rocket. At the same time, the space shuttle's gravitational force pulls up equally on Earth. These forces form an action-reaction pair. They are equal and opposite, and act on different objects.

FIGURE 7–9. A net force must be present for the space shuttle to lift off.

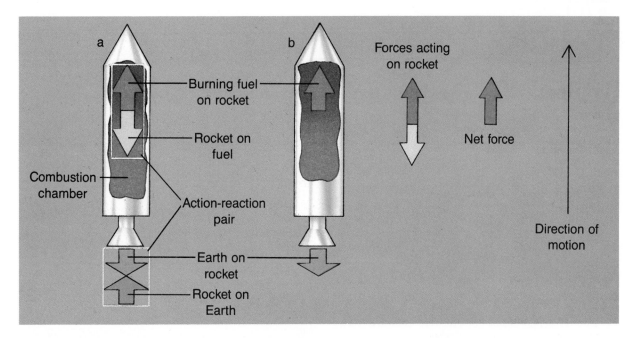

The rocket fuel burning in the combustion compartment creates a large upward force on the space shuttle. This upward force is greater than the downward force Earth exerts on the rocket. There is a net upward force. If you look carefully at the diagram, you'll see that the two forces are both working on the same object, the rocket. Also, they are unequal in size. These two forces are not action-reaction forces. Recall from Newton's second law that a net force must be present in order for motion to occur.

Let's review Newton's three laws of motion. Newton's first law describes how an object moves when there is no net force acting on the object. His second law describes how an object moves when a net force is applied to it. His third law describes how objects are affected by action-reaction pairs.

FIGURE 7–10. Each pair of action-reaction forces is equal (a). The forces acting on the rocket alone are unequal, and a net upward force is produced (b).

7:6 Circular Motion

Many objects don't move in straight lines. A tether ball wrapping around its pole is an example of circular motion, or motion in a circle. The acceleration of the tether ball as it moves in a circular path is toward the center of the circle. Thus, the force causing this acceleration must also be toward the center of the circle. The force that acts toward the center of the circle is called **centripetal** (sen TRIHP ut ul) **force.**

Problem: What are the action-reaction forces acting on the inside of a moving balloon?

Materials

fishing line
masking tape
balloons
　(3 different types)

meter stick
soda straw
scissors

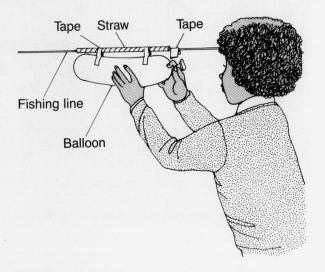

Tape　Straw　Tape

Fishing line

Balloon

Procedure

1. Copy the data table.
2. Use the scissors to cut the soda straw in half.
3. Tie one end of the fishing line to a permanent fixture at one end of the classroom. Push the line through one of the straw pieces. Tie the other end of the line to a heavy table or a permanent fixture so that the line is taut and level.
4. Your group will test each balloon to determine how far it will travel along the fishing line. Write a hypothesis stating which balloon will travel the longest distance.
5. Choose a balloon for the rocket. Inflate the balloon and hold the end closed. Another group member should tape the balloon to the straw on the line. Use a piece of masking tape to mark the location of the back end of the balloon on the fishing line.
6. Release the balloon and observe what happens. Use the meter stick to measure the distance from the tape marker to where the balloon stopped. Record the type of balloon and the distance traveled in the data table.
7. Remove the balloon.
8. Repeat steps 5 through 7 for the two remaining balloons.

Data and Observations

Description of balloon	Distance traveled

Questions and Conclusions

1. Which balloon traveled the farthest?
2. What is Newton's third law of motion?
3. What observation did you make that indicated air escaping from the balloon?
4. What were the action-reaction forces acting on the inside of the balloon before it was released?
5. What were the action-reaction forces acting on the inside of the balloon after it was released?
6. How does your hypothesis compare with the results of the activity?

a

b

What provides the centripetal force on the tether ball? The rope attaching the ball to the pole provides the force. What would happen if the rope suddenly broke? Without centripetal force, there is no circular motion. The ball would fly off in a straight line.

How does centripetal force work on a car rounding a curve? The frictional force of the road on the tires is toward the center of the curve. What would happen if friction were reduced by oil or ice on the road? Centripetal force would also be reduced. Wet pavement or high speeds can cause tires to slip. Roads that are banked can give more force toward the center. Notice the banked track in Figure 7–11b that provides additional centripetal force so that racing cars can move around curves faster.

FIGURE 7–11. The force of the rope keeps the ball moving in a circle (a). Banked curves increase centripetal force and allow racing cars to round curves faster (b).

Why are some roads banked?

SCIENCE AND SOCIETY

7:7 Satellites and Space Garbage

Artificial satellites (SAT uh lites) in orbit around Earth show circular motion. Gravitational force between the satellite and Earth provides centripetal force. If gravitational force were to suddenly disappear, the satellite would continue out into space in a straight line.

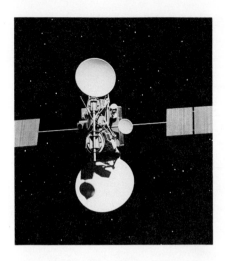

FIGURE 7–12. Satellites are used for communication and navigation, and to collect weather data.

SKILL BUILDER

Outlining

Outline the material in Sections 7:5 through 7:7. If you need help, refer to Outlining on page 527.

Questions

1. What is the main idea of these sections?
2. How many major subdivisions are included in your outline? List them.
3. What is the purpose of an outline?

Artificial satellites serve a variety of purposes. **Communication satellites** receive, amplify, and relay telephone, TV, and radio signals. Using radio signals, these satellites can link computers on all parts of Earth's surface. Thus, they can be used to transmit medical and educational information. **Weather satellites** monitor weather conditions. They send data to ground stations by way of microwaves. These satellites have led to improved weather forecasting and more timely warnings of approaching severe weather. Satellites are now being developed to aid in air traffic control and other areas of navigation. By the end of the century, your car may have a receiver that uses satellite data to help you determine your location instead of a paper map.

Satellites have a limited lifespan. Eventually, they wear out and must be replaced. Currently, old satellites are not removed from orbit when new ones are launched. Old satellites become "space garbage." Collisions with old satellites can damage or destroy working satellites, space shuttles, and future space stations. How dangerous do you think space garbage is? How could space garbage be cleaned up?

REVIEW

6. State Newton's third law of motion.
7. Describe the forces acting on your body as you sit in a chair.
8. What force causes circular motion?
9. List two uses of satellites.
10. Why do old satellites cause problems for space shuttle orbiters?

CHAPTER 7 REVIEW

SUMMARY

1. Motion is the changing of an object's position and is described in terms of an object's speed and velocity.   7:1
2. Inertia is an object's resistance to change in velocity.   7:2
3. Acceleration is the rate at which velocity changes. Newton's second law states that acceleration of an object depends on the mass of the object and the net force acting on it.   7:3
4. Earth's gravitational force is the net force on a falling object. When air resistance balances gravitational force, falling objects reach a constant terminal velocity.   7:4
5. Newton's third law of motion states that when one object exerts a force on a second object, the second object exerts an equal and opposite force on the first object.   7:5
6. The force that makes an object move in a circle or curve is always directed toward the center and is called centripetal force.   7:6
7. Satellites are used for weather information and communication. Space is becoming littered with nonfunctioning satellites that are a threat to working satellites and space shuttles.   7:7

VOCABULARY

a. acceleration
b. air resistance
c. average speed
d. centripetal force
e. communication satellites
f. inertia
g. motion
h. Newton's first law of motion
i. Newton's second law of motion
j. Newton's third law of motion
k. position
l. speed
m. terminal velocity
n. velocity
o. weather satellites

Match each description with the correct vocabulary word from the list above.
1. measure of how fast an object moves
2. $F = m \times a$
3. changing of position
4. change in velocity divided by time
5. constant velocity reached by a falling object
6. tendency of an object to resist a change in motion
7. force acting towards the center
8. force exerted by air on a moving object
9. total distance divided by total time
10. speed and direction

CHAPTER 7 REVIEW

MAIN IDEAS

A. Reviewing Concepts

Choose the word or phrase that correctly completes each of the following sentences.

1. You should wear a seat belt in a car to act against your body's _____.
   - **a.** energy
   - **b.** inertia
   - **c.** momentum
   - **d.** weight

2. A(n) _____ is necessary to accelerate an object.
   - **a.** net force
   - **b.** mass
   - **c.** motion
   - **d.** inertia

3. The rate at which distance is covered is _____.
   - **a.** acceleration
   - **b.** force
   - **c.** speed
   - **d.** velocity

4. The average speed of a car traveling 240 km in 3 hours is _____.
   - **a.** 60 km/h
   - **b.** 12.5 km/h
   - **c.** 80 km/h
   - **d.** 720 km/h

5. A car that goes from 0 km/h to 60 km/h in 5 seconds is an example of _____.
   - **a.** acceleration
   - **b.** speed
   - **c.** velocity
   - **d.** inertia

6. The acceleration of objects in free fall near Earth's surface is about _____.
   - **a.** 5 m/s^2
   - **b.** 10 m/s^2
   - **c.** 15 m/s^2
   - **d.** 20 m/s^2

7. The scientist who did experimental work in the early 1600s with force and motion was _____.
   - **a.** Aristotle
   - **b.** Galileo
   - **c.** Einstein
   - **d.** Kepler

8. An object's place or location is called its _____.
   - **a.** inertia
   - **b.** motion
   - **c.** position
   - **d.** velocity

9. Stationary reference points are used to judge _____.
   - **a.** inertia
   - **b.** motion
   - **c.** mass
   - **d.** force

10. _____ describes an object's speed and direction.
    - **a.** Inertia
    - **b.** Speed
    - **c.** Velocity
    - **d.** Position

11. Average speed is calculated by _____.
    - **a.** dividing total distance by time
    - **b.** dividing time by total distance
    - **c.** multiplying distance and time
    - **d.** subtracting the distance from time

12. The average speed of a car that travels 500 km in 10 hours is _____.
    - **a.** 50 km/h
    - **b.** 60 km/h
    - **c.** 70 km/h
    - **d.** 80 km/h

13. According to Newton's first law of motion, every object has _____.
    - **a.** acceleration
    - **b.** force
    - **c.** inertia
    - **d.** motion

14. A bowling ball's inertia is _____ that of a volley ball.
    - **a.** more than
    - **b.** less than
    - **c.** the same as
    - **d.** twice

15. A train traveling 120 km/h due south is a description of _____.
    - **a.** acceleration
    - **b.** force
    - **c.** mass
    - **d.** velocity

B. Understanding Concepts

Answer the following questions using complete sentences.

16. Which law of motion explains why it takes more force to accelerate a large mass than a small mass?
17. Contrast speed and velocity.
18. Contrast velocity and acceleration.
19. What is the SI unit for force?
20. What force accelerates an object in free fall?
21. How can old satellites cause problems for space shuttle orbiters?
22. How does the acceleration of a falling

object on the moon compare with the same object falling on Earth?

23. How does a constant acceleration affect velocity?

24. What is terminal velocity?

25. How does the third law of motion explain the forces involved when you hit a wall?

C. Applying Concepts

Answer the following questions using complete sentences.

26. Why might a car slide when it hits an icy spot on a curving road?

27. How are artificial satellites helpful?

28. When is it hard to detect motion?

29. When a cowhand whirls a lasso, what force pulls the lasso inward? What happens if the rope is released?

30. Can two cars have the same speeds but different velocities? Explain.

SKILL REVIEW

If you need help, refer to the Skill Handbook, pages 526 to 537.

1. Copy the data table. Drop a sheet of paper from a height of 2 m. Record how long it takes to fall. Repeat this two times. Crumple the paper into a ball and drop it three times. Record your data.

Drop	Time to Fall 2 m	
	Flat Sheet	Crumpled
1		
2		
3		

2. What were the dependent and independent variables in Question 1?

3. What can you infer about the amount of air resistance on the flat sheet versus the amount on the crumpled sheet?

4. What type of graph should you use to compare the average speeds of a train, a bike, and a car?

5. If you constructed a double line graph showing the accelerations of the space shuttle and a motorcycle, which would have the steeper line?

PROJECTS

1. Devise a solution for ridding our upper atmosphere of space garbage. Keep cost effectiveness in mind.

2. Make a rocket car. Punch a hole in one end of a light box. Blow up a balloon and insert its mouth into the hole. Place the box on parallel straws or round pencils. Release the balloon. Experiment to see what factors will make the rocket car go farther.

READINGS

1. Fleisher, Paul. *Secrets of the Universe: Discovering the Universal Laws of Science.* New York NY: Macmillan, 1987.

2. Stwertka, Albert and Eve. *Physics: From Newton to the Big Bang.* Danbury, CT: Watts, 1986.

3. White, Jack. *The Hidden World of Forces.* New York NY: Dodd, Mead and Co., 1987.

Fluids

CHAPTER 8

Career: Service Station Mechanic

Jenny and Tony were on a cross-country car trip with their parents when warning lights on the dashboard suddenly came on. Their father pulled the car over to the side of the road and turned off the engine. Dad started the car again, but the warning lights were still lighted. Dad decided that he didn't want to risk damaging the engine. The family would just sit in the car and wait for help. Within 15 minutes, a state patrol car stopped to see if they were in trouble. The officer called a tow truck, and the car was towed to a service station.

The service station mechanic checked the fluid levels in the car and found that the oil was low. On inspection, he found a leaking gasket. The mechanic explained that oil is used while the engine is running. The oil pump draws oil out of the oil pan and pumps it over all the moving parts of the engine. The oil reduces friction between the moving parts of the engine and prolongs the life of the engine. Excess oil then drains back into the oil pan. Because Dad hadn't checked the oil often enough on the trip, he hadn't been aware that more oil was being used because of the leak.

A fluid is material that flows. In a car, the volume, density, and pressure of a fluid are important to the smooth functioning of the car's mechanical parts. This chapter discusses properties of fluids and the important laws and principles of fluids.

F.Y.I. Motor Vehicle Manufacturers Association of the United States, Inc., 7430 Second Avenue, Detroit, MI 48202

What Are Fluids?

GOALS
You will study . . .
1. properties of fluids.
2. fluid pressure.

What is one difference between a liquid and a gas?

F.Y.I. At sea level, one cubic meter of air at 20°C has a mass of about 1.3 kg.

8:1 Fluid Properties

You may have filled a glass with water or poured a cup of milk today. Perhaps you blew air into a balloon. A **fluid** is a material that can flow. Liquids and gases are called fluids because they flow. You experience the properties of fluids every time you feel a breeze, take a breath, go swimming, or turn on a faucet. Water can be poured from one container to another. You are familiar with Earth's oceans. They contain much water. However, did you know that you live in an ocean of gas? This ocean of gas is the atmosphere.

Gases and liquids do not behave alike in all respects. A gas will expand to fill a closed container, but a liquid will not. You could say that gases are "springy." They can easily be squeezed and expanded. The particles in a gas are much farther apart and move more freely than the particles in a liquid. Gas particles do not have as much attractive force for each other as the particles in a liquid. You may have noticed that when you put air in a bicycle tire the air spreads equally throughout the inside of the tire. When you blow up a balloon, the air expands all parts of the balloon. If you put a small amount of liquid in a large container, the liquid does not spread throughout the container. It fills only a certain amount of the container. A liquid has a definite volume. If you pour 500 mL of milk into a 2000-mL pitcher, you will still have only 500 mL of milk in the pitcher. Because gas

FIGURE 8–1. Liquids keep their volume but take the shape of their container.

particles move so freely, you can detect the odor of perfume across a room quickly. It is also the reason gas companies put odor compounds into natural gas. Natural gas is colorless and odorless. By adding odor compounds, leaks can be caught quickly before an explosion or fire can occur.

Why is an odor added to natural gas?

8:2 Pressure

Gently push against the side of your face with the palm of your hand. Now, using the same amount of force, push against the side of your face with the tip of your index finger. Is there a difference in the feeling of each? The area of contact of your finger tip was much smaller. You pushed with the same force, but the feeling was different. Applying the same force to a smaller area increased the pressure you exerted on your face. **Pressure** is the force applied per unit of area. Pressure is calculated by dividing the total force by the area of the surface. That is,

What is pressure?

$$Pressure = \frac{force}{area}$$

$$P = \frac{F}{A}$$

Air pressure at sea level is 101 300 N/m^2.

Why does a gas exert pressure? As with all matter, the particles of a gas are in constant motion. When the

F.Y.I. The SI unit for pressure is one newton per square meter and is called a pascal (Pa).

What Are Fluids? 151

particles strike the surfaces of their container they push on them. Large numbers of particles constantly striking and bouncing off the surface cause the pressure. If you have particles of gas in a small container, the pressure will be greater than if the same number of particles is in a large container. If you push in on an inflated balloon, the particles of the gas in the balloon are squeezed into a smaller volume. As a result, the particles hit the surface more often, thereby increasing the pressure.

Recall that pressure is force per unit of area. In a fluid such as water, the pressure on an object is the force the fluid exerts per unit of area of the object. The amount of force per unit of area depends on the weight of the column of fluid above each unit of area. In other words, pressure on any object in a fluid depends on the depth of the object in the fluid. The deeper the object is submerged in the fluid, the greater the pressure. Look at Figure 8–3. Which container has the greatest pressure at the bottom? Container B has the greatest pressure at the bottom. The water is deeper, and thus the amount of weight (force) pressing on a unit area of the bottom is greater.

You may have observed that dams are built much thicker at the bottom than at the top. The reason for this is so they can withstand the pressure from the deep water behind them. Maybe you have been aware of pressure when you dived into a swimming pool or lake. Diving chambers and submarines that can descend to great depths in the ocean must be built to withstand very high pressures.

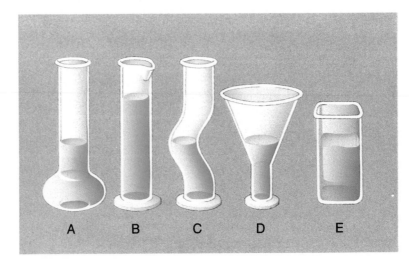

FIGURE 8–3. The shapes of these containers differ. The container with the most liquid has the greatest pressure on the bottom.

The Leaking Tub

It was a warm, sunny Saturday morning. Since the weather was comfortable, Bob decided to give his Irish setter, Sandy, a bath. It was Bob's responsibility to groom Sandy. He brushed her every day and usually gave her a bath twice a month.

Bob got a large tub out of the garage and placed it on the lawn. He then put the garden hose in the tub and turned on the faucet. While the tub was filling with water, Bob and Sandy played fetch. After they had played for several minutes, Bob turned off the hose and gathered the soap and towels. Since Sandy didn't like baths, he put her on a leash and led her to the tub.

When Bob arrived at the tub, he noticed that the ground around the tub was wet. Since the tub had not overflowed, Bob looked for leaks. He found two identical holes on opposite sides of the tub. One hole was near the top of the tub, and the other hole was nearer to the middle. Bob observed that the water from the first hole was only spraying a short distance from the tub. But, water from the lower hole was spraying out much farther. Bob wondered why. How can you explain why the water from the lower hole sprayed farther than the water from the higher hole?

Air is a fluid also. You and every object at Earth's surface are submerged in an ocean of air. If you move to higher altitudes, the pressure of the atmosphere is less than it is at sea level. Atmospheric pressure is caused by the weight of air pressing on each unit area of an object.

REVIEW

1. Why are gases and liquids called fluids?
2. How are gases and liquids different?
3. How is pressure related to force and area?
4. Compare distances between particles in a gas and a liquid.
5. How does the pressure on the bottom of an aquarium half full of water compare with the pressure in a full aquarium?

Problem: How can you compare the densities of different liquids?

Materials

pan balance
graduated cylinder
small plastic cups (4)
large plastic cup
water

rubbing alcohol
cooking oil
corn syrup
masking tape

Procedure

Part A

1. Copy the data table.
2. Label the cups water, oil, alcohol, and syrup. Find and record the mass of each empty cup.
3. Use a clean graduated cylinder to measure 25 mL of water. Pour the water into one cup. Find and record the mass of the cup and water.
4. Calculate and record the mass of the sample. Use the equation:

$$\text{mass of cup with liquid} - \text{mass of cup} = \text{mass of sample}$$

5. Repeat steps 3 and 4 with each test liquid. Be sure to clean the graduated cylinder before adding a new liquid.
6. Calculate the density of each sample. Use the equation: $density = \dfrac{mass}{volume}$

Part B

7. Predict the position of the liquids if they were each poured into one large plastic cup.
8. Carefully pour each liquid down the side of the large plastic cup. Do not move the large cup. Look at the cup from the side and observe the positions of the liquids.
9. Give the cup of liquids to your teacher for disposal.

Questions and Conclusions

1. List the order of the densities in Part A from least dense to most dense.
2. List the order of the layers in Part B from top to bottom.
3. How do the calculated densities of the liquids compare to their positions in the large cup?
4. In Part B, what information did you use to make your prediction?
5. In Part B, how did your prediction compare to your observations of the position of the liquids in the cup?
6. How can you compare the densities of different liquids?

Data and Observations

Measurements	Water	Oil	Alcohol	Syrup
Mass of cup with liquid (g)				
Mass of empty cup (g)				
Mass of sample (g)				
Volume of sample (mL)				
Density of sample (g/mL)				

8:3 Fluids at Rest

Judy was swimming with her younger sister, Chris. Chris stubbed her toe, and Judy picked Chris up to comfort her. As she lifted her sister, Judy noticed that Chris didn't seem to be as heavy as she did normally. Recall that Earth and all objects exert a force on each other. However, fluids exert a force on objects that are in them. **Buoyant force** is the upward force of a fluid on an object in it.

You have probably noticed that you seem almost weightless in water. The density of the human body is almost the same as the density of water. Therefore, the buoyant force of water is just enough to support the weight of the average person. The apparent weight of an object in a liquid is the object's weight in air minus the buoyant force of the liquid. Perhaps you have seen films of people diving for treasure or exploring old shipwrecks. Have you noticed that many objects such as old jars or cannons seem lighter and easier to move underwater? Once they are hauled up and break the water's surface, they suddenly seem much heavier. You are observing the effects of buoyant force.

In the third century B.C., Archimedes, a Greek philosopher, proposed an explanation for why objects float or sink. **Archimedes' principle** states that the buoyant force on an object in a fluid is equal to the weight of the fluid displaced by the object.

GOALS

You will study . . .
1. properties of fluids at rest and in motion.
2. the effect of pressure of a gas due to a change in volume and the effect on the volume of a gas due to a change in temperature.
3. air pollution.

How do you determine apparent weight?

FIGURE 8–4. Buoyant force exerts an upward force on all objects in liquids.

Suppose you have an iron block and a pine wood block, each 1000 cm^3 in volume. Because iron is more dense, the iron block weighs 77 N while the wood weighs only 4 N. Now, suppose you place these blocks in a bucket of water. As the iron is lowered into the bucket, it begins to displace water. Therefore, a buoyant force begins to act upward on the iron. When the iron block is completely submerged, it has displaced 1000 cm^3 of water. Water weighs about 10 N per 1000 cm^3. So, according to Archimedes' principle, the buoyant force acting on the iron is 10 N. But the iron weighs 77 N, so there is not enough buoyant force to counteract its weight, and the iron sinks.

As the wood is lowered into the water, a buoyant force begins to act on it, too. By the time 400 cm^3 of the block is underwater, it has displaced 400 cm^3 of water. Four hundred cm^3 of water weighs 4 N. This gives a buoyant force of 4 N, which is the weight of the block. Thus, the block is held up by the buoyant force and does not sink further.

An object will float when it displaces enough fluid to equal its weight. A life jacket is light but allows you to displace more water. Therefore, you float more easily. If the density of an object is greater than the fluid it is in, the object will sink. If the density of an object is less than the density of the fluid, the object will float. Submarines pump water into and out of chambers in order to regulate the depth at which they operate. How does Archimedes' principle explain this? Archimedes' principle can be applied to fish also. Fish have air sacs that allow them to swim at different depths.

When will an object float?

FIGURE 8–5. The amount of water displaced by the iron block is not enough to allow it to float (a). The wood block displaces enough water to equal its weight, and floats (b).

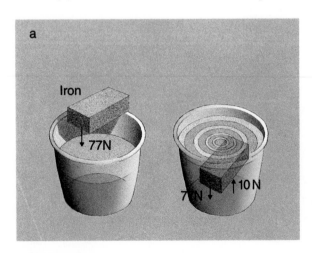

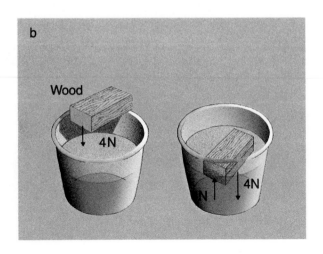

a

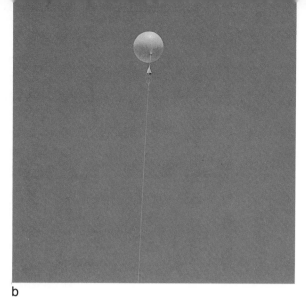
b

Air is a fluid, and Archimedes' principle works there as well as in liquids. Balloons blown up with air sink because the density of the balloon with compressed air inside is greater than the surrounding air. You are familiar with balloons that float in air, however. These balloons are filled with helium, a gas that is less dense than air. You may recall that you are advised to drop to the floor and crawl out of a burning building. This is because warmer air is less dense than colder air and is pushed upward by the buoyant force.

FIGURE 8–6. Weather balloons (a) are inflated with helium, so they rise to a level in the atmosphere where the density of the helium equals the density of the surrounding air (b).

SKILL BUILDER

Observing and Inferring

Suppose you have two 1-L beakers. One beaker contains water. The other beaker contains alcohol. You place a rubber ball in the water, and it floats. You place an identical rubber ball in the alcohol, and it sinks. Make inferences based on your observations to answer the questions below. If you need help, refer to Observing and Inferring on page 535.

Questions

1. Does water or alcohol have a greater buoyant force?
2. Are the rubber balls denser than the water? Are they denser than the alcohol?
3. Suppose you placed one of the rubber balls in salt water. Would it float or would it sink? Explain.

To what height will a helium balloon rise?

It also explains why hot-air balloons can rise and carry a load. Unlike water, air becomes less dense as you go up. Weather balloons are inflated with just enough helium gas so that they rise to a certain level and float there. This level is the height at which the density of the balloon equals the density of the air around it.

Remember that the particles of gases and liquids are free to move in any direction. For this reason, pressure on an object within a fluid is exerted at all points on the object. This is why a deep-sea diving chamber must be strong on all sides. Likewise, if you increase the pressure on a container of fluid, the increased pressure is exerted everywhere within the fluid. Suppose you squeeze one end of a balloon. The other end bulges because of the increased pressure. A French scientist, Blaise Pascal (1623–1662), first described this property of fluids. **Pascal's principle** states that pressure applied to an enclosed fluid will be felt equally throughout the fluid. This means that if the pressure of water is increased at a pumping station, the pressure will be increased by the same amount throughout the water lines. Of course, if many people turn on their water at once, the pressure drops throughout the water lines.

State Pascal's principle.

Pascal's principle can be used to construct machines that multiply force. Hydraulic lifts and hydraulic brakes are examples. See Figure 8–7. Hydraulic lifts are used in warehouses to raise heavy objects. Force is applied to a small piston. The small piston and a large piston are linked and contain fluid.

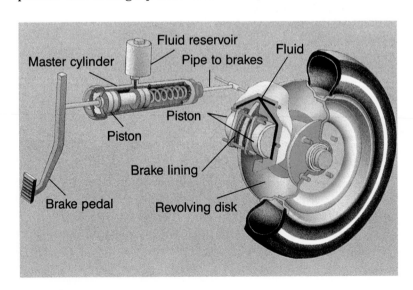

FIGURE 8–7. Pressure on the brake pedal pushes a piston into the fluid-filled master cylinder. Fluid is pushed into lines connected to fluid in the wheel cylinders. The fluid presses brake linings together against revolving disks attached to the wheels.

FIGURE 8-8. Airplanes stay aloft because lift is created by higher pressure pushing up on the bottom of the wings, with lower pressure on top of the wings because air is rushing over them faster.

Suppose you exert a pressure of 20 newtons per square centimeter on the small piston with an area of 10 cm^2. This pressure is transmitted everywhere in the fluid. The pressure acts on the large piston, exerting a force of 20 newtons per cm^2. However, the large piston has an area of 100 cm^2. Therefore, the large piston could lift a load of 20 N/cm$^2 \times 100$ cm$^2 = 2000$ newtons. The force used on the small piston has been multiplied ten times using Pascal's principle.

8:4 Fluids in Motion

Try this experiment. Hold a 5 cm-wide strip of notebook paper in front of your mouth and blow across the top of the paper. The strip will rise. There must be a force pushing the paper up. In 1738, Daniel Bernoulli (1700–1782), a Swiss mathematician, discovered a relationship in fluids between speed and pressure. **Bernoulli's principle** states that the pressure in a fluid decreases as the speed of the fluid increases. How does this explain your observation with the rising strip of paper? The pressure in the fast-moving air rushing across the top of the paper was less than in the air below the paper. As a result, the pressure below the paper exerted an upward force causing the paper to rise. This force is called lift.

State Bernoulli's principle.

What caused the paper to rise?

How Do Fluids Behave? 159

Why do wings produce lift?

The wings of an airplane are designed so that the air travels a longer distance over the top. Thus, the air must travel faster, creating an area of lower pressure above the wing. Air pressure below the wing produces a net upward force or lift. The lift force carries the aircraft upward and supports it during level flight. Why do you suppose low-speed gliders must have very long wings?

You may have noticed that the bottom of a shower curtain moves toward the water when the shower is turned on. Maybe you have observed paper moving into the stream of a fan or vent. The increased speed of the fluids has caused a decrease in pressure on one side, and the atmospheric pressure on the other side makes the curtain and paper move in the direction of the lower pressure. If you look at the bottom of the shower curtain, you will see weights or magnets that are placed there to overcome the tendency of the curtain to stick to your legs.

TECHNOLOGY

Gliders and Ultralights

Today's skies are full of many types of aircraft. You may have seen hang gliders and ultralights. Hang gliders are flying wings. These gliders have no engine and rely on wind currents to keep them aloft. The pilot is suspended beneath the triangle-shaped wing and steers it by shifting his or her body weight. These are usually flown in mountainous regions where updrafts frequently occur.

Ultralights evolved from hang gliders. These, too, are one-person crafts. Most have a large forward wing and a small rear wing and tail. The wings provide lift, and a small engine with a propeller pushes the craft forward. Pilots ride in a sitting position beneath the wings.

Hang gliders and ultralights are made of light-weight metals and plastics. The wings are nylon fabric stretched tightly over skeleton frames.

ADVANCE

Ultralights are being used to dust crops. Pilots spray pesticides, herbicides, and fertilizers on vegetable and fruit crops. Ultralights can fly 3-5 m above fields at 25 km/h. The amount of chemicals, water, and fuel used is much less than a conventional aircraft would require. Farmers save money and protect the environment because pollution is reduced.

Problem: How does the shape of an airplane wing create lift?

Materials

paper (2 sheets)   index cards (2)
metric ruler   drinking straw
thumbtack   scissors
empty spool   transparent tape

Procedure

Part A

1. Fold one index card in half lengthwise. Place the card on a table.
2. Hypothesize what will happen when you blow between the card and the flat surface with a straw. Record your hypothesis.
3. Try to blow the card across the table by blowing hard with a straw beneath the card. Record your observations.

Part B

4. Push a thumbtack through the center of an unfolded index card. Place the point of the tack in the hole of the spool, and hold the card in place.
5. Hypothesize what will happen when you blow into the hole and release your hold on the card.
6. Blow through the hole in the spool and release the card. Try this with the card facing toward the ceiling, floor, and

sideways. Record your observations in the data table.

Part C

7. Use the scissors to cut a piece of paper 5-cm wide and 20-cm long. Tape the ends of the paper together. Bend the paper in the shape of an airplane wing. The bottom of the wing should be flat, and the top should be curved. Hold the straw horizontally. Hang the wing on the straw so the bottom faces you.
8. Hypothesize what will happen when you blow directly at the wing. Write the hypothesis in the data table.
9. Blow directly at the wing. Write your observations in the data table.

Questions and Conclusions

1. What did you observe in Part A?
2. In Part B, what happened when you stopped blowing?
3. What effect does moving air have on pressure compared to stationary air?
4. Over which surface did molecules of air have to travel faster to reach the back of the wing at the same time?
5. How does the shape of an airplane wing create lift?

Data and Observations

	Hypotheses	Observations
Part A		
Part B		
Part C		

8:5 Gas Laws

What happens as you blow air into a balloon? You increase the number of particles inside the balloon. Remember that these particles are moving in all directions. The pressure inside the balloon increases, and the balloon gets larger. If you squeeze the balloon to a smaller volume, the pressure will increase. The pressure increases because the particles are striking the inside surface of the balloon more often. The relationship between pressure and volume was first described in 1662 by Robert Boyle (1627–1691), an English scientist. **Boyle's law** states that if you push an amount of a gas to a smaller space the pressure of the gas increases. If you increase the volume, the pressure will decrease. Boyle's law assumes that the temperature and amount of gas do not change.

About 100 years after Boyle's discovery, the relationship between temperature and volume of a gas was described by Jacques Charles (1746–1823), a French scientist. **Charles's law** states that if the temperature of a gas increases, the gas will expand to a larger volume. Charles's law assumes that the pressure and amount of gas do not change. It also assumes that the gas is loosely contained so that it is free to change volume. When the temperature of a gas increases, the particles move faster. They begin to strike the walls of the container more often. If the walls are free to expand, the gas pushes them out. Thus, the volume increases. Look at Figure 8–9. The volume of the balloon increases as it is moved from an ice-water to a hot-water bath.

Why does pressure increase in a balloon when squeezed?

State Boyle's law.

State Charles's law.

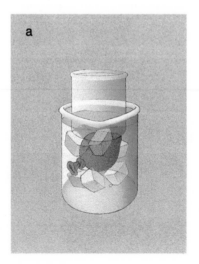 

FIGURE 8–9. The volume of air inside this balloon increases as it is moved from the ice water (a) to the hot water (b).

162 Fluids

SCIENCE AND SOCIETY

8:6 Air Pollution

The ocean of air in which we live is necessary for life. However, sometimes it has caused great harm. London, England experienced a short period of extreme air pollution in 1952. People who had respiratory problems were seriously affected, and as many as 4000 deaths may have been linked to the pollution. Similar occurrences took place in Belgium in 1930, in Pennsylvania in 1948, and again in London in 1962. It was not until 1948 that people realized that air pollution along with a temperature inversion could cause deaths in people whose lungs had been weakened by illness or disease. A temperature inversion occurs when an upper level of warm air overlies cooler air and prevents the upward movement of air. The warmer air acts as a lid. Cooler air is trapped near the surface with pollutants held in place.

When does a temperature inversion occur?

Human health is influenced by the pollutants in air. The pollutants enter the body by ingestion, by absorption through the skin and eyes, and by inhalation. Long-term exposure to pollutants has been linked to a variety of respiratory diseases. Persons most likely to be affected by air pollution are those who are very young or very old, those who have lung or heart problems, and those who have allergies to the pollutants.

How do pollutants enter the body?

Air pollution causes damage to buildings, statues, metals, paints, and plants. Weather is also affected by air pollution. Certain particles in the atmosphere absorb energy and warm Earth's atmosphere and surface, creating the "greenhouse effect."

One area of air pollution that is causing concern is the destruction of the ozone layer in the atmosphere.

FIGURE 8–10. Human health is affected by air pollution such as smog.

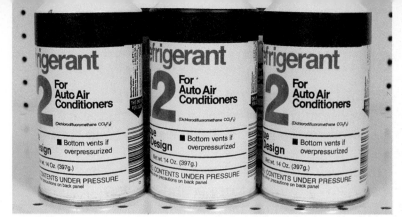

FIGURE 8–11. World governments are encouraging industries in trying to find ways to cut back on the use of CFCs as a means of protecting Earth's ozone layer.

What does ozone do?

Ozone is a form of oxygen consisting of three atoms of oxygen combined to form a molecule. Ozone filters out much of the damaging portion of ultraviolet radiation from the sun. A small reduction in the ozone layer will produce an increase in the amount of ultraviolet radiation reaching Earth. Increased amounts of ultraviolet radiation could increase the number of cases of skin cancer, reduce crop productivity, and produce a slight warming of Earth's atmosphere.

Name three effects of increased ultraviolet radiation.

Chlorofluorocarbons destroy large quantities of ozone. **Chlorofluorocarbons,** known as CFCs, are chemicals that contain chlorine, fluorine, and carbon. They are used as refrigerants and in the making of polyurethane foams such as those used in making seat cushions. CFCs have also been used for metal cleaning and in fast freezing of foods. Some nations have agreed to cut production of chlorofluorocarbons by 50 percent over the next decade. Even if the production of all CFCs were to be stopped, the level of CFCs in the atmosphere today would still be noticeable for some time.

Air pollution is a global problem. What part do people play in finding solutions for this problem? Often it is possible to find ways to avoid using materials that pollute the air, but these may be more costly. Will you be willing to pay a higher price for goods if this will contribute to a cleaner atmosphere? Why or why not?

F.Y.I. The atmospheric lifetime of one chlorofluorocarbon, CCl_2F_2, is more than 100 years.

REVIEW

6. State Pascal's principle.
7. What does the buoyant force of a fluid depend on?
8. Why is it easier to lift a rock in water than on land?
9. How are pressure in a fluid and the speed of the fluid related according to Bernoulli's principle?
10. Contrast Boyle's law and Charles's law.

CHAPTER 8 REVIEW

SUMMARY

1. Gases and liquids are called fluids because they flow. Gases can be squeezed and expanded, but liquids cannot. 8:1
2. Pressure is defined as the force applied per unit area. 8:2
3. Archimedes' principle states that the buoyant force on an object in a fluid is equal to the weight of the fluid it displaces. Pascal's principle states that the pressure applied to a confined fluid is transmitted unchanged throughout the fluid. 8:3
4. Bernoulli's principle states that the pressure in a fluid decreases as the speed of the fluid increases. 8:4
5. Boyle's law states that pushing an amount of a gas into a smaller space causes the pressure of the gas to increase if the temperature remains constant. Charles's law states that if the temperature of a gas increases the gas will expand to a larger volume. 8:5
6. Air pollution damages buildings, vegetation, the atmosphere itself, and along with a temperature inversion, can cause deaths. The destruction of the ozone layer will produce an increase in the amount of ultraviolet radiation that reaches Earth. 8:6

VOCABULARY

a. Archimedes' principle
b. Bernoulli's principle
c. Boyle's law
d. buoyant force
e. Charles's law
f. chlorofluorocarbons
g. fluid
h. ozone
i. Pascal's principle
j. pressure

Match each description with the correct vocabulary word from the list above.
1. any substance that flows
2. force per unit area
3. gives the relationship between volume and pressure
4. the speed of a fluid increases as the pressure decreases
5. a form of oxygen
6. pressure is transmitted unchanged throughout a confined fluid
7. contain chlorine, fluorine, and carbon
8. upward force on an object in a fluid
9. gives the relationship between volume and temperature
10. the buoyant force on an object in a fluid is equal to the weight of the fluid displaced by the object

CHAPTER 8 REVIEW

MAIN IDEAS

A. Reviewing Concepts

Choose the word or phrase that correctly completes each of the following sentences.

1. The relationship between speed and pressure in fluids is known as _____.
   a. Archimedes' principle
   b. Bernoulli's principle
   c. Boyle's law
   d. Charles's law

2. Pressure in a fluid depends on the _____.
   a. volume of the fluid
   b. weight of the column of fluid above an object
   c. depth of the object in the fluid
   d. both b and c

3. Archimedes explained why _____.
   a. hydraulics work   c. objects sink
   b. objects float   d. both b and c

4. A dam is thicker at the bottom because pressure is greatest _____.
   a. at the bottom   c. in the middle
   b. at the top   d. all of these

5. _____ force is the upward force exerted on an object by the displaced fluid.
   a. Gravitational   c. Magnetic
   b. Electrical   d. Buoyant

6. The buoyant force on a submerged stone depends on the _____.
   a. weight of the stone
   b. mass of the stone
   c. weight of displaced fluid
   d. none of these

7. A gas in a closed container will _____.
   a. expand to fill the container
   b. occupy one-half of the container
   c. sit on the bottom of the container
   d. none of these

8. An increase in the temperature of a gas causes the particles to move _____.
   a. the same speed   c. slower
   b. faster   d. all of these

9. On a mountain, atmospheric pressure is _____ sea level pressure.
   a. more than   c. equal to
   b. less than   d. none of these

10. Chlorofluorocarbons contain _____.
    a. Cl and F only   c. Cl, F, and C
    b. F and C only   d. O and H only

11. _____ explained the principle behind hydraulic machines.
    a. Boyle   c. Charles
    b. Bernoulli   d. Pascal

12. If a 100-N object displaces 60 N of water its apparent weight is _____.
    a. 160 N   c. 60 N
    b. 100 N   d. 40 N

13. Squeezing a balloon causes the pressure to _____.
    a. increase   c. stay the same
    b. decrease   d. none of these

14. Air travels faster over the wing of an airplane, producing _____ pressure under the wing.
    a. lower   c. equal
    b. higher   d. no

15. _____ explained the relationship between the temperature of a gas and its volume.
    a. Bernoulli   c. Charles
    b. Pascal   d. Boyle

B. Understanding Concepts

Answer the following questions using complete sentences.

16. What is the difference between gases and liquids?

17. Why does a shower curtain move to the inside of the shower?

CHAPTER 8 REVIEW

18. What are some uses of CFCs?
19. Why is the ozone layer important?
20. What happens to the density of air when the air is compressed?
21. How does pressure differ from force?
22. Why can you support yourself in water easier than in air?
23. How does a life jacket help you float?
24. What is a temperature inversion?
25. What happens to an object that cannot displace its weight in a liquid?

C. Applying Concepts

Answer the following questions using complete sentences.

26. Why will an egg float in salt water but not in fresh water?
27. How much water must a large ship displace in order to float?
28. What would you expect to happen to barometer readings as you go from sea level to the mountains? Why?
29. Waterbeds are sometimes used for people confined to bed because they are less likely to develop bruises and bedsores. Why?
30. Would an empty ship sink deeper in water than the same ship filled with feathers? Why?

SKILL REVIEW

If you need help, refer to the Skill Handbook, pages 526 to 537.

1. Classify each of the following as a fluid or a nonfluid: milk, air, wood, gold, ice, and liquid water.
2. What SI unit is used to express the volume of fluids? What SI units are used to express pressure?

3. Outline Sections 8:4 and 8:5.
4. A balloon is moved from an ice-water bath to a hot-water bath. What effect do you observe? What caused it?
5. Suppose you observe that a large area of ozone has been destroyed. What effects do you infer this will have on people, plants, and animals?

PROJECTS

1. Assemble a Cartesian diver. Fill a 2-L plastic bottle with water. Fill a dropper with just enough water so it floats near the top of the bottle. Put the lid on the bottle. Squeeze the bottle. The dropper should sink. Demonstrate to the class and explain the movements.
2. Construct three different wings out of balsa wood. Build stands for the wings out of pipe cleaners that hold them about 8 cm above the surface. Place each wing and stand on a pan balance. Place a fan in front of the wing. Measure the lifting ability of each wing by the decrease of mass on the balance.

READINGS

1. Arnold, Guy. *Gas.* New York: Franklin Watts, 1985.
2. Sprackling, Michael. *Liquids and Solids.* New York: Metheun, 1985.
3. Starr, D. "How to Protect the Ozone Layer." *National Wildlife,* Dec. 1987/Jan. 1988, pages 26–28.

FUN WITH

You are in a car passing a truck on the highway. Why does the car seem to be pulled toward the truck? When the vehicles pass, the space between them narrows and air pressure decreases. Greater air pressure on the one side of the car pushes the car toward the truck.

QUIZ

Juan took the bus to the museum. The bus traveled about 25 km/h. Just before his stop, Juan got up and walked toward the front of the bus at 5 km/h. What is his speed as seen by the other passengers? By people at the stop?

Calvin and Hobbes

JOKE

Q. What runs but never walks?
A. a river

Sue and Alex went to the carnival. Sue decided to take Alex on the Roundup. They strapped themselves in. Once in motion, the floor dropped out from under the riders. Alex was frightened, but he held on tightly. The floor rose to its original position as the ride slowed. Why didn't the riders fall when the floor dropped?

168

SCIENCE

Edison invents electric light.

1902

First microwave oven is marketed.

1974

1879

Marie and Pierre Curie discover radium.

1947

Ali knocks out Foreman to regain world heavyweight title.

Why do scissors cut paper?

Scissors are compound machines made of two levers that move in opposite directions. The levers pivot around a fulcrum. It is easier to cut an object close to the pivot because the mechanical advantage is greatest there.

Did you know that an ant can transport about 600 times its own weight?

Riddle

Q. A rooster lays an egg on a barn roof. Which direction does it roll? **A.** Roosters don't lay eggs!

QUESTION AND ANSWER

Why does a boomerang return?

A return boomerang is flat on one side and convex on the other like an airplane wing. Such a boomerang must be thrown vertically. Because of Bernoulli's principle, low pressure will form on the convex side of a spinning boomerang. The boomerang will accelerate toward its low pressure side. This causes a boomerang to fly in a circle and return close to the point where it was thrown.

TEASER

FUN RECIPE

SPICED APPLE CIDER

Pour 2 cups of unsweetened apple cider or apple juice into a heavy saucepan. Add 2 whole cloves and 1 stick of cinnamon. Heat the ingredients until hot but not boiling. Remove from heat and let stand for 10 minutes. Remove the cloves and cinnamon stick. Serve in mugs.

169

Answers
Quiz: 5 km/h; 30 km/h
Teaser: When the Roundup reaches a certain speed, the riders are thrown away from the center of rotation. Centripetal force holds them in place.

UNIT 3

Planet Earth

Hundreds of small rivers contribute to the Mississippi River. The river carries large amounts of sediment that are deposited in the Gulf of Mexico. What forces work together to form the Mississippi delta? Water slides are like river systems. Channels carry water and you to a pool at the bottom of the hill. How else is a water slide like a river system?

171

Our Earth

Career: Aerial Photographer

A photograph in the newspaper showed an aerial view of the new school and its grounds. The building was marked by an *X,* the track by an *O,* and the sports fields by *Y*s. Rich's hobby was photography, and he wondered how such a clear picture was made. He decided to visit the survey company that took the picture.

At the survey office, Rich was met by the owner of the company, Scott Booth. He showed Rich some of the aerial photographs that he had taken of the surrounding area. His company owned several airplanes, and he told Rich that he used different cameras and airplanes for different assignments. For the school's aerial photo, he had the pilot fly low and bank in a circle around the area. Mr. Booth kept the plane's door open and the camera level with the horizon while he snapped 30 pictures. Since he was moving, he used a camera with a fast shutter and fast film to prevent any blurring.

Mr. Booth showed Rich one of the airplanes used to take photographs for mapmaking. It had a large camera mounted to the floor. Mr. Booth explained that this special camera uses a large roll of film that takes 100 pictures.

Maps are models of Earth's surface and can show many types of features. In this chapter, you will study the characteristics and models used to represent Earth.

F.Y.I. Ferris State University, Big Rapids, MI 49307

What Shape Is Earth?

GOALS

You will study . . .
1. the shape, size, and other properties of Earth.
2. how Earth's shape and size have been determined.
3. Earth's gravitational and magnetic properties.

9:1 Earth's Shape

If you've ever held a basketball or volleyball in your hand, you've held a sphere. A **sphere** is a round, three dimensional object whose surface at all points is the same distance from its center. Earth's shape is spherical. Because Earth is so large, people on its surface cannot clearly see its shape. At one time people thought Earth was flat because it appears to stretch out flat in all directions. Let's take a look at some facts that indicate Earth's shape is spherical.

Two pieces of evidence that prove Earth is spherical can easily be seen. First, if a person on the shore watches a ship approach from sea, its mast comes into view first. Gradually, more and more of the ship appears. The curved shape of Earth's surface keeps the main part of the ship from view, as shown in Figure 9–1. A second proof of Earth's shape is seen in photographs taken from space. These pictures show Earth to be spherical.

Earth is not a perfect sphere. It is slightly flattened at the geographic poles, which are located at the north and south ends of Earth's axis. Earth's **axis** is an imaginary line around which Earth spins. Measurements show that Earth's diameter is 42 kilometers less from pole to pole than at the equator. Earth's **equator** is an imaginary line circling the globe equally distant at all points from the poles. The equator separates Earth into two equal halves, the Northern Hemisphere and the Southern Hemisphere.

What is Earth's equator?

FIGURE 9–1. A ship's mast is the first part that can be seen as it approaches land.

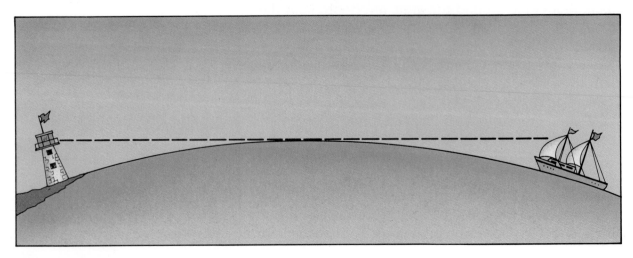

FIGURE 9–2. Earth's spherical shape can be seen from space.

9:2 Earth's Physical Properties

The physical properties of Earth are measured by scientists in many different branches of earth science. Geology is the study of Earth, its form and composition, and the processes of change in the past and present. Meteorology is the study of Earth's atmosphere. Weather and the forces and processes that cause it are the focus of meteorology. The oceans are studied in the branch of earth science called oceanography. Astronomy is the study of the universe and how Earth relates to other objects in space.

What is meteorology?

FIGURE 9–3. Astronomy is the branch of earth science that studies Earth's relationship to other objects in space.

How has Earth been measured?

What is the diameter of Earth at the poles? At the equator?

Table 9–1 lists some of Earth's physical properties. How were these measurements obtained? Technology has made obtaining measurements of Earth's size and shape fairly easy. Satellites and surveying equipment using laser beams are used to measure some of Earth's physical properties.

Table 9–1

Physical Properties of Earth	
Diameter (poles)............................	12 714 km
Diameter (equator)..........................	12 756 km
Circumference (poles)......................	40 008 km
Circumference (equator)....................	40 075 km
Mass..................................	5.96×10^{24} kg
Density	5520 kg/m^3

   The physical properties mass and density can be used to compare Earth to other planets in the solar system. For example, the planet Jupiter's mass is about 318 times more than Earth's mass. On the other hand, Jupiter's density is much less than Earth's. Earth is the most dense planet in the solar system. This means that Earth has more mass per unit volume than any other planet in the solar system.
   As stated earlier in Chapter 5, gravity is a force that every object exerts on every other object. Earth has a gravitational force on objects just as the gravity from other objects affects Earth. The sun's gravitational force causes Earth to curve toward it. The force of gravity exerted by one object on another is determined by the masses of the objects and the distance between their centers. More gravitational force is exerted between objects having large masses or when objects are very close to each other. You can easily lift a baseball but not a car. The car has more mass, and thus the gravitational force between it and Earth is greater. You could say that the car has a heavy weight. If you were in the top of a very tall building and weighed yourself, your weight would be slightly less than if you weighed yourself in the basement. This is because the force of gravity decreases the farther you are from Earth's center.

FIGURE 9–4. Earth's gravity is pulling this parachutist toward the ground.

Another physical property of Earth is magnetism. You may have used a compass to determine direction or a bar magnet to pick up paper clips or other metallic objects. Objects having magnetic properties have a magnetic field around them. A magnetic field is an area of magnetic lines of force. Figure 9–6 shows Earth's magnetic field. A field of magnetic force exists inside and around Earth just as it exists inside and around a magnet. The small metal needle in a compass lines up with Earth's magnetic field and always points toward a magnetic pole.

What is a magnetic field?

FIGURE 9–5. A compass needle points toward a magnetic pole.

FIGURE 9–6. These lines of force represent Earth's magnetic field.

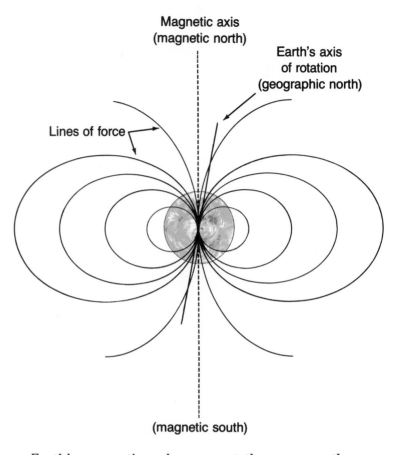

Magnetic axis
(magnetic north)

Earth's axis
of rotation
(geographic north)

Lines of force

(magnetic south)

Earth's magnetic poles are not the same as the geographic poles that are the ends of its axis. The magnetic poles are located at two points on Earth's surface where the magnetic field is strongest. Since a compass needle points to the north magnetic pole in the Northern Hemisphere, an adjustment must be made to obtain the compass reading for geographic north. The angle of difference between geographic north and magnetic north is called **declination.** This value is placed on maps and must be added to or subtracted from compass readings in order to find true geographic north.

What is declination?

REVIEW

1. What is one way to show that Earth is a sphere?
2. On what factors does gravitational force depend?
3. What is meteorology?
4. Why is declination important for finding accurate directions with a compass?
5. Why would a football not be considered a sphere?

9:3 Earth Movements

Some early astronomers thought Earth was the center of the universe. They thought Earth stayed in one place and everything else moved around it. If you watch the sun, moon, and stars, they do appear to move across our sky. These objects change positions in our sky mainly because Earth moves. Earth spins on its axis and travels around the sun at the same time.

The spinning of Earth about its axis is called **rotation.** Earth takes one day, about 24 hours, for one rotation. This period of time is referred to as a solar day, since we measure Earth's rotation by the position of the sun. Evidence of Earth's rotation is the regular change from daylight to nighttime over most of Earth's surface. If observed from above the North Pole, Earth spins in a direction opposite the hands of a clock, or counterclockwise. This also means that Earth rotates west to east.

Have you ever seen a pendulum swinging in a clock? A pendulum is a heavy object suspended so it can swing freely. In 1851, a French physicist, Jean Foucault, suspended a heavy iron ball from a long, thin wire in an attempt to prove that Earth rotated.

GOALS

You will study . . .
1. the difference between Earth's rotation and revolution.
2. how seasons occur on Earth.

What is rotation?

FIGURE 9–7. A Foucault Pendulum shows that Earth rotates.

He set the ball swinging along a north-south line. Foucault knew that a pendulum in motion would not change direction from the line it is swinging in. However, about one hour after he started the pendulum, it seemed to have changed direction. Several hours later, the direction of the pendulum's swing appeared to be east to west. What caused this change? The swinging pendulum did not change direction, Earth did. Earth was rotating under the Foucault pendulum. Foucault had succeeded in proving that Earth rotates.

As Earth rotates, it also revolves around the sun. **Revolution** is the movement of one object around another object. The path of a revolving object is called an **orbit.** The movement of Earth in its orbit takes a little more than one year to complete. Earth's orbit is an ellipse, which is an elongated, closed curve. Thus, the distance between Earth and the sun changes. The closest Earth gets to the sun is about 147 million km, which occurs around January 3. The farthest point is about 152 million km, which occurs around July 4. Even though Earth is closest to the sun in January and farthest away in July, Earth's temperatures are not affected much by its distance from the sun. You will study the cause of temperature change and Earth's seasons in Section 9:4.

What is an orbit?

What is the shape of Earth's orbit?

FIGURE 9−8. Individual cars on this ride spin as they travel around in a circle. Earth spins as it moves around the sun.

Problem: What is the difference between the rotation and revolution of Earth?

Materials

light source (unshaded)   wastebaskets (2)
tape   meter stick
globe   chalk
string (7 m)

Procedure

1. Tie the ends of the string together to form a loop. Place the loop in a circular shape on the floor.
2. Inside the circle place two wastebaskets spaced about 2 m apart. Take the slack from the string by pulling the loop tight at one point.
3. Using the string as a guide, draw a chalk line around the wastebaskets.
4. Remove the wastebaskets and the string, and describe the shape of the chalk line in the data table. Place the light source in the center of the shape.
5. Turn on the light representing the sun. **CAUTION:** *The light may get hot.* Place the globe on the chalk line.

6. Rotate the globe counterclockwise.
7. Describe the rotation of the globe in the data table.
8. Move the globe counterclockwise on the chalk line around the light source.
9. Describe the revolution of the globe in the data table.

Data and Observations

Movement of globe	Observations
Shape of orbit	
Rotation of globe	
Revolution of globe	

Questions and Conclusions

1. How is the shape of Earth's orbit different from a circle?
2. What name describes the shape of Earth's orbit?
3. How would you describe Earth's rotation?
4. How long does it take for Earth to make one rotation?
5. How long does it take for Earth to make one revolution?
6. What movement of Earth causes day and night?
7. What is the difference beween rotation and revolution?

9:4 Seasons

The amount of energy the entire Earth receives from the sun during a year changes very little. However, the amount of energy received by any one place on Earth varies throughout the year. These changes in the amount of energy received from the sun result in seasons.

If you set your book up on end on your desk top, the front cover of your book is perpendicular to the desk top. Earth's axis is not aligned this way. Instead, Earth's axis is tilted 23 ½° from a line perpendicular to its orbit around the sun.

Because Earth is tilted while it revolves around the sun, half of the year the Northern Hemisphere is toward the sun. During the other half of the year, the Southern Hemisphere is toward the sun. When a hemisphere is toward the sun, there are more daylight hours, and the sun's rays hit that hemisphere at a higher angle. In other words, the sun is higher in the sky for longer periods of time. This results in more direct, intense heating, higher temperatures, and the season known as summer.

What causes different seasons?

FIGURE 9–9. Earth's axis remains tilted as Earth revolves around the sun. This tilt causes the amount of energy received by Earth to vary during the year.

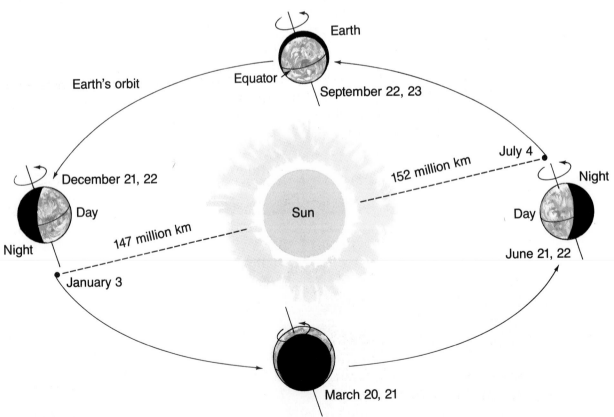

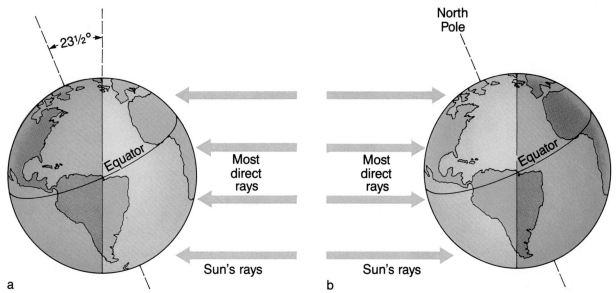

a

b

As Earth continues around the sun, seasons change. Fall occurs in the Northern Hemisphere as it moves away from its summer position of being tilted toward the sun. Winter occurs in the Northern Hemisphere when it is most tilted away from the sun. Spring occurs in the Northern Hemisphere as it moves from its winter to its summer position.

FIGURE 9–10. When the Northern Hemisphere is tilted away from the sun, lack of direct rays result in winter (a). When tilted toward the sun, direct rays result in summer (b).

SKILL BUILDER

Observing and Inferring

Refer to Figure 9–9. Observe the different positions of Earth as it revolves around the sun. If you need help, refer to Observing and Inferring on page 535.

Questions

1. What season is just beginning in the Southern Hemisphere on March 21?
2. Would you find more snow and cold temperatures or more rain and warm temperatures in the Southern Hemisphere in July?
3. What season is just beginning in the Northern Hemisphere on June 21?
4. Which hemisphere receives the most sunlight in January?
5. How does Figure 9–9 help to explain the change of seasons in each hemisphere?

a

b

FIGURE 9–11. These photographs were taken on the same day, one in the Northern Hemisphere (a) and one in the Southern Hemisphere (b).

Because of the tilt of Earth's axis, the sun's position relative to Earth's equator constantly changes. The longest day of the year is called summer solstice. **Solstice** occurs when the sun reaches its greatest distance north or south of the equator. The summer solstice occurs on June 21 or 22 for the Northern Hemisphere. On this day, the Northern Hemisphere is tilted more directly toward the sun.

The shortest day of the year is called winter solstice. It occurs on December 21 or 22 for the Northern Hemisphere. On this day, the Northern Hemisphere is tilted most directly away from the sun.

An **equinox** occurs when the sun is directly above Earth's equator and day and night are of equal length. This happens twice each year. The first day of spring is called the spring equinox. This occurs on March 21 or 22 in the Northern Hemisphere. The first day of fall is called the fall equinox. This occurs on September 21 or 22 in the Northern Hemisphere.

When does equinox take place?

REVIEW

6. What are Earth's two main motions?
7. What property of pendulums allowed Foucault to prove that Earth rotates?
8. Where is the sun on the summer solstice in the Northern Hemisphere?
9. How long are day and night on the first day of spring and fall?
10. How long would it take for Foucault's pendulum to make one complete rotation if it were placed at the North Pole?

Problem: How does the angle of light affect temperature?

Materials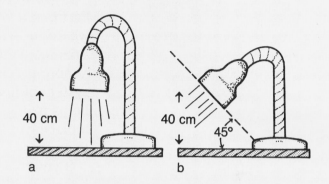

Celsius thermometer   meter stick
scissors   protractor
tape   watch
black construction paper
gooseneck lamp with 75-watt bulb

Procedure

1. Fold a piece of black construction paper in half, and form an envelope by taping the two sides together.
2. Adjust the gooseneck lamp so that the shade is directly facing the table as shown in diagram a.
3. Slide the end of the thermometer into the envelope and place the thermometer directly under the lamp while it is still off.
4. Read the thermometer and record the temperature in a data table like the one shown.
5. Predict the effect of light on the temperature.
6. Turn on the lamp. Observe and record the temperature in the table every three minutes.
7. Turn off the lamp. Allow the lamp and the shade to cool. **CAUTION:** *The lamp and the shade may be very hot.*
8. Remove the thermometer.
9. Adjust the gooseneck lamp so that the end of the shade is slanted at a 45° angle to the table top.
10. Hypothesize how light at a low angle will affect the temperature compared to how light from directly above the thermometer affects temperature.
11. Repeat steps 4 through 8.

Data and Observations

	Temperature at			
	Start	3 min	6 min	9 min
Direct light				
Angled light				

Questions and Conclusions

1. What happened to the temperature of the thermometer when light was directed on it?
2. Did direct light or angled light give off more heat? Explain why.
3. If the angle of the shade was tilted at a less than 45° angle, what effect would it have on temperature?
4. How does the angle of light affect temperature?
5. During what season does a location on Earth get direct sunlight from a high angle?
6. During what season does a location on Earth get sunlight from a low angle?
7. What causes the seasons to change during the year? Explain.

GOALS

You will study . . .

1. how to find locations on Earth using lines of latitude and longitude.
2. why daylight saving time is used.
3. map projections.

What are parallels?

What are meridians?

FIGURE 9–12. Latitude describes distance north or south of the equator (a). Longitude describes distance east or west of the prime meridian (b).

9:5 Latitude, Longitude, and Time Zones

If you were asked to locate a place somewhere on Earth, how would you do it? If someone asked you where the Grand Canyon is, you could say it is in Arizona. While that would be a correct answer, there is a more precise way to describe locations on Earth. A system of imaginary lines has been developed that helps people describe exact locations. The location of a place can be identified by the point at which these lines cross.

If you look closely at a globe of Earth, you will see lines drawn on it. The equator is drawn around Earth halfway between the North and South Poles. **Latitude** is a term used to describe distance in degrees north or south of the equator. Lines of latitude are drawn east and west parallel to the equator. Degrees of latitude range from 0° at the equator to 90° at either the North Pole or the South Pole. Lines of latitude also are called parallels.

Lines drawn north and south at right angles to the equator are called meridians. **Longitude** is a term used to describe distances in degrees east or west of 0° meridian. The **prime meridian** is the 0° meridian that passes through Greenwich, England.

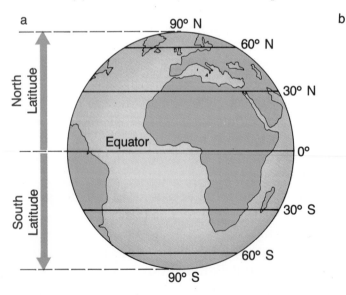

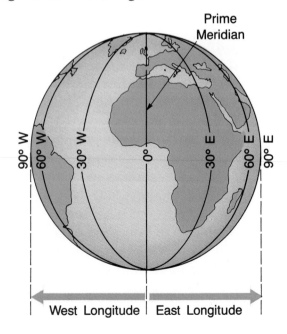

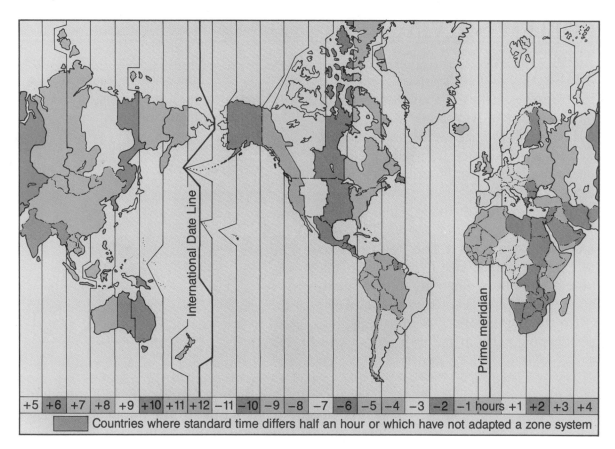

| +5 | +6 | +7 | +8 | +9 | +10 | +11 | +12 | −11 | −10 | −9 | −8 | −7 | −6 | −5 | −4 | −3 | −2 | −1 hours | +1 | +2 | +3 | +4 |

Countries where standard time differs half an hour or which have not adapted a zone system

Longitude lines have a use other than indicating distances east or west of the prime meridian. They are also used to indicate time zones. Time zones are geographic areas having the same time. For example, Detroit, Michigan, and Tampa, Florida are in the same time zone. We keep time according to the position of Earth in relation to the sun. Because Earth is constantly rotating, time is constantly changing. The sun rises earlier in Atlanta, Georgia than it does in Seattle, Washington. Therefore, when the sun is rising in Atlanta, it is still dark in Seattle, and thus the time is several hours earlier.

Each time zone represents one hour. Since there are 24 hours in one complete rotation of Earth, there are 24 international time zones. Each time zone is roughly 15° wide. Although time zones are based on meridians, they do not strictly follow lines of longitude. If half of a city were in one time zone, and the other half in another time zone, great confusion would result. To prevent this from happening, time zone boundaries are moved around cities and other areas wishing to keep the same time.

FIGURE 9–13. Time zones are roughly determined by longitudinal lines.

Why does time change?

What does a time zone represent?

PROBLEM SOLVING

Time Traveler

In November, Lisa's father went on a long business trip to Japan. Lisa's birthday was also in November. Lisa's father did not want to miss her birthday, but he had no choice. Since he would be away, he told her he would bring her a gift from Japan. He also said he would telephone her on her birthday.

As her birthday got closer, Lisa got more excited about it. She was eager to talk to her father. Lisa did not want the phone to be busy when her father called, so she asked her friends not to call her.

On the day before Lisa's birthday, the phone rang early in the morning. It was Lisa's father calling to wish her a happy birthday. Did Lisa's father make a mistake? Why do you think he called her the day before her birthday?

The **International Date Line** is the 180° meridian that is directly opposite the prime meridian. The International Date Line is one-half of one day or 12 time zones from the prime meridian. If you were traveling west across the International Date Line, you would lose one day. If you were traveling east across the International Date Line, you would gain one day.

SCIENCE AND SOCIETY

9:6 Daylight Saving Time

Much of the United States uses a system known as **daylight saving time** between the months of April and October. During daylight saving time, clocks are set one hour ahead so darkness comes one hour later than usual. Mornings are also affected because darkness lasts one hour longer. In October, clocks are set back to standard time.

The Uniform Time Act was passed in 1966 by the United States Congress. This act was an attempt to organize the country's use of daylight saving time. Individual states may choose not to use daylight saving time. States that lie in two separate time zones may elect to use daylight saving time in one portion and standard time in the other portion of the state.

F.Y.I. Daylight saving time was first suggested in a comical essay by Benjamin Franklin in 1784.

There are several advantages to the use of daylight saving time. There is more daylight in the evening for outdoor work and recreation. Less energy is used because lights are used less.

Daylight saving time also has some disadvantages. People who leave for work early in the morning must do so in darkness. School-age children must stand and wait for their bus or walk to school in darkness. Some people think that daylight saving time is a good idea, and some think it is a bad idea. What do you think?

F.Y.I. An office building in Minneapolis–St. Paul, Minnesota, once had different times on different floors during part of daylight saving time.

9:7 Models of Earth's Surface

A model is a representation of an object or an idea of how an object looks. Models, such as those of Earth, are usually scaled down in size. Since Earth's shape is spherical, a globe makes a good model. A map is also a type of model. Because flat maps are easier to carry around than globes, several methods have been developed to make flat maps. A method that is used to project latitude and longitude lines, points, and locations from a curved surface to a flat piece of paper is called a **map projection.**

What is a map projection?

TECHNOLOGY

Photogrammetry

Making measurements using photography is a process known as photogrammetry. This process most often uses aerial photographs as the basis for drawing maps. Aerial photographs present a problem though, because they are distorted. Hilltops, for example, look larger than valleys because the hilltops are closer to the airplane taking the picture.

An instrument called a stereoplotter is used to correct the distortions in aerial photographs. The stereoplotter requires two pictures from different locations of the area to be mapped. A map can then be drawn from the three-dimensional image made from the two photographs by the stereoplotter.

ADVANCE

Landsat is a mapping satellite. It uses light to record highly detailed images of Earth's surface. Computers are used to interpret Landsat's data and process the color-enhanced photographs. The different colors indicate cities, forests, and large bodies of water.

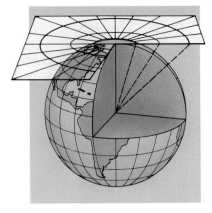

a

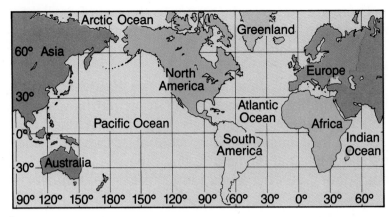

b

FIGURE 9–14. a polar map projection (a) and a Mercator projection (b) On Mercator maps, polar areas appear larger than they actually are.

What are three map projections?

Three types of map projections are Mercator, polar, and conic. In a Mercator map projection, latitude and longitude lines intersect at right angles and longitude lines appear parallel. In reality, longitude lines are far apart at the equator, and get closer at Earth's poles. Because the longitude lines are spread out on a Mercator map projection, a large distortion problem develops. The polar areas appear much larger on the map than they really are.

A polar map projection is made by placing a flat sheet of paper over Earth's pole and projecting points out from the surface of the globe. On these maps, Earth's pole is at the center of the map. Longitude lines extend straight out like spokes on a wheel, and latitude lines appear as circles. Polar projections produce the most accurate maps of polar areas.

Conic map projections are considered accurate for small areas. To make a conic projection, a flat piece of paper is rolled into a cone. The cone is then fitted over a globe, making contact with a latitude line. Points and lines are then projected into the cone.

REVIEW

11. What is latitude?
12. How many degrees are there between the prime meridian and the International Date Line?
13. If you were traveling east toward the International Date Line on Tuesday, what day would it be on the other side of the line?
14. Explain how a polar map projection is made.
15. If it is 4 A.M. in Los Angeles, what time is it in New York City?

CHAPTER 9 REVIEW

SUMMARY

1. Earth's shape is spherical. Earth is separated into Northern and Southern Hemispheres by an imaginary line called the equator. 9:1
2. The main branches of earth science include geology, meteorology, oceanography, and astronomy. A measure of the force of gravity on an object is its weight. 9:2
3. Earth rotates on its axis and revolves around the sun. 9:3
4. Earth's revolution around the sun and the tilt of its axis cause seasons. 9:4
5. Latitude lines are parallel to the equator. Latitude is measured in degrees north or south of the equator. Longitude is measured in degrees east or west of the prime meridian. 9:5
6. During daylight saving time, clocks are set ahead one hour so darkness comes one hour later than at standard time. 9:6
7. Three types of map projections are Mercator, polar, and conic. 9:7

VOCABULARY

a. axis
b. daylight saving time
c. declination
d. equator
e. equinox
f. International Date Line
g. latitude
h. longitude
i. map projection
j. orbit
k. prime meridian
l. revolution
m. rotation
n. solstice
o. sphere

Match each description with the correct vocabulary word from the list above.
1. distance in degrees east or west of the prime meridian
2. the movement of one object around another object
3. a round three-dimensional object whose surface at all points is the same distance from the object's center
4. distance in degrees north or south of the equator
5. a time when the sun reaches its greatest distance north or south of the equator
6. methods whereby latitude, longitude, points, and locations are projected from a curved surface to a flat map surface
7. the 0° meridian that passes through Greenwich, England, from which longitude is measured
8. the spinning of Earth about its axis
9. the path of a revolving object
10. an imaginary line circling the globe equally distant at all points from the poles

CHAPTER 9 REVIEW

MAIN IDEAS

A. Reviewing Concepts
Choose the word or phrase that correctly completes each of the following sentences.

1. Earth's shape is approximately _____.
   - **a.** spherical
   - **b.** a circle
   - **c.** an ellipse
   - **d.** flat

2. When Earth _____, it moves around the sun.
   - **a.** spins
   - **b.** revolves
   - **c.** swings
   - **d.** rotates

3. The diameter of Earth at the equator is _____.
   - **a.** 40 075 km
   - **b.** 12 756 km
   - **c.** 20 714 km
   - **d.** 40 008 km

4. When the North Pole is tilted most directly toward the sun in June, a(n) _____ occurs.
   - **a.** hemisphere
   - **b.** equinox
   - **c.** solstice
   - **d.** eclipse

5. Objects that are _____ have a greater amount of gravitational force between them.
   - **a.** far apart
   - **b.** touching
   - **c.** the same size
   - **d.** none of these

6. The angle of difference between geographic north and magnetic north is the _____.
   - **a.** declination
   - **b.** density
   - **c.** diameter
   - **d.** distance

7. Earth's axis is tilted _____.
   - **a.** 360°
   - **b.** 180°
   - **c.** 23½°
   - **d.** 90°

8. Spring equinox occurs in the Northern Hemisphere on _____.
   - **a.** March 21-22
   - **b.** Sept. 21-22
   - **c.** Dec. 21-22
   - **d.** June 21-22

9. Earth's magnetic field can be found _____ Earth.
   - **a.** around
   - **b.** on
   - **c.** inside
   - **d.** all of these

10. If it is 9:00 A.M. on the west coast of the United States, it is _____ on the east coast.
    - **a.** 4:00 A.M.
    - **b.** 5:00 A.M.
    - **c.** noon
    - **d.** 3:00 A.M.

11. Daylight saving time occurs between _____.
    - **a.** March and August
    - **b.** April and October
    - **c.** April and September
    - **d.** January and November

12. A distance in degrees of latitude is _____.
    - **a.** 80° east
    - **b.** 45° north
    - **c.** 25° west
    - **d.** 7° east

13. A map projection with the greatest distortion near the poles is called a _____ map.
    - **a.** Mercator
    - **b.** polar
    - **c.** conic
    - **d.** prime meridian

14. _____ describes distance east or west of the prime meridian.
    - **a.** Latitude
    - **b.** Revolution
    - **c.** Rotation
    - **d.** Longitude

15. _____ deals with studying the weather.
    - **a.** Geology
    - **b.** Oceanography
    - **c.** Meteorology
    - **d.** Astronomy

B. Understanding Concepts
Answer the following questions using complete sentences.

16. How is Earth's curved path around the sun described?

17. What is meteorology?

18. Why would there be more gravitational force between a car and a truck than between two bicycles?

19. How are the physical properties of Earth used?

20. What are some benefits of daylight saving time?

21. Why are polar areas on a Mercator map distorted?
22. If it is 3:00 P.M. in Memphis, Tennessee, what time is it in San Francisco, California?
23. Why do degrees of latitude only range from 0° to 90°?
24. Why is the summer solstice the longest day of the year?
25. Why don't we experience summer when Earth is closest to the sun?

C. Applying Concepts

Answer the following questions using complete sentences.

26. What would seasons be like if Earth's axis were not tilted?
27. How are positions on Earth's surface described using a globe or map?
28. Why don't time zones always follow lines of longitude?
29. Explain why a polar map projection would not be the best map to use when studying the equator.
30. Why is it necessary to adjust for declination when using a compass?

SKILL REVIEW

If you need help, refer to the Skill Handbook, pages 526 to 537.

1. You watch a Foucault pendulum. What can you infer about Earth?
2. Copy and complete the table below.

Cause	Effect
Earth is tilted 23½° on its axis	
	regular change from night to daylight

3. Below is a table listing cities in the U.S. and other parts of the world. The latitude or longitude of these cities is also listed. Complete the table.

Latitude	Longitude	City
40°N	83°W	Columbus, OH
38°N		San Francisco, CA
	38°E	Moscow, USSR
34°S		Sydney, Australia

4. Outline Section 9:4 of this chapter.
5. You see a ball roll off a table. You correctly assume this is because of Earth's gravity. What observations and inferences did you make?

PROJECTS

1. Construct a sundial. Attach a pencil to a board so it is perpendicular to the board. On a sunny day, watch the shadow produced by the pencil. Mark on the board where the shadow falls during each hour of daylight. Observe your sundial for a week and write a report explaining your project.
2. Construct a model of Earth revolving around the sun.

READINGS

1. Brandt, Keith. *Earth*. Mahwah, N.J.: Troll Associates, 1985.
2. Bromwell, Martyn. *Planet Earth*. Danbury, CT: Watts, 1987.
3. Peltier, W.R. "Global Sea Level and Earth Rotation." *Science*. May 13, 1988, pp. 895–901.

Rocks and Minerals

CHAPTER 10

Career: Potter

Ned went to North Carolina to visit his aunt and uncle for two weeks. One day, they took him to the country to visit some craftmakers. Ned was especially interested in the pottery shop. As Ned stopped to watch, there was already a group of people gathered around watching as the potter threw a glob of red clay onto a wheel. The potter explained that the wheel turns when a foot pedal is pumped. The foot pedal gives the potter control over the wheel.

As the wheel turned, the potter explained that the red clay gets its color from iron oxides. Ned was fascinated as the potter formed an opening in the clay ball and began to make a wide bowl. The potter explained that clay is similar to a soft plastic and can be shaped into many different kinds of pots, bowls, jugs, and vases. Handles can be added later. The potter explained to Ned and the others that it is fun to experiment with different colors and types of clay and to observe the colors after they are fired in a kiln. Before Ned left the shop, he bought a small blue jug as a souvenir.

Clay is a fine-grained material composed of minerals. In this chapter, you will study about minerals and how to identify them. You will also study different types of rocks and how they form.

F.Y.I. Whatcom Community College Pottery Studio, 237 West Kellogg, Bellingham, WA 98226

GOALS

You will study . . .
1. Earth materials called minerals.
2. how minerals are identified.

What is a mineral?

10:1 Minerals

Could you identify a mineral if you saw one? Have you ever held a mineral in your hand? Chances are that you have; you just may not have realized it. Rock salt, diamond, graphite, and gold are minerals. A **mineral** must meet five requirements. (1) Minerals are not living. (2) Minerals are formed in nature. (3) Minerals are solids. (4) The atoms in a mineral form a crystalline pattern. (5) The chemical composition of a mineral is fixed within narrow limits.

There are over 3000 minerals in Earth's crust. Most minerals in the outer 10 km of Earth form when hot molten material, called **magma**, cools. Evaporation of solutions results in the formation of minerals such as rock salt and calcite. Heat and pressure on rocks can cause minerals to form. Biotite and garnet form when heat and pressure are applied to shale.

Minerals can be classified by composition. The major groups of minerals are silicates, carbonates, oxides, sulfides, sulfates, halides, and native elements. Mineral groups, what they are made of, and some

FIGURE 10–1. Gold (a), diamond (b), graphite (c), and rock salt (d) are minerals.

a

b

c

d

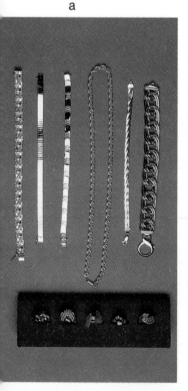

examples of each are listed in Table 10–1. Perhaps you will recognize some you have used. The largest group of minerals is the silicates. Notice that silicates are made of silicon (Si), oxygen (O_2), and one or more other elements. There are about 12 common rock-forming minerals, most of which are silicates. Quartz, feldspar, biotite, and hornblende are silicates.

What are silicates?

FIGURE 10–2. Quartz, feldspar, biotite, and hornblende are silicate minerals.

Table 10–1

Classification of Minerals		
Mineral group	**General composition**	**Examples**
Silicates	compounds containing silicon, oxygen, and sometimes other elements	Quartz (SiO_2) Biotite (K (Mg,Fe) ($AlSi_3O_{10}$) $(OH)_2$) Feldspar ($CaAl_2Si_2O_8$)— ($NaAlSi_3O_8$)—($KAlSi_3O_8$)
Carbonates	compounds containing carbonate (CO_3^{2-}) group	Calcite ($CaCO_3$) Dolomite ($Ca,Mg(CO_3)_2$)
Oxides	compounds containing oxygen and one or more other elements	Hematite (Fe_2O_3)
Sulfides	compounds containing sulfur and one or more other elements	Pyrite (FeS_2) Galena (PbS)
Sulfates	compounds containing sulfate (SO_4^{2-}) group	Gypsum ($CaSO_4 \cdot 2H_2O$)
Halides	compounds containing a halogen and another element	Halite (NaCl) Fluorite (CaF_2)
Native elements	elements not combined with other elements	Gold (Au) Graphite (C)

10:2 Identifying Minerals

With over 3000 known minerals, how can anyone tell them apart? How can you tell one food from another? You can test for and observe the physical properties of the foods. Physical properties that give clues to a food's identity are color, feel, and taste. Physical properties can also be used to identify minerals. These properties include luster, hardness, color, streak, cleavage, fracture, heft, and form. You shouldn't try to memorize the properties of every mineral. Instead, you should learn how to test a mineral for its specific properties. After testing a mineral, compare the properties you observed with those listed in mineral tables.

Luster describes how light is reflected from a mineral's surface. Does the mineral shine like a metal? Minerals such as galena and pyrite shine like metal and are said to have metallic luster. Metallic luster is like the shine of the chrome handlebars of a new bike. When a mineral does not shine like metal, its luster is nonmetallic. Nonmetallic lusters are described as dull, pearly, or glassy.

In some cases, the color of a mineral can give a clue to what it is. Sulfur, for example, is yellow to yellow-brown in color. This, along with its smell, makes sulfur an easy mineral to identify.

Differences in what a mineral is made of, however, can change its color. Hematite is an iron oxide that can be red, red-brown, medium gray, or dark gray in color. Hematite's streak is always the same, red-brown. **Streak** is the color of a mineral in powdered form. Streak usually does not change for different samples of the same mineral. Streak is determined by rubbing a mineral across a piece of unglazed porcelain tile called a streak plate.

What is luster?

What is streak?

FIGURE 10–3. Streak is the color of a mineral in powdered form (a). Nonmetallic luster can be dull, pearly, or glassy (b).

a

b

Table 10–2

Hardness Scale		
Mohs' minerals	**Hardness**	**Common items**
Talc	1	
Gypsum	2	
	2.5	fingernail
Calcite	3	copper penny
Fluorite	4	
	4.5	iron nail
Apatite	5	
	5.5	glass
Orthoclase	6	
	6.5	steel file
Quartz	7	streak plate
Topaz	8	
Corundum	9	
Diamond	10	

Hardness is a measure of how easily a mineral can be scratched. Table 10–2 lists a set of Mohs' minerals and other items used to test minerals for hardness. To test for hardness, scratch the unknown mineral against each Mohs' mineral or each item listed in the table. A mineral will scratch all items softer than itself and will be scratched by all items harder than itself. Minerals of the same hardness will usually scratch one another.

How do you test a mineral's hardness?

F.Y.I. Friedrich Mohs, a German Scientist, worked out a scale of hardness for minerals.

PROBLEM SOLVING

Valuable or Not?

Brandi and Wendy were walking home after an enjoyable day of window shopping at the mall. They were talking about recent fashions when Brandi noticed a sparkle in the grass near the sidewalk. She looked more closely and found what she thought was a "ruby" earring. Wendy, however, thought the "ruby" might not be real. She said it might be nothing more than red glass. How can the girls determine whether the "ruby" is or is not real?

What Are Minerals? 199

a   b

Hardness is an important property. The usefulness of a mineral is often determined by how hard or how soft it is. Some lubricants are made from graphite. Graphite is very soft. In motor oil, graphite can help an engine last longer by preventing moving parts from rubbing against each other and wearing out.

Other properties can be useful in identifying minerals. Heft is how heavy a mineral feels. Heft can be determined by tossing a mineral up and down in your hand. Form is the overall shape of the mineral. A mineral sample can be a single crystal, a group of crystals, or a dense mass. Some minerals, such as magnetite, are magnetic. Others, such as calcite, react with hydrochloric acid. When this reaction occurs, carbon dioxide bubbles form.

The way a mineral breaks is either by cleavage or fracture. Cleavage is the name given to breakage of a mineral along smooth, flat planes. Two minerals that break in this way are mica and feldspar. Cleavage can be compared to a cake being separated between iced layers. Fracture describes breaks along irregular surfaces. Grabbing a chunk out of the side of the cake can be compared to fracture. Hematite and quartz are minerals that fracture.

F.Y.I. Eye surgery can be done with a diamond-tipped scalpel. Diamond wafers are used as tiny windows in some spacecraft, since they are able to withstand extreme temperatures.

How does cleavage differ from fracture?

REVIEW

1. Define a mineral.
2. What is the largest group of minerals?
3. What is luster?
4. What is streak?
5. Some marine organisms build shells of calcite. Are these seashells minerals?

Problem: How can you identify unknown minerals?

Materials

mineral samples
hand lens
streak plate
copper penny
mineral identification books
table knife
plate glass
steel file
quartz

Procedure

1. Using your text as a reference, determine the physical properties of each mineral sample. Record your data in a table similar to the one shown.
2. Examine each sample and record its color and luster in the data table.
3. Rub each sample across the streak plate and record the color of the streak.
4. Examine each sample for cleavage or fracture and record your observations in the data table.
5. Perform a hardness test and record the results for each sample.
6. Use your textbook and the mineral identification books to aid in identifying each mineral sample.

Questions and Conclusions

1. Which two properties did you find most useful in identifying minerals?
2. Explain why these properties were most useful.
3. Which property did you find least helpful? Explain why.
4. Explain how unknown minerals can be identified.
5. What conclusions can you draw from this activity?
6. Explain what you would do if you were given an unknown mineral to identify.

Data and Observations

Sample	Color	Luster	Streak	Cleavage/fracture	Hardness	Mineral
1						
2						
3						

GOALS
You will study . . .
1. the three types of rocks and how they form.
2. how the processes of rock formation make up the rock cycle.

What is a rock?

10:3 Igneous Rocks

How old were you in May of 1980? That's when Mount St. Helens, a volcano in the state of Washington, blew its top. Molten material and ash were thrown hundreds of kilometers into the air. When the molten material cooled and solidified, igneous rocks formed. What are rocks? How do rocks form? **Rocks** are combinations of one or more minerals. Rocks are classified according to how they form. There are three kinds of rocks—igneous (IHG nee us), metamorphic (met uh MOR fihk), and sedimentary (sed uh MENT ree).

Magma forms deep in Earth where temperatures and pressures are high. Magma has a low density and sometimes rises to Earth's surface. When magma flows onto Earth's surface, it is called lava. When lava or magma cools and becomes solid, **igneous rocks** form. The type of igneous rock that forms is based on whether the molten material cools within Earth or on its surface.

Intrusive igneous rocks form when magma cools underground. Because the magma is insulated by the surrounding rock, it cools slowly. Slow cooling allows large mineral particles, or grains, to form. Thus, intrusive rocks have relatively coarse textures. Granite is an intrusive igneous rock. Study Figure 10–5. Large masses of magma that solidify far below Earth's surface are called batholiths. Batholiths often form the core of large mountain systems. Laccoliths are mushroom-shaped, intrusive rock bodies. Smaller igneous rock bodies are dikes and sills. Dikes cut across existing rock layers. Sills lie parallel

FIGURE 10–5. Intrusive igneous rock structures include batholiths, laccoliths, dikes, and sills (a). Extrusive rock bodies include lava flows and volcanoes (b).

a

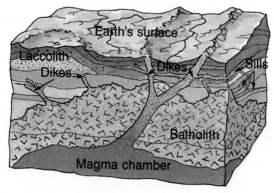

b

to surrounding rock layers. In both cases, the magma is forced into cracks or between layers of existing rocks where it cools and solidifies.

When lava cools quickly on Earth's surface, extrusive igneous rocks form. Rapid cooling allows very little time for mineral grains to form. Rhyolite and basalt are extrusive igneous rocks. Two other examples of extrusive rocks are pumice and obsidian. Pumice and obsidian cool so rapidly that no grains form. These two rocks are called volcanic glass. Lava and other materials may build up cone-shaped mountains called volcanoes. Volcanoes and lava flows also are extrusive rock bodies.

List two examples of extrusive igneous rocks.

F.Y.I. In February of 1943, Paricutín volcano in Mexico started as a 25-m crack in a farmer's cornfield. By the next morning it was about 10 m high. Within one year, it was over 300 m high. It now stands over 400 m high.

TECHNOLOGY

Piezoelectricity

In 1880, Pierre and Jacques Curie noted that quartz crystals have a property known as piezoelectricity (pee ay zoh uh lek TRIHS ut ee). If quartz crystals are stretched or compressed, a flow of electrons is produced. This flow produces a negative charge at one end of the crystal and a positive charge at the other end.

In 1921, this property of quartz was first used to control radio frequencies. When quartz is placed in a radio circuit, the frequency of receiving or sending is controlled by the vibrations of the quartz.

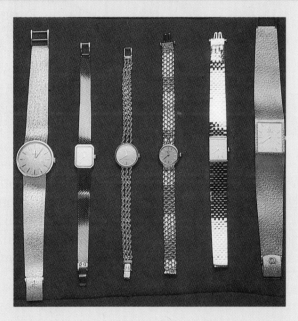

ADVANCE

Tiny quartz plates are placed in the analog quartz watches shown in the photograph. The quartz is subjected to an electrical current powered by the watch battery. The size of the quartz plate determines the number of vibrations it has in a given time. This set vibration controls the back-and-forth electronic circuit of the watch. The electronic circuit generates pulses that cause the second hand to move. The minute and hour hands, however, are moved by gears powered by the second hand.

What changes in rocks occur during metamorphism?

10:4 Metamorphic Rocks

Have you ever gone to lunch, opened up your lunch bag, and realized your apple spent the morning resting on the cream-filled cake? The cake has changed in form. This happened due to pressure from the apple and heat in your locker. Rocks can be affected by changes in pressure and temperature, too. Rocks that change in form due to increases in pressure and temperature are **metamorphic rocks.** Metamorphic rocks form from existing rocks.

The temperatures and pressures that cause metamorphic rocks to form are not as great as those that cause igneous rocks to form. Thus, there is no melting during metamorphism. Metamorphic changes usually occur between 12 and 15 km below Earth's surface. Temperatures there range from 150° to 800°C. Magma, on the other hand, forms as deep as 200 km below Earth's surface where temperatures often exceed 800°C.

During metamorphism, rocks change in a number of ways. Mineral grains move around or become larger. Metamorphic rocks that have had their mineral grains moved around include slate, schist, and gneiss. These rocks have a banded appearance. Rocks in which the mineral grains have become larger are quartzite and marble. These rocks are usually made of only one mineral and don't have a banded appearance. The rock's composition can change and new minerals can form. Shale is a rock made of clay minerals. During metamorphism, these minerals can change to mica, forming slate.

FIGURE 10–6. Heat and pressure change shale, granite, and limestone to slate, gneiss, and marble.

10:5 Sedimentary Rocks

Do you have a junk drawer or box at home? If you do, it probably fills up quickly. When you need something from the drawer, you must dig down through layers and layers of elastic bands, paper, rulers, and so on. When you get to the item you wanted, you may find it crushed with other things sticking to it. **Sedimentary rocks** are rocks made of loose materials that have been cemented together. These materials may include rock fragments, pebbles, sand, mud, and plant and animal remains. The loose materials are called sediments. Sediments are found almost everywhere. As sediment accumulates, the material near the bottom is compacted, or pressed together. Over time, minerals may be deposited in the spaces between the sediments. These minerals act as cement and "glue" the materials together, forming sedimentary rocks. Cementing minerals include calcite, silica, and iron oxide.

List three cementing materials in sedimentary rocks.

Sediments often accumulate on the seafloor, on lake bottoms, or in swamps. In these areas, the remains of dead animals and plants may become part of the sediment. Over time, these remains can become fossils. **Fossils** are the remains or evidence of prehistoric life preserved in Earth's crust. In general, sedimentary rocks are the only rocks that contain fossils.

Moving water, wind, and ice can carry sediments. The energy of the water, wind, or ice determines the kinds of sediments that are carried and deposited. Currents of air and water sort sediment by size. The stronger the current, the larger the sediment that is carried. Sediments of all sizes are deposited by moving ice. Sediments are also moved by gravity.

FIGURE 10–7. Large sediments make up a conglomerate (a). Sediment size decreases in sandstone (b), siltstone (c), and shale (d).

a

b

c

d

There are two kinds of sedimentary rocks—clastic and nonclastic. Clastic rocks form from pieces of other rocks and minerals or from shells. Clastic rocks are named based on the size or shape of their fragments. Rounded particles form conglomerates. Sand-sized grains form sandstones. Silt forms siltstones. Clay forms shales. Some sea animals, called corals, have hard shells made of calcite. Corals live in thick reefs that, when compacted, form limestone.

How do nonclastic sedimentary rocks form?

Nonclastic rocks are sedimentary rocks that form from solution or from organic processes. Mineral-rich water may evaporate and leave deposits. Rock salt forms in this way. Bituminous coal is a nonclastic rock formed by plant debris buried in a swamp.

a

b

FIGURE 10–8. Conglomerates have rather large, rounded fragments (a). Shale is composed of clay fragments that have been compacted (b).

Table 10–3

Types of Rocks				
		Formation	**Texture**	**Examples**
Igneous	Intrusive	forms deep within Earth	coarse grained	granite
	Extrusive	forms near Earth's surface	fine grained	rhyolite, basalt
			has holes glassy	pumice obsidian
Metamorphic	Banded	heat and pressure rearrange mineral grains	shows mineral bands	slate schist gneiss
	Massive	heat and pressure make mineral grains larger	enlarged grains	marble quartzite
Sedimentary	Clastic	cementing and compacting of rock and mineral fragments	microscopic grains sand-sized grains round pebbles	shale sandstone conglomerate
	Nonclastic	precipitation evaporation compaction of plant remains	coarse to microscopic cubic-cleavage fragments coarse to microscopic	limestone rock salt coal

ACTIVITY 10-2

Problem: How can you classify different rocks?

Materials

rock samples
hand lens
goggles
5% HCl
water
paper towels
cloth towel
rock identification books

hammer
streak plate
copper penny
table knife
plate glass
steel file
quartz
apron

Procedure

1. Wrap a rock sample in the cloth towel. Break off a small piece of each sample with the hammer. **CAUTION:** *Wear goggles when using the hammer.*
2. Examine each rock piece. Observe and record the texture of each sample. Texture describes the shape and arrangements of the rock grains.
3. Observe and record the presence of minerals, the size and shape of the grains, and the arrangement of the grains for each sample.
4. Use the streak plate, penny, table knife, plate glass, steel file, and quartz to identify the minerals you see.
5. Record other observations such as rock color, size and number of openings, banding, fossils, and smell. Test a fresh surface of each rock with HCl. **CAUTION:** *HCl is an acid and may cause burns. Wear goggles and apron. Rinse spills immediately with water.*
6. Classify and record each sample as igneous, metamorphic, or sedimentary. Use your textbook and identification books to identify each rock.

Questions and Conclusions

1. Which property did you find most useful in determining the rock type?
2. Which property was least helpful?
3. Which rocks were most difficult to identify? Explain your answer.
4. How can you classify rocks?
5. How can you identify rocks?

Data and Observations

Sample	Texture	Mineral observations	Other observations	Rock type	Rock name
1					
2					
3					
4					
5					

10:6 The Rock Cycle

When exposed at Earth's surface, the minerals that make up a rock change. Wind, water, and ice break a rock into sediments. Wind, water, ice, and gravity move these sediments. Chemical and physical changes that rocks undergo at or near Earth's surface are called weathering. The moving and depositing of sediment is called erosion.

High temperatures and pressures deep within Earth change rocks and form magma. When magma cools, igneous rocks form. Weathering and erosion may break up and move the igneous rock fragments. Heat and pressure can change igneous or sedimentary rock into metamorphic rock. There is no set order to the continual changes that rocks undergo. The way one rock changes to another and the processes by which these changes take place is the **rock cycle.**

What is the rock cycle?

The full cycle of changes does not always occur. The arrows across Figure 10–9 show that some of the processes may shortcut the cycle. For example, igneous rock may become metamorphic rock if enough heat and pressure occur. Igneous rock may also become sedimentary rock if erosion and deposition occur. What other shortcuts do you see?

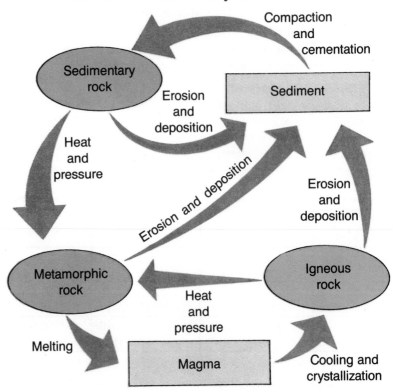

FIGURE 10–9. The many processes that change rocks make up the rock cycle.

a

b

SCIENCE AND SOCIETY

10:7 Coal

Fossil fuels are compounds of hydrogen and carbon. They form as a result of the decay of plant and animal remains. Earth's fossil fuels formed millions of years ago. They are nonrenewable. **Coal** is a fossil fuel composed of plant remains that have been compacted to form a rock.

Coal forms when plant remains fall to swamp floors and are quickly buried. Bacterial processes increase the amount of carbon in the remains. With time, the remains are compacted to form peat. Pressure from overlying sediments and chemical reactions change peat to lignite. As these processes continue, lignite becomes bituminous coal, a sedimentary rock. Bituminous coal is darker, harder, and contains more carbon than lignite. Increased temperatures and pressures can change bituminous coal into anthracite.

Coal beds are mined using one of two methods. Surface mining is used when coal beds lie close to the surface. Soil and rock above the coal are removed and piled to the side. The coal is then removed and hauled away. If the mine is worked correctly, the soil and rock are returned, covered with topsoil, and replanted.

In underground mining, tunnels are dug deep in the ground to reach the coal seam. Explosives may be used to break up the coal, or machines may loosen the coal and load it for removal. In some underground mines, pillars of coal are used to support the roof. Longwall mining uses a machine that holds up the roof of the mine as it removes the coal. As the machine moves through the coal seam, the roof is allowed to cave in behind the machine.

FIGURE 10–10. The mining equipment used in surface mining (a) and in underground mining (b) is quite different.

What is coal?

What are the four stages of coal formation?

F.Y.I. A bed of coal may be only 1/10 the thickness of the bed of peat from which it formed.

F.Y.I. Surface mining also is called strip mining.

FIGURE 10–11. Bituminous coal is a sedimentary rock that is mined for use as a fuel.

F.Y.I. About 30 percent of the world's known coal reserves are in the United States.

Coal is an economical energy resource that could last for hundreds of years. Over three-fourths of the coal produced in the United States is used by power plants to generate electricity.

Burning coal releases smoke, ash, and sulfur and nitrogen oxides. The oxides can react with moisture in the air to form acid precipitation. Acid rain or snow can damage plants and kill fish.

Mining coal also can harm the environment. Surface mining can scar Earth's surface with open pits if the land is not reclaimed, and landslides and erosion are likely to occur. Water flowing through the ground may become polluted.

Does the need for coal balance the problems that mining and using it create? If we decide not to use coal because of environmental problems, what will we use to generate electricity?

SKILL BUILDER

Graphing

In 1987, 78 percent of the coal mined in the United States was used to generate electric power. Nine percent of the coal was exported. Twelve percent was used by industries. Only one percent was used to heat homes. Use these figures to make a pie graph of coal usage in the United States in 1987. If you need help, refer to Graphing on pages 532–533.

Questions

1. What was the largest section of your pie graph?
2. How much coal was used by industry and in electricity generation?
3. How much of the total coal mined in the United States is represented by your pie graph?

REVIEW

6. What are igneous rocks?
7. List four kinds of metamorphic rocks.
8. What is coal?
9. What is the final stage in coal formation?
10. Why do you think that fossils are usually found only in sedimentary rocks?

CHAPTER 10 REVIEW

SUMMARY

1. Minerals are not living, formed in nature, solids, composed of crystals and have a definite composition. Most minerals form from magma.   10:1
2. Physical properties such as luster, hardness, streak, cleavage, heft, and form are used to identify minerals.   10:2
3. Igneous rocks form when molten material cools and solidifies. Intrusive igneous rocks solidify deep within Earth and have relatively coarse textures. Extrusive igneous rocks solidify at or near Earth's surface. Few grains form because of rapid cooling.   10:3
4. Metamorphic rocks form as a result of increases in temperature and pressure. Mineral grains may move around or become larger. The rock's composition can change and new minerals can form.   10:4
5. Sedimentary rocks, clastic and nonclastic, form from the compaction and cementation of sediment. Fossils are found mainly in sedimentary rock.   10:5
6. The process by which rocks change form is called the rock cycle. The full cycle does not always occur; shortcuts happen.   10:6
7. The sedimentary rock, coal, is a nonrenewable fossil fuel. Surface and underground mining methods are used to mine coal.   10:7

VOCABULARY

a. coal
b. fossil fuels
c. fossils
d. hardness
e. igneous rocks
f. luster
g. magma
h. metamorphic rocks
i. mineral
j. rock cycle
k. rocks
l. sedimentary rocks
m. streak

Match each description with the correct vocabulary word from the list above.
1. how light is reflected from a mineral's surface
2. rocks that solidify from magma or lava
3. remains or evidence of prehistoric life preserved in Earth's crust
4. combinations of one or more minerals
5. a nonliving, naturally occurring, crystalline solid with a fixed chemical composition
6. a measure of how easily a mineral can be scratched
7. rocks that form due to increases in pressure and temperature
8. a fossil fuel made from plant remains
9. the color of a powdered mineral on unglazed porcelain
10. rocks formed by compacting and cementing sediment

CHAPTER 10 REVIEW

MAIN IDEAS

A. Reviewing Concepts

Choose the word or phrase that correctly completes each of the following sentences.

1. Mohs' mineral scale is used to test the _____ of a mineral.
   a. luster   c. color
   b. hardness   d. streak
2. Minerals form from cooled magma, evaporation, _____, and pressure.
   a. plants   c. heat
   b. fractures   d. rocks
3. Hot molten material deep within Earth is _____.
   a. lava   c. coal
   b. streak   d. magma
4. A mineral with metallic _____ reflects light from its surface.
   a. hardness   c. luster
   b. streak   d. heft
5. The movement and depositing of sediment is called _____.
   a. erosion   c. fossil formation
   b. metamorphism   d. weathering
6. A rock that forms when magma cools and becomes solid is _____ rock.
   a. igneous   c. sedimentary
   b. lava   d. metamorphic
7. _____ rocks form from pieces of other rocks and minerals or shells.
   a. Coal   c. Clastic
   b. Lava   d. Nonclastic
8. Rocks that form underground at 200°C are _____.
   a. clastic   c. metamorphic
   b. igneous   d. sedimentary
9. Because magma cools slowly, _____ or particles develop when igneous rock forms.
   a. streak   c. fossils
   b. grains   d. marble

10. _____ rocks would most likely contain fossils.
    a. Sedimentary   c. Igneous
    b. Metamorphic   d. Intrusive
11. _____ is the process whereby wind, water, and ice break rock into sediment.
    a. Erosion   c. Compaction
    b. Metamorphism d. Weathering
12. Coal formation begins when _____ remains are compacted.
    a. plant   c. metamorphic
    b. lignite   d. igneous
13. Bituminous is an example of a(n) _____ rock.
    a. extrusive   c. sedimentary
    b. metamorphic d. intrusive
14. Mineral breakage along smooth, flat planes is _____.
    a. luster   c. fracture
    b. cleavage   d. heft
15. A(n) _____ igneous rock forms when lava cools quickly on Earth's surface.
    a. intrusive   c. clastic
    b. extrusive   d. nonclastic

B. Understanding Concepts

Answer the following questions using complete sentences.

16. List several ways that minerals can form.
17. Describe the conditions under which metamorphic rocks form.
18. List a major advantage and disadvantage of surface mining.
19. How do sedimentary rocks form?
20. Explain how an igneous rock can become a metamorphic rock.
21. Compare the depths and temperatures at which igneous and metamorphic rocks form.
22. List the main groups of minerals.

23. Explain the difference between fracture and cleavage.

24. Describe how a metamorphic rock can become a sedimentary rock.

25. Explain the steps involved in coal formation.

C. Applying Concepts

Answer the following questions using complete sentences.

26. Sally found a rose-colored mineral. She used mineral identification tests and determined it scratched a steel file but not corundum. It did not react with HCl, but it did break along uneven surfaces. Use Table 10–2 to identify Sally's mineral.

27. Granite and rhyolite are igneous rocks. Which would you expect to have larger crystals? Why?

28. Over time, limestone may be changed into marble. How would the mineral grains change?

29. Juan found a chunk of bituminous coal near his house. He examined the coal with a hand lens and found what he thought was an impression of a leaf. Was Juan's identification correct? Explain your answer.

30. Why do you think talc rather than quartz is used in body powder?

SKILL REVIEW

If you need help, refer to the Skill Handbook, pages 526 to 537.

1. Refer to Table 10–2 in your textbook to answer the following. Will quartz scratch glass? Will quartz scratch corundum? Will an iron nail scratch a diamond? Which two Mohs' minerals can you scratch with your fingernail?

2. You determine that a mineral sample has a hardness of 7 on the Mohs' scale, fractures along an uneven surface, and is crystalline. You correctly identify the mineral sample as quartz. Identify your observations and inferences.

3. Burning coal pollutes the air and *causes* lakes and rivers to become more acidic. Name one *effect* this can have.

4. Use Section 10:6 of this chapter to help you place the following events in the correct sequence.

| magma cools | weathering breaks rock into pieces | pieces are carried away and deposited |
| sedimentary rock forms | pieces become compacted | igneous rock forms |

5. Outline Sections 10:3 and 10:4.

PROJECTS

1. Write a report about the processes of forming certain crystals in space. Determine if there are definite advantages to forming crystals in zero gravity. Is this process economical?

2. Environmentalists are concerned about pollution caused by burning coal. Develop a survey to determine how concerned your friends are about this issue. Report your findings to your class.

READINGS

1. Baines, Rae. *Rocks and Minerals.* Mahwah, NJ: Troll Associates, 1985.

2. Gattis, Lou. *Basic Rocks and Minerals for Pathfinders: A Young Enrichment Skill.* Altamonte Springs, FL: Cheetah Publications, 1987.

3. Kraus, Pansy. *Introduction to Lapidary.* Radnor, PA: Chilton, 1987.

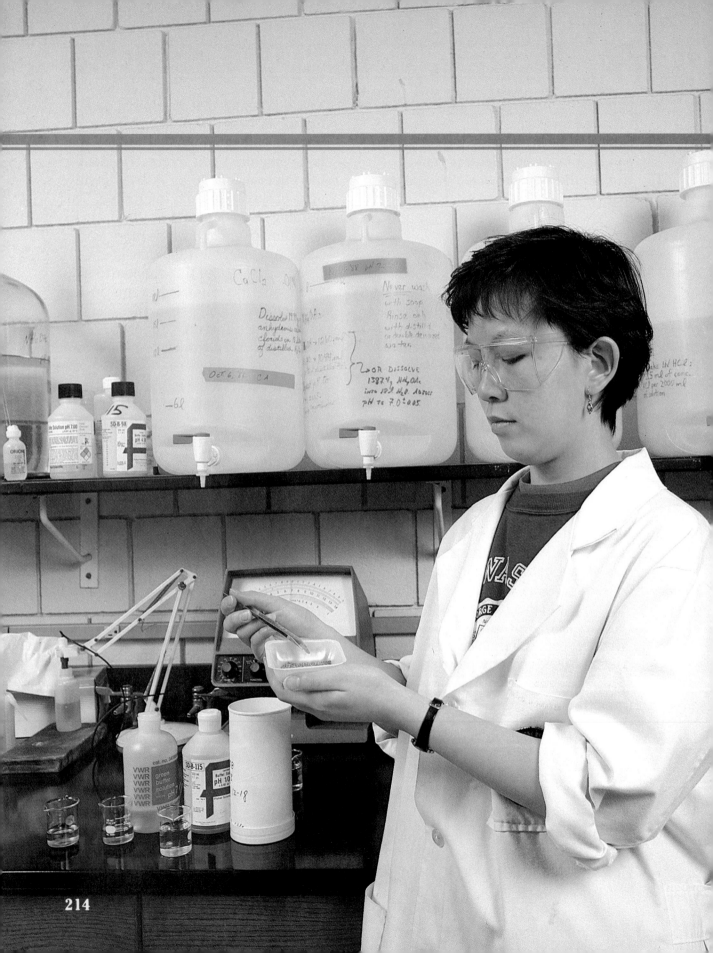

Weathering and Erosion

CHAPTER 11

Career: Soil Scientist

Steve's family was buying the old farm just outside of town. No one had farmed there for several years. Steve's parents were worried that nothing would grow except weeds. Steve's mother called the soil-testing lab at the local agricultural college. They told her to collect soil samples from several areas in the fields. Then she was to label each sample so that she would know which area it came from.

Steve and his mother then took the samples to the lab. The soil scientist ran the proper soil tests and interpreted the results. Each sample was tested for nutrients such as phosphorous, potassium, and nitrogen, for its acidity, and for certain physical properties.

The soil scientist showed Steve and his mother a large soil survey map of the county. It showed the different types of soil in the county, as well as streams, roads, and houses. The map helped the soil scientist decide which soil tests to perform. After each sample was tested, the scientist recommended the best types of fertilizer to use and suggested which crops would grow best in each type of soil.

In this chapter, you will study how weathering and erosion produce soil. You will also study different types of soil, their physical properties, and how soil erosion can be prevented.

F.Y.I. Agricultural Technical Institute (ATI), Wooster, OH 44691

How Hard Is a Rock?

GOALS

You will study . . .

1. physical and chemical weathering.
2. how weathering and erosion change Earth's surface.

What causes weathering?

11:1 Weathering

The physical and chemical processes that break down rocks at Earth's surface are called **weathering.** Weathering is caused by water, wind, ice, plant roots, and the actions of animals. There are two types of weathering: physical weathering and chemical weathering. Physical weathering causes a change in the size of rocks. Chemical weathering changes the composition of rocks.

Have you ever eaten large biscuits of shredded wheat for breakfast? If so, you probably broke the biscuits in half first so that they would fit into your bowl. You also may have broken the cereal into bite-sized pieces with your spoon. The physical breakdown of rocks on Earth's surface is similar to the breaking of the biscuits of shredded wheat.

If you have ever made the mistake of putting a glass container filled with lemonade into the freezer and forgetting about it, you have seen the results of physical weathering. When water freezes, it expands. In the freezer, the expanding water broke the jar. Similarly, water can get into cracks and pores in rocks and freeze. The ice exerts pressure on the rocks, causing the cracks and pores to become larger. When freezing alternates with periods of thawing, the rocks are broken into smaller fragments. This type of physical weathering is called ice wedging.

FIGURE 11–1. The breaking-up of the cereal (a) is similar to the breakup of rocks (b) during physical weathering.

a

b

a

b

Another way that physical weathering occurs is when the soil is removed from deeply-buried bodies of rock, exposing them at the surface. The removal of the soil reduces the pressure on the rock. Outer layers of the exposed rock expand and peel off, much like the layers of an onion. This process is called sheeting.

Animals and plants also cause physical weathering. Burrowing animals such as earthworms or moles leave tunnels in the soil. These tunnels can fill with water that soaks down to the rock and causes ice wedging. Plant roots sometimes grow into cracks in rocks. As they grow, the roots force the rocks apart. Have you contributed to physical weathering of rocks? Perhaps you have broken rocks into smaller pieces or chipped away at a large stone.

What happens to your bike if it is left out in the rain? It doesn't take long for rust to begin forming on exposed metal parts. Oxygen is reacting with iron in the bike parts to form rust. This process is similar to chemical reactions that affect rocks at Earth's surface.

Water is the most important agent of chemical weathering. Materials dissolved in water combine with some minerals in rocks to form new substances. Oxygen, for example, is often dissolved in water. When oxygen-rich water moves through or comes into contact with rocks rich in iron, the iron will combine with the oxygen to form iron oxide or rust. This chemical change is similar to the change that takes place as rust forms on your bike. Another reaction involves carbonic acid, which forms when carbon dioxide dissolves in water. Granite is often weathered by this acid.

FIGURE 11–2. Plant roots and the action of other organisms help break up rocks (a). The rusting of a bike is similar to some of the processes of chemical weathering (b).

What causes rust?

FIGURE 11–3. Some organisms such as lichens release acids that chemically weather rocks.

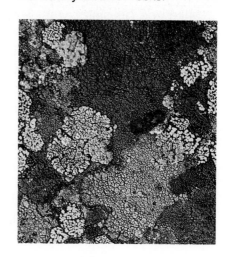

How Hard Is a Rock? 217

F.Y.I. Memorials made of granite last much longer than those made of limestone or marble. Carbon dioxide in the air reacts with moisture to form carbonic acid. The acid then reacts with the calcite in the limestone or marble. The reaction products are removed in solution.

How does the size of rock fragments affect the rate of weathering?

Three things affect the rate of weathering. First, the size of the rock fragments affects weathering. Have you ever watched ice melt in a glass of iced tea? A large ice cube takes longer to melt than crushed ice. This is because a lot of smaller ice fragments have a greater surface area than one large ice fragment. Thus, the smaller fragments tend to melt faster. The same thing happens with rocks. Lots of small fragments weather faster than one large fragment because the small fragments have more surface exposed.

The composition of a rock also affects the rate of weathering. For example, granite is more resistant to weathering than marble or limestone. It is for this reason that many headstones in cemeteries are made of granite rather than marble or limestone. The Capitol Building in Washington, DC, is made of limestone. In recent years, this building has weathered to the point that major repairs are necessary.

A third factor that affects the rate of weathering is climate. Chemical weathering tends to be more rapid in areas with hot, humid climates. In areas such as the tropics, high temperatures, lots of water, and decaying vegetation speed up chemical weathering. Physical weathering is more rapid in places that have temperate climates where periods of freezing and thawing alternate.

PROBLEM SOLVING

The Old Statue

On a family picnic, Mike's younger sister noticed an old statue in the park. Mike and his sister went to the statue to take a closer look. Mike told his sister the statue was made of polished marble. Then, Mike pointed out how the surface was pitted in some places and had large cracks in others. He also noticed moss growing on the base of the statue. His sister asked what had caused the marble to fall apart. How could Mike explain what had happened to the statue? How could Mike demonstrate the effects of this weathering process at home?

a

b

11:2 Erosion

Weathered particles often are moved from one place to another. This results in erosion. **Erosion** is the transportation of weathered particles by water, wind, ice, or gravity. Water is probably the most important agent of erosion. Water erodes rocks and soil as it flows over Earth's surface. You have probably seen the gullies formed by water erosion along road cuts and in farm fields. You will study more about erosion by water and ice in Chapter 12.

Wind is an important agent of erosion in deserts and other dry areas. Wind erodes Earth's surface by deflation (dih FLAY shun) and abrasion (uh BRAY shun). Deflation removes loose material from the ground surface. You may have experienced deflation when playing softball on a dry, dusty field. Just when you are ready to swing at the ball, a gust of wind blows dust in your face, and you strike out. Abrasion is the scouring action of particles carried by the wind. It is similar to the process of sandblasting sometimes used to clean buildings.

FIGURE 11–4. The U.S. Capitol building is weathering quickly because of its composition (a). Humans use the process of abrasion to clean buildings (b).

How does wind erode Earth's surface?

F.Y.I. In the fall of 1933, soil was picked up by wind on the Great Plains and blown as far east as Washington, DC.

How Hard Is a Rock? 219

a

b

c

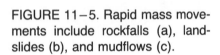

FIGURE 11–5. Rapid mass movements include rockfalls (a), landslides (b), and mudflows (c).

Gravity is often the first agent of erosion to affect a surface. Weathered materials move down a slope due to gravity. This type of erosion is called mass movement. Rockfalls, landslides, mudflows, and creep are examples of mass movements. **Rockfalls** occur when pieces of rock fall from a high place to a low place. Rockfalls may occur along road cuts in mountains. **Landslides** occur when large amounts of rock and soil move rapidly down a slope as a unit. If the soil is very wet, the mass movement is called a mudflow. The force of a mudflow can move houses in its path. **Creep** is a relatively slow downslope movement of material at Earth's surface. Tilted fence posts, telephone poles, and trees often indicate that creep is occurring. Creep is the result of freezing and thawing of soil particles on a slope.

REVIEW

1. What is weathering?
2. How do physical and chemical weathering differ?
3. What is erosion?
4. What is abrasion?
5. Is the rust on cars the result of physical or chemical weathering? Explain your answer.

Problem: How does slope affect erosion?

Materials

stream table
sand
500-mL beaker
watering can
water
bricks (2)
metric ruler
plastic pail

Procedure

1. Fill the stream table with damp sand. Spread the sand so that the surface is flat. Measure and record the depth of the sand.
2. Arrange the stream table as shown. Place a brick under one end.
3. Add 1 L of water to the watering can.
4. Empty the watering can on the sand at the raised part of the stream table.
5. Measure and record the height of the sand where the water was poured.
6. Hypothesize what effect increasing the slope will have on the erosion of sand.
7. Repeat steps 1 through 5 using two bricks.

Data and Observations

Slope	Height of sand before watering	Height of sand after watering
one brick		
two bricks		

Questions and Conclusions

1. What agents eroded the sand in the activity?
2. Calculate the difference in height of the sand for a slope of one brick and for a slope of two bricks.
   Use the formula

   difference = height before watering − height after watering

3. How does slope affect erosion? Explain your answer.
4. What do you predict would happen if the slope of the stream table were increased to three bricks? Explain your answer.
5. If you had a fan, explain how you might use the materials in this activity to test how wind affects erosion.

GOALS

You will study . . .
1. different types of soils.
2. soil horizons that make up a soil profile.
3. the effects of soil erosion and how erosion can be controlled.

F.Y.I. It is estimated that over 15 000 different soil types exist in the United States.

On what does soil texture depend?

FIGURE 11−6. Soil texture can be described as clay-rich (a), sandy (b), or loamy (c).

11:3 Soil

Have you ever walked through a flower garden or seen someone plant a tree? The material in which the flowers were growing or the tree was planted is soil. **Soil** is a mixture of weathered rock and organic matter at Earth's surface. The organic matter in soil, called humus, consists of living and partly decayed plant and animal materials. The amount of organic matter contained in soil varies. Organic matter and weathered rock make up about half the volume of soil. Air and water contained in open spaces or pores within the soil make up the other half.

Soil can be described by its physical properties. These properties include color, moisture content, and texture. The color of a soil is related to its organic content. Soils rich in humus are black to dark brown. These soils contain many open spaces and thus are often very moist. Soils with less humus tend to be brown to yellow-brown. They have fewer open spaces and so can't hold much water. Soils with a low organic content are pale brown to yellow. Open spaces in these soils are few, and water content is low.

The texture of a soil depends on the types of weathered materials that make up the soil. Soil rich in clay feels smooth, and it tends to stick to your fingers. Clay-rich soils hold a lot of water. Sandy soils are gritty and crumble between your fingers. Sandy soils are very porous and water tends to flow right through them. Loam is a mixture of clay, sand, and other eroded particles. Loam holds water well, and is the best soil for growing most houseplants and gardens.

a

b

c

222   Weathering and Erosion

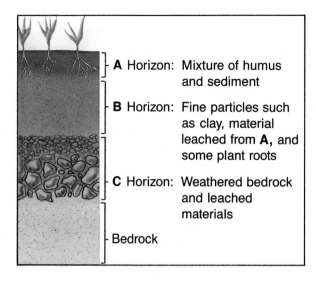

A Horizon: Mixture of humus and sediment

B Horizon: Fine particles such as clay, material leached from **A,** and some plant roots

C Horizon: Weathered bedrock and leached materials

Bedrock

FIGURE 11–7. A mature soil profile has three horizons.

11:4 A Soil Profile

Soil forms as the result of weathering over hundreds or thousands of years. Five factors affect the type of soil that develops. These factors are the type of bedrock present, the climate, the slope of the land, the presence of organisms, and the amount of time the soil has been forming. Soils range from depths of a few centimeters to over 60 m. A description of the layers that make up a soil is a **soil profile.** In a well-developed soil, three distinct layers, the *A, B,* and *C* horizons, exist. The *A* horizon is the top layer. It contains humus, which gives it a dark color. Worms and other organisms in the *A* horizon leave tunnels in the soil that allow oxygen to mix with the soil.

Have you ever placed a wet, red tee shirt on top of a pair of white shorts? If you have, you may have experienced leaching as the dye from the shirt dripped down with the water to the shorts. In soil, **leaching** is a process by which some soil components in upper layers are carried to lower layers by water.

The *B* horizon is lighter in color than the *A* horizon due to a lower organic content. The *B* horizon is often rich in clay and iron oxides, which leach down from the *A* horizon. The oxides give the *B* horizon a red color.

The *C* horizon lies below the *B* horizon. The *C* horizon is rich in materials leached from the *B* horizon. The *C* horizon also contains partly weathered bedrock fragments. Below the *C* horizon is the bedrock.

How deep is soil?

F.Y.I. The bedrock or parent material of a soil profile is also called the *D* horizon.

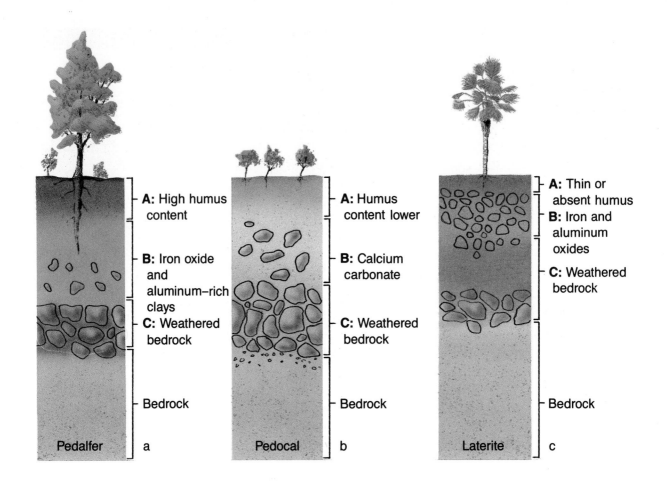

A: High humus
content

B: Iron oxide
and
aluminum–rich
clays

C: Weathered
bedrock

Bedrock

Pedalfer   a

A: Humus
content lower

B: Calcium
carbonate

C: Weathered
bedrock

Bedrock

Pedocal   b

A: Thin or
absent humus

B: Iron and
aluminum
oxides

C: Weathered
bedrock

Bedrock

Laterite   c

FIGURE 11–8. Pedalfers form in humid, temperate climates (a). Pedocals form in dry temperate climates (b). Laterites form in hot, wet, tropical climates (c).

What are the three major types of soils?

F.Y.I. The word *pedalfer* comes from the Greek word pedon, which means soil, combined with the chemical symbols Al (aluminum) and Fe (iron). *Pedocal* is derived from pedon (soil) and cal (calcite).

11:5 Soil Types

Soils are grouped into three major types based on their composition: pedalfers, pedocals, and laterites. Pedalfers form in the humid, temperate climate of the eastern United States. The large amounts of precipitation in these areas, over 60 cm per year, leach out much of the calcium carbonate. **Pedalfers** are soils that contain large amounts of iron oxide and aluminum-rich clays. Due to the iron content, the soil tends to have a brown to reddish brown color. The soil supports a forest type of vegetation and develops large amounts of humus from decaying organic matter.

In the dry, temperate climate of the western United States, annual precipitation is less than 60 cm per year. Rain often evaporates before it enters the soil to leach away minerals such as calcium carbonate. Soils rich in calcium carbonate are called **pedocals.** This type of soil supports grassland and brush vegetation. The clay content of pedocals is less than for pedalfers.

Hot, wet, tropical climates produce soils known as laterites. The large amount of water that flows through this soil produces heavy chemical weathering and leaches out calcium carbonate and other minerals. **Laterites** are red-orange soils rich in iron and aluminum oxides. They contain little humus. For this reason, they are usually not very fertile.

Soils have many small holes or pores between the individual soil particles. A measure of the amount of a soil's volume that is composed of pores is called its **porosity.** Very porous soils are able to hold large amounts of water. If the pores are connected, the water can flow through the soil. The ability of a soil to allow water to flow through it is called its **permeability.** A soil can have a high porosity, but if the pores are not connected, the permeability can be very low. A soil's permeability can be tested using a "perc" test. In these tests, the downward movement of water in soil is timed.

SKILL BUILDER

Observing and Inferring

Suppose you live in a community where both clay-rich soils and sand-rich soils can be found. You observe that after a heavy rainfall, large puddles have formed in some areas but not in others. You investigate and find that the areas with clay-rich soils are the ones with large puddles. This standing water stays even after the rain stops. The areas with sand-rich soils are well drained. No large puddles have formed in these areas. Make inferences based on your observations to answer the questions below. If you need help, refer to Observing and Inferring on page 535.

Questions

1. Do clay-rich soils or sand-rich soils have a greater permeability?
2. Which type of soil will be the wettest several days after the rain?
3. Many people add sand to their gardens. Why do you think it's necessary for them to do so?

F.Y.I. Laterite soils are very dry and hard. Some people use these soils to make bricks.

ACTIVITY 11–2 A "Perc" Test

Problem: How can you compare the permeability of different soils?

Materials

coffee cans (open at both ends) (3)
500-mL beaker   spade
bucket   metric ruler
water   permanent marker
watch

Procedure

1. Use the metric ruler and permanent marker to mark the outside of each coffee can 3 cm from one end.
2. Get permission to test three different locations on the school grounds. List each in the data table.
3. Use the spade to dig a small hole about 20 cm deep in each location.
4. Observe and record the color, texture, and organisms present in the soil at each location. Also record the types and amounts of the particles in each sample.
5. Predict the permeability of the soil in each location. Write your predictions in the data table.
6. Use your foot to press a can into the soil up to the 3 cm mark at each location.
7. Add 500 mL water to the beaker and pour into each can.
8. Use the watch to measure how long it takes for all the water in each can to sink into the soil. This procedure is known as a "perc" test. Record the amount of time in the data table.

Questions and Conclusions

1. Which location had the most permeable soil? How can you tell the soil was most permeable at this location?
2. Which location had the least permeable soil? How can you tell the soil was least permeable at this location?
3. How can you explain the differences in permeability of the soil samples?
4. Which soil sample did you predict would be most permeable? The least permeable?
5. What variables were controlled in your test?
6. What conclusions can you draw from this activity?
7. How can you compare the permeability of soil in different locations?

Data and Observations

Location	Observations of soil	Prediction	Amount of time to sink in

SCIENCE AND SOCIETY

11:6 Soil Erosion

Soil is a very important natural resource. It is used to grow crops. Soil supports a variety of vegetation and provides a living place for many small organisms. It takes from 10 to 30 years to produce 1 mm of topsoil. Poor farming methods and other activities of humans contribute to soil erosion. How can soil erosion be prevented or reduced?

Some farmers plow fields parallel to the slope of the land. Erosion occurs as water carries fine materials down the plowed furrows. Contour plowing is a farming method in which fields are plowed and planted across a slope. This method of plowing produces barriers that decrease soil erosion by water.

F.Y.I. When minimum tillage and contour farming are used together on a field, soil erosion can be reduced by as much as 98%.

Why is soil important?

TECHNOLOGY

Soil Conservation

During the 1930s, the Great Plains area of the United States experienced severe drought conditions. Crops that were planted could not live without water and failed. The soil was exposed to severe erosion, and winds blew much of the topsoil away.

To avoid a repeat of this occurrence, the United States government instituted soil conservation measures in 1935. One of the methods used involved planting windbreaks along the edges of farms in the Great Plains. These long rows of trees were planted in a north-south direction. They slowed the wind and thus reduced soil erosion. The use of contour plowing also helped reduce erosion.

ADVANCE

Minimum tillage is becoming a popular way of plowing fields. The process involves very little surface disruption. Fields are not plowed before planting. Instead, a special machine digs furrows in the ground right through the residue from previous crops. Instead of plowing for weed control, chemicals are used. Since minimum tillage provides a nearly continuous vegetation cover, soil erosion can be reduced by up to 90 percent. Another advantage of minimum tillage is that it costs less than "regular" tilling. Machines pass through the fields fewer times, so less fuel is used.

FIGURE 11–9. Contour planting helps cut down on soil erosion.

What is crop rotation?

F.Y.I. Windbreaks are also called shelterbelts.

If the same crops are planted in a certain area year after year, the soil becomes depleted of so many plant nutrients that the soil becomes infertile. Few crops can be grown in infertile soil. The uncovered soil is easily eroded by water and wind. Crop rotation is a method of farming used to keep soil nutrients from being depleted. Certain root crops such as beets remove large amounts of nutrients from the soil. Plants such as clover and soybeans restore nutrients to the soil. The two crops are rotated from year to year to keep the soil nutrient-rich.

If the ground has no plant cover in areas where strong winds exist, winds can remove topsoil. Planting of ground cover and erecting windbreaks in these areas help reduce soil erosion. Most ground covers are quick-growing plants with very shallow roots that help hold topsoil in place. These plants include clover, alfalfa, and hay. Windbreaks are rows of trees or shrubs planted along the side of a field that prevent wind from eroding topsoil from an area.

REVIEW

6. What is soil?
7. How is color related to the organic content of a soil?
8. Describe the *A* horizon of a mature soil.
9. Which soil type is rich in oxides of iron and aluminum?
10. If you were a farmer, what are two ways you could reduce soil erosion on your land?

CHAPTER 11 REVIEW

SUMMARY

1. Physical and chemical processes that break down rocks at Earth's surface are called weathering. Physical weathering breaks rocks into smaller fragments. Chemical weathering changes rock composition. 11:1
2. Erosion is the transportation of weathered fragments by water, wind, ice, and gravity. Water is probably the most important agent of erosion. Wind erodes by deflation and abrasion. Mass movements are caused by gravity. 11:2
3. Soil is a mixture of weathered rock and organic matter at Earth's surface. Soils can be described by color, moisture content, and texture. 11:3
4. A mature soil has three distinct horizons: *A, B,* and *C.* The *A* horizon contains organic matter. The *B* horizon is often rich in clay and iron oxides. The *C* horizon overlies the bedrock from which the soil formed. 11:4
5. Humid, temperate climates produce pedalfer soil. Dry, temperate climates produce pedocals. Tropical climates produce laterites. Porosity and permeability are measurements of how well water moves through soil. 11:5
6. Poor farming methods and lack of proper ground cover are contributing to a drastic increase in soil erosion. 11:6

VOCABULARY

a. creep
b. erosion
c. landslides
d. laterites
e. leaching

f. pedalfers
g. pedocals
h. permeability
i. porosity
j. rockfalls

k. soil
l. soil profile
m. weathering

Match each description with the correct vocabulary word from the list above.
1. relatively slow downslope movement of Earth materials
2. a process by which some soil components are dissolved and carried downward by water
3. soils rich in iron oxide and aluminum-rich clays
4. processes that break down rocks at Earth's surface
5. rapid mass movements of a unit of large amounts of rock and soil
6. red-orange soils rich in iron and aluminum oxides
7. mixture of weathered rock and organic matter
8. large pieces of rock falling from a high place to a low place
9. transportation of weathered Earth materials
10. soils rich in calcium carbonate

MAIN IDEAS

A. Reviewing Concepts

Choose the word or phrase that correctly completes each of the following sentences.

1. _____ changes the composition of a rock.
   a. Chemical weathering
   b. Mass movement
   c. Ice wedging
   d. Physical weathering
2. _____ is physical weathering.
   a. Rusting   c. Ice wedging
   b. Creep   d. Leaching
3. Weathering is affected by _____.
   a. rock size   c. climate
   b. rock   d. all of these
      composition
4. A measure of the amount of a soil's volume composed of pores is _____.
   a. erosion   c. leaching
   b. porosity   d. permeability
5. The scouring action of particles carried by wind is _____.
   a. deflation   c. creep
   b. abrasion   d. leaching
6. Which of the following is an example of chemical weathering?
   a. ice wedging   c. rusting
   b. plant roots   d. sheeting
      cracking rocks
7. Soils that form in humid, temperate climates are _____.
   a. pedalfers   c. laterites
   b. pedocals   d. all of these
8. Soil is _____ percent air and water.
   a. 10   c. 50
   b. 25   d. 75
9. Soils rich in _____ feel smooth and sticky to the touch.
   a. clay   c. sand
   b. silt   d. organic matter

10. Soils rich in _____ feel gritty to the touch.
    a. clay   c. silt
    b. sand   d. organic matter
11. Which soil horizon might contain weathered bedrock?
    a. *A*   c. *C*
    b. *B*   d. none of these
12. The ability of a soil to allow water to flow through it is _____.
    a. porosity   c. leaching
    b. permeability   d. gravitability
13. Soils that contain little organic matter and form in hot wet tropical climates are _____.
    a. laterites   c. pedalfers
    b. pedocals   d. all of these
14. A description of the layers that make up a soil is a _____.
    a. soil profile   c. laterite
    b. "perc" test   d. pedalfer
15. _____ increases soil erosion.
    a. Lack of ground cover
    b. Plowing parallel to the slope
    c. Strong winds
    d. All of these

B. Understanding Concepts

Answer the following questons using complete sentences.

16. How does physical weathering differ from chemical weathering?
17. Define erosion, and list the four agents of erosion.
18. What factors affect the rate of weathering of a rock?
19. Why is soil important?
20. What is deflation?
21. What soil type is common in the western United States where the climate is dry?

22. What is found in the open spaces and pores within soil?
23. What are some characteristics of a black or dark brown soil?
24. Describe loamy soil.
25. Describe the horizons in a soil profile.

C. Applying Concepts

Answer the following questions using complete sentences.

26. What type of weathering would be more effective in a desert area? Explain.
27. How could a soil that is very porous *not* be permeable?
28. How might a forest fire affect weathering processes in a certain area?
29. How does amount of rainfall affect leaching?
30. How does contour plowing reduce soil erosion?

SKILL REVIEW

If you need help, refer to the Skill Handbook, pages 526 to 537.

1. You observe a large piece of rock moving rapidly down a steep slope. Which erosional agent do you infer is responsible?
2. Make a pie graph of the composition of an average dry soil. Label the percentage made up of organic matter and weathered rock. Label the percentage made up of open space.
3. Suppose you make a pie graph of a very sandy soil. Would the pore space area on your graph be larger or smaller than it was in Question 2?
4. Outline Section 11:2.

5. Suppose you are going to classify soil samples as pedalfers, pedocals, and laterites. What characteristics of the soil will you use?

PROJECTS

1. Obtain samples of the *A* horizon of soil near your home, near the school, and at three other locations in your community. Be sure to receive the permission of the property owner before you obtain your samples. Record the color, texture, and moisture content of each sample. Relate these soil properties to the types and amounts of vegetation found at each location.
2. Place samples of limestone, granite, and sandstone in clear, plastic containers. Label each with the type of rock in the container. Half fill each container with vinegar. Make daily observations of your samples for a two-week period. Record your observations. Hypothesize which rocks are more susceptible to chemical weathering. Relate this to the mineral content of each rock.

READINGS

1. Booth, Eugene. *Under the Ground*. Milwaukee, WI: Raintree Pubs., 1985.
2. McLarney, B. "Control Stream Erosion." *Mother Earth News*. May-June, 1986, pp. 16–19.
3. Milne, Lorus J. and Milne, Margery. *A Shovelful of Earth*. New York, NY: H. Holt and Co., 1987.

Career: Hydrogeologist

It seemed like everyone was complaining about the weather. There hadn't been much rain in the spring, and summer was even drier. The farmers' crops weren't growing well, and the grass was brown and prickly.

The water department put the city on water restrictions to save water. The city's water supply was from underground, and without good rainfall there might not be enough water to get through the winter. No one was allowed to water lawns or to wash cars.

Mr. Parker's job was more important than ever. As a hydrogeologist, he was responsible for testing the city's water supply. He took water samples from special wells and analyzed them for the presence of metals such as lead and mercury, fertilizers, pesticides, and other impurities that may have entered the groundwater. Mr. Parker's job is important even when the water supply is not low. One time, he found some benzene in one of his samples and traced it to an old buried storage tank that was leaking. If he finds too much pollution, bottled water will be used for drinking.

When rain or snow sinks into the ground, it becomes groundwater. It can wash metals and other pollutants into drinking water. In this chapter, you will study surface water and groundwater, and how they become polluted.

F.Y.I. American Geophysical Union, 200 Florida Avenue, N.W. Washington, DC 20009

GOALS

You will study . . .
1. the water cycle.
2. how rivers form and develop.
3. how water changes Earth's surface.

What percentage of Earth's surface is covered by water?

12:1 The Water Cycle

Look at a globe. Try to estimate the amount of Earth's surface that is covered with water. What's your guess? Thirty percent? Fifty percent? Seventy-five percent? Water covers over 71 percent of Earth's surface. All water that exists on Earth makes up the **hydrosphere.** The hydrosphere includes all the water in Earth's oceans, lakes, streams, ice, atmosphere, and ground. About 97 percent of Earth's water is contained in the oceans. Over 2 percent of Earth's total water supply is ice. Less than 1 percent of Earth's water is streams, lakes, groundwater, and water vapor.

Suppose it's your turn to wash the dinner dishes. You turn on the faucet and fill the sink with warm, soapy water. Half an hour later, you wash the last pan. You look around to make sure you haven't forgotten anything. You pull the plug. You hear a *blurp* and the water disappears down the drain. What will happen to the water now? It probably leaves your house or apartment and flows through the city sewers to the water treatment plant. There, the water is processed and returned to a local stream or reservoir. Eventually, someone else will use it or it will flow into the ocean.

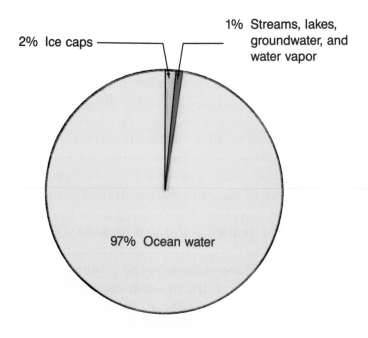

2% Ice caps

1% Streams, lakes, groundwater, and water vapor

97% Ocean water

Earth's Hydrosphere

FIGURE 12–1. The hydrosphere is made up of all of Earth's water resources.

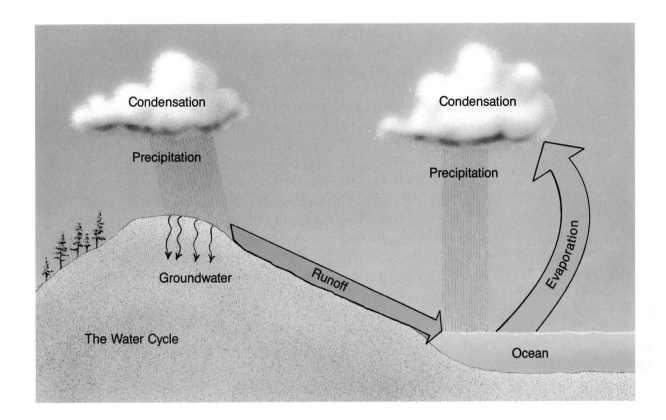

In the image, the following labels appear: Condensation, Precipitation, Condensation, Precipitation, Evaporation, Groundwater, Runoff, The Water Cycle, Ocean

In a similar way, water in Earth's hydrosphere is continually moved from one place to another. This movement of water is called the **water cycle.** The energy needed to power the water cycle is supplied by the sun. Solar energy warms water on Earth's surface. The water molecules may become warm enough to evaporate. **Evaporation** is the process in which a liquid changes to vapor. Water vapor may collect around tiny particles of dust or salt in the air and change to a liquid. Recall that the process in which a gas changes to a liquid is condensation. If the water droplets become too heavy, they will fall as precipitation. Precipitation is water that falls back to Earth's surface as rain, snow, or ice. Precipitation results in the removal of water from the air and its return to Earth.

Most precipitation falls over the oceans. The precipitation that falls on land becomes either groundwater or runoff. You will learn more about groundwater in Section 12:3. **Runoff** is precipitation that flows along Earth's surface. Runoff flows downhill due to gravity and will eventually flow back into lakes or the oceans.

FIGURE 12–2. The water in Earth's hydrosphere is continually moved from one place to another in the water cycle.

F.Y.I. Water vapor is also released into Earth's atmosphere by the process of transpiration in plants.

Where does runoff flow?

12:2 Rivers

The Mississippi River is the longest river in the United States. It is over 3750 km long and in some places is over 1350 m wide. How did this river form? Was it always this big? The mighty Mississippi began millions of years ago as runoff.

As runoff travels to the ocean, it flows over many types of land surfaces. Some types of rock and soil are easy for the runoff to erode, while others are more difficult. The runoff will begin eroding the easier surfaces first. Runoff cuts a channel by removing the loose and weak material. Additional runoff will then follow this channel and cut it deeper and wider. These small runoff streams eventually flow into larger streams. A **stream** is a body of flowing water. Small streams flow into larger streams, and the larger streams flow into major rivers. This system of water channels that drains an area is called a drainage system.

Drainage systems create patterns on the land. The type of pattern depends on the original shape of the land and the rocks over which the streams flow. In an area with a central high point such as a volcano or hill, the streams flow away from the central high. This produces a radial pattern. It resembles the spokes of a bicycle wheel. Where the land is mostly flat, drainage patterns resemble a tree. The main river is the "trunk" of a tree. The smaller streams are the "branches." The Mississippi River has such a drainage pattern.

How did the Mississippi River begin?

F.Y.I. The mouth of a river is the point where it empties into another body of water.

FIGURE 12–3. A radial pattern develops around high points (a). A treelike pattern forms in flat areas (b).

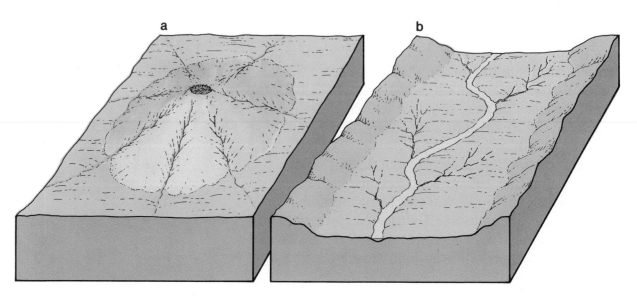

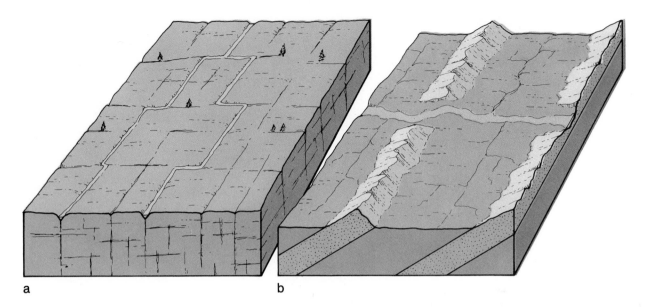

a   b

When the rocks underlying streams are fractured in regular patterns, the drainage pattern "copies" the fractures. Streams flow along the weak zones and produce a rectangular pattern on the land. In places where bands of resistant rock alternate with bands that erode more easily, a trellis pattern develops. The main river cuts across unfractured, resistant rock, and the smaller streams flow only in the weak zones.

As streams flow over land, they erode and deposit Earth materials. Recall that these materials are called sediments. Sediments that are too large and heavy to be carried are rolled along the bottom of the channel. Some sediments are dissolved by the water and carried in solution. Many of the harmful pollutants found in streams are carried in this way.

In addition to eroding, streams deposit materials as they flow through their valleys. **Bars** are long ridges of sand and gravel that are deposited in the stream's channel. As a stream deposits a bar in one place, it will erode the channel's bank in another. This causes the stream channel to wander back and forth. The curves that are formed in a stream are called **meanders.**

When a stream overflows its banks, material is deposited on the land on either side of the channel. This area is called the floodplain. **Levees** (LEV eez) are ridgelike deposits that are built up along the sides of a stream. They are formed by successive floods over a period of many years.

FIGURE 12–4. Rectangular (a) and trellis (b) drainage develop because of the underlying rock.

F.Y.I. The Mississippi River carries over 750 million metric tons of eroded material to the Gulf of Mexico each year.

How is a floodplain formed?

FIGURE 12–5. Bars, levees, and floodplains form along a meandering stream.

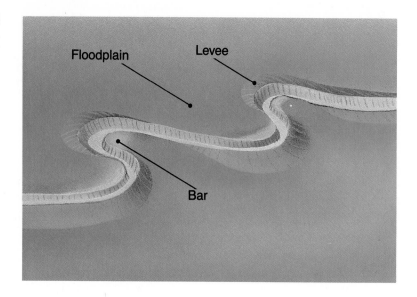

Floodplain   Levee

Bar

At its mouth, a stream flows into a larger body of water. Here, the water loses energy as its speed decreases. Sediment is deposited in a fan-shaped body called a **delta.** The Mississippi Delta forms where the Mississippi River flows into the Gulf of Mexico.

Where does the Mississippi Delta form?

TECHNOLOGY

Flood Control

Dams have been used for flood control for thousands of years. The type of dam and the materials from which it is constructed depend on the geology and climate of an area. In broad river valleys, dams are constructed of soil and rock. In narrow river valleys, concrete dams are built.

When river valleys are dammed, large reservoirs of water form behind the dam. Dams usually have gates that raise and lower or valves that open and close. The water level in the reservoir is regulated by these gates or valves. By controlling the level of the reservoir, dams control the amount of water that flows down the river valley. In times of heavy precipitation, water can be held in the reservoir so the river valleys don't flood.

ADVANCE

To protect the city of London, England, a movable dam has been installed on the Thames River. The dam has ten floodgates that rest on the river bottom. If a storm develops and flooding is possible, the gates are raised to form a 15-m high dam.

Problem: How do different surfaces affect the amount of runoff?

Materials

stream table   piece of sod (20 cm^2)
500-mL beaker   bricks (2)
sprinkling can   plastic pail
water   flat rock (about 20 cm^2)
soil mixture

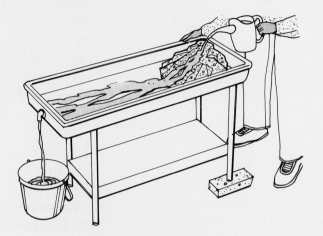

Procedure

1. Copy the data table.
2. Arrange the stream table as shown. Place the bricks under one end.
3. Hypothesize how different surfaces such as rock, soil, and vegetation affect the amount of runoff.
4. Place the rock in the upper end of the stream table.
5. Pour 1 L of water into the sprinkling can. Steadily sprinkle the water from the can over the rock.
6. Measure the amount of runoff in the bucket at the other end of the table. Record the amount of runoff and your observations in your data table.
7. Remove the rock. Pack soil to a depth of about 5 cm into the upper end of the stream table.
8. Pour 1 L of water into the sprinkling can. Steadily empty the can over the soil.
9. Measure the amount of runoff in the bucket at the other end. Record the amount of runoff and your observations.
10. Replace the soil with the piece of sod. Repeat steps 8 and 9 with the sod.

Data and Observations

Surface	Runoff amount	Water color	Surface appearance
Rock			
Soil			
Sod			

Questions and Conclusions

1. How do the amounts of runoff for each surface compare?
2. How do the colors of the runoff from the soil and sod compare?
3. What differences did you observe on the surfaces after each was sprinkled?
4. How do the results of the activity compare with your hypotheses?
5. How can you explain why sod had less runoff than the other two surfaces?
6. How do different surfaces affect runoff?
7. How could you test the effect of slope on the amount of runoff of sod?

What Is the Hydrosphere? 239

12:3 Groundwater

Precipitation that soaks into the ground through small pores or openings becomes **groundwater.** The amount of precipitation that soaks in depends on the porosity and permeability of the ground. Have you ever dug a hole in the sand at the beach? You probably dug only a few inches before the hole filled with water. This is because the groundwater filling the pore spaces flowed out into the hole. You dug into a zone saturated with water. The upper surface of the zone saturated with groundwater is the **water table.** The water table may be right at Earth's surface or hundreds of meters deep.

When the water table occurs at the land surface, a swamp forms. Swamps are very shallow bodies of water. If the water table drops even a few centimeters, the swamp may dry up. Sometimes the land dips below the water table. These low areas fill with water, and lakes, ponds, or streams develop. Occasionally the water table meets the land surface on the side of a hill. The groundwater flows out onto the surface. This is called a spring.

You learned that water flows through permeable soils. Water also flows through rock. Permeable rocks filled with water are called **aquifers.**

What determines the amount of groundwater that soaks into the ground?

FIGURE 12–6. The locations of swamps, streams, lakes, and springs depend on the depth of the water table.

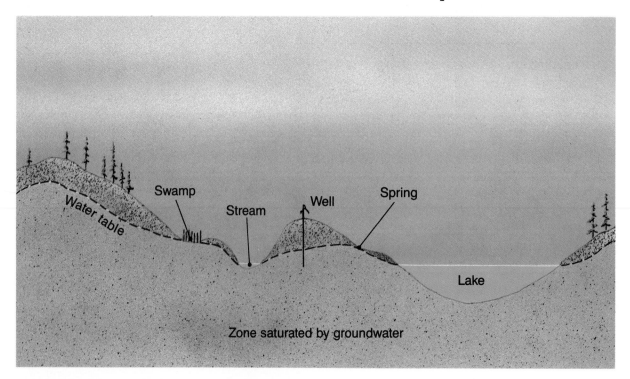

Aquifers form when a layer of permeable rock is trapped between two layers of impermeable rock. The groundwater fills the pore spaces in the permeable rock. Layers of sandstone are common aquifers. Sandstones have large, connected spaces. Wells are often drilled through layers of soil and impermeable rock to reach aquifers. Such wells are important sources of fresh water. Groundwater provides drinking water for 53 percent of the population of the United States. At least some of the water you drink probably comes from groundwater.

Groundwater is also an erosional agent. It carves out underground caverns. Caverns are hollowed out chambers in limestone rock. Why do caverns form only in limestone? Rainwater reacts with carbon dioxide in the air and forms carbonic acid. This carbonic acid dissolves the calcite crystals in limestone. The dissolved calcite is then carried away by the flowing groundwater. Since part of the rock has been removed, a hollowed out chamber is left in the limestone. Not all caverns are filled with groundwater. If the level of the water table drops, the cavern fills with air. One chamber in New Mexico's Carlsbad Caverns is the size of 14 football fields.

BIOGRAPHY

Ruth Patrick
1907–

Dr. Ruth Patrick has devoted her life to clean rivers. As a child, she loved to examine the life forms that lived in water. She began a department of freshwater studies at the Academy of Natural Sciences. She won the Tyler Ecology Award in 1975.

Groundwater often contains dissolved calcium carbonate ($CaCO_3$). As this groundwater drips through the ceiling of caverns, carbon dioxide (CO_2) escapes from the water. As this happens, calcite is deposited on the ceiling forming an iciclelike structure called a stalactite (stuh LAK tite). The water then drops to the floor of the cavern and evaporates. As the water evaporates, calcite forms a deposit called a stalagmite (stuh LAG mite) on the cave floor. Stalactites and stalagmites often grow together to form a column. This process is extremely slow. During your lifetime, a stalactite or stalagmite might grow only one centimeter.

Groundwater that contains dissolved minerals such as calcium, magnesium, and iron is called "hard" water. Since hard water stains sinks and clothes, many people "soften" their water. Water softeners replace the dissolved minerals with sodium. Sodium does not stain materials, and soap lathers more in soft water. Can you think of a disadvantage of using sodium? People with high blood pressure and heart problems must limit the amount of sodium they consume.

PROBLEM SOLVING

Hard Water

Kevin was responsible for doing his own laundry. His mother had instructed him in how to separate laundry into different color and fabric loads, how to select water temperature and cycle, and how long to keep the clothes in the dryer. Kevin also learned when to add bleach and detergent, and how much of each to add. Since last year, he had learned a lot about washing clothes.

One day, much of the soap in Kevin's wash did not rinse out although he followed his normal procedures. His clothes seemed as clean as usual but they were streaked with suds. Kevin then remembered that a water softener had been installed in the house. How should Kevin adjust his washing procedures? How does softened water affect washing?

SCIENCE AND SOCIETY

12:4 Using Groundwater

In many places, groundwater is the only source of fresh water available. Groundwater supplies the water needs for people, livestock, crops, and industry.

Much groundwater is clean enough to drink without any type of treatment. The rocks and soil that groundwater flows through are natural filters. They absorb the impurities dissolved in the water. In many cases, water goes directly from the ground into your drinking glass. However, more and more groundwater is being contaminated. Septic tanks, broken sewage pipes, agricultural fertilizers, and garbage dumps all pollute groundwater. Sewage may flow directly into aquifers. Rainwater seeps through garbage dumps and carries the pollution into the ground. Toxic chemicals from farmland also mix with groundwater in this way.

Wells must be drilled so that groundwater can be pumped to the surface. Over time, the water that is removed by humans is replaced by precipitation. This replacement may be slow. If large volumes of water are removed by humans, the water table can be lowered many meters. It may take thousands of years for the water table to return to its original level. Removal of large volumes of groundwater also can cause collapse of soil and rock underground. This, in turn, can cause the land surface to sink.

If large volumes of groundwater are removed from areas near the oceans, salt water can flow into the empty area and remain for long periods of time. Wells that once pumped fresh water could pump only salt water.

What can happen to land if large amounts of groundwater are removed?

All life on Earth is dependent on groundwater. Yet, if too much is removed or polluted, we risk the chance of losing this important resource. What can be done to solve this problem?

REVIEW

1. What percentage of Earth's surface is covered by water?
2. Explain evaporation and condensation.
3. What is groundwater?
4. Why does sandstone make a good aquifer?
5. Why must humans be careful when using groundwater?

What Are Glaciers?

GOALS

You will study . . .
1. erosion and deposition by glaciers.
2. possible causes of ice ages.

Where do glaciers form?

F.Y.I. Glaciers can form at the equator at high elevations such as in the Andes mountains of Colombia.

12:5 Glaciers

Look at Figures 12–9 and 12–10. These spectacular landforms were created by glaciers. **Glaciers** are large masses of ice in motion. They form at high elevations and in polar regions where snow does not completely melt in the summer. There are two types of glaciers: alpine glaciers and continental glaciers. Alpine glaciers form at high elevations. Continental glaciers form near the poles and spread toward the equator. Continental glaciers presently cover most of Greenland and Antarctica.

Have you ever slid into home base during a baseball game? You probably made gouges in the ground, and your pants were probably covered with dirt.

FIGURE 12–9. The Matterhorn is a famous mountain peak of the Alps.

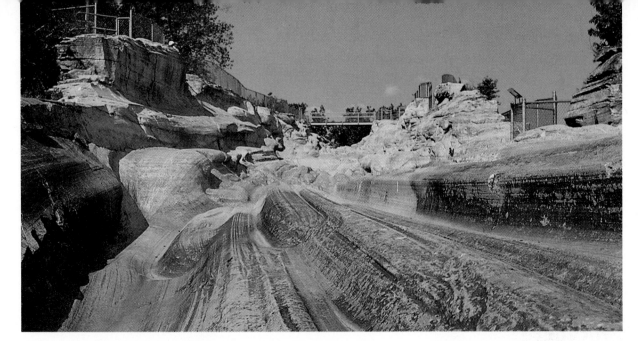

Just as the dirt sticks to your pants, rocks and soil become embedded in a glacier. As the glacier moves, the rocks and soil carried by the ice scour the land. Gouges made by glaciers are called striations (stri AY shunz). Some striations are as much as 1 m wide and 1 m deep! A well-known set of striations is located on Kelleys Island, Ohio. Together, these striations form a groove 10 m wide and 5 m deep.

Glaciers also erode Earth's surface by a process called ice wedging. Ice at the bottom of glaciers can melt and flow into cracks in rocks. As the water refreezes, it expands. This expansion breaks up rocks into smaller blocks. These smaller blocks are then carried away by the glacier.

Glaciers also change Earth's surface by depositing rocks and soil. Material carried by glaciers is deposited as the glacier melts. Material deposited directly by the ice of a melting glacier is **till.** Till is an unsorted, unlayered jumble of rock and soil. Accumulations of till form features called moraines. Terminal moraines are ridges of till deposited at the front edge of a glacier. Ground moraine is a sheetlike deposit of till dropped from the bottom of a glacier. Material deposited by glacial meltwater is **outwash.** Unlike till, it is deposited by running water. Different sized materials settle out of water at different rates. Because of this, outwash is layered. The larger particles are on the bottom and the smaller ones are on top.

FIGURE 12–10. Rocks carried along the bottom of a glacier scour out large grooves in underlying rocks.

What are the gouges made by glaciers called?

F.Y.I. The northern portion of Long Island, NY, is a terminal moraine. The southern portion is a large outwash deposit.

Problem: How do sediments settle out of water?

Materials

graduated cylinder
clear plastic
  cups (5)
water
spoon
gravel (50 mL)

salt (50 mL)
sand (50 mL)
clay (50 mL)
colored pencils (3)
watch or clock with
    second hand

Procedure

1. Copy the data table.
2. Label the cups A, B, C, D, and E.
3. Use the graduated cylinder to measure 25 mL of gravel and pour it into cup A. Pour 25 mL of salt into cup B. Pour 25 mL of sand into cup C and 25 mL of clay into cup D.
4. Pour the remaining gravel, salt, sand, and clay into cup E.
5. Add water to each cup until it is about two-thirds full.
6. Hypothesize what will happen to the sediments in each cup when stirred and allowed to settle.

7. Stir each cup thoroughly. Record your observations in the data table.
8. Observe the cups at five-minute intervals for 15 minutes and record your observations in the data table.
9. After 15 minutes, use the colored pencils to draw and label your observations of cup E. Use a different color for each layer in the cup.

Data and Observations

Cup	Start	5 minutes	10 minutes	15 minutes
A				
B				
C				
D				
E				

Questions and Conclusions

1. Which two sediments settled out most quickly?
2. Which two sediments did not settle out? Explain why.
3. How did the mixture change with time?
4. Describe the mixture in cup E. Are the sediments layered?
5. Explain how the results of the activity compare with your hypothesis.
6. How can you explain what happens to gravel, salt, sand, and clay carried by streams?

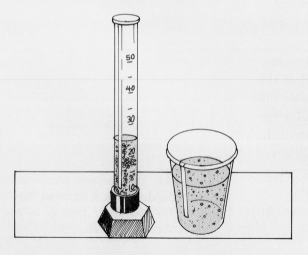

SKILL BUILDER

Cause and Effect

Joshua filled a glass jar with water and sealed it. He then placed it outside and left it overnight. The outside temperature dropped below freezing and the water in the jar froze. When Joshua returned for the jar, he found it had broken. Answer the questions below. If you need help, refer to Cause and Effect on page 536.

Questions
1. Why did the jar break?
2. What name is given to the breaking up of rock by freezing water?

12:6 Ice Ages

A period of time when glaciers cover a large portion of Earth's surface is called an **ice age.** The most recent ice age began about 8 million years ago and ended about 7000 years ago. The average global temperature during the last ice age was about 4°C lower than present day temperatures.

Many features you see today are the result of ice ages. The Great Lakes formed when continental glaciers deepened river valleys. Rivers once existed where the Great Lakes are today. Ice and moraines dammed the river valleys and lakes formed.

Many lakes located in the western United States are left over from the ice age. Great Salt Lake in Utah, for example, was once part of a much larger lake called Lake Bonneville. The Bonneville Salt Flats are part of the dried up lake bottom of the ancient ice age lake.

Glaciation also affects sea level. When water is frozen into glacial ice, sea level is lowered. This causes land at the shoreline to extend much farther out to sea. When glaciers melt, sea level rises and floods the low coastal plain.

Some of the effects of changes in sea level are offset by changes in the elevation of the land. Huge masses of ice cause the land to sink. When the ice melts, the land begins to rise back up. This slow rising of the land, called isostatic rebound, continues even today. In

F.Y.I. Kettle lakes are depressions formed when blocks of ice remain stagnant and melt.

What happens to sea level when glaciers melt?

FIGURE 12–11. During the last ice age, much of North America was covered by continental glaciers such as this one.

F.Y.I. During the most recent ice age, the ice sheet was as thick as 2 km in the area where Boston, MA, is located today.

places that were glaciated during the last ice age, the land is rising about 1 cm per year.

The causes of ice ages seem to be related to changes in Earth's tilt on its axis, the shape of Earth's orbit, and the wobble of Earth on its axis. Earth resembles a toy top that wobbles as it slowly spins. As Earth wobbles, its tilt also changes. The tilt of Earth's axis varies from about 22° to 25°. When the tilt is at a minimum, the poles receive less energy from the sun. Scientists believe that more ice forms during these times. When Earth's orbit becomes more circular, Earth is farther from the sun. Thus, temperatures are cooler than normal. The ice that forms near the poles spreads toward the equator. A combination of all these events may be the cause of ice ages.

REVIEW

6. What are glaciers?
7. What are the two types of glaciers?
8. How do striations form?
9. How does till differ from outwash?
10. What is an ice age?

CHAPTER 12 REVIEW

SUMMARY

1. The movement of water in Earth's hydrosphere from one place to another is the water cycle. Processes involved in the water cycle include evaporation, condensation, and precipitation. 12:1
2. Runoff forms channels as it flows. Runoff channels join to form larger and larger streams. The type of drainage pattern that develops depends on the original shape of the land and the underlying rocks. Streams erode and deposit Earth materials as they flow. 12:2
3. Groundwater is precipitation that soaks into the ground through pore spaces. The location of swamps, ponds, streams, and springs is determined by the level of the water table. Aquifers are permeable rocks containing groundwater. 12:3
4. Groundwater is a valuable source of fresh water. Removal and pollution of groundwater causes many environmental problems. 12:4
5. Large masses of ice in motion are glaciers. Alpine glaciers form at high elevations. Continental glaciers form in polar regions. Glaciers, like rivers, change Earth's surface by eroding and depositing materials. 12:5
6. An ice age is a period of time when glaciers cover a large portion of Earth. Ice ages are related to changes in Earth's rotation and orbit. 12:6

VOCABULARY

a. aquifers
b. bars
c. delta
d. evaporation
e. glaciers
f. groundwater
g. hydrosphere
h. ice age
i. levees
j. meander
k. outwash
l. runoff
m. stream
n. till
o. water cycle
p. water table

Match each description with the correct vocabulary word from the list above.
1. the upper surface of the zone saturated by groundwater
2. process in which a liquid changes to vapor
3. the movement of water within the hydrosphere
4. water that flows along Earth's surface
5. a period of time when glaciers cover a large portion of Earth
6. ridges of sand and gravel deposited along the sides of streams
7. large masses of ice in motion
8. a curve in a stream
9. a body of flowing water
10. unsorted material deposited by glaciers

CHAPTER 12 REVIEW

MAIN IDEAS

A. Reviewing Concepts

Choose the word or phrase that correctly completes each of the following sentences.

1. About _____ of Earth's water is contained in the oceans.
   - **a.** 30 percent
   - **b.** 50 percent
   - **c.** 75 percent
   - **d.** 97 percent

2. The energy needed to power the water cycle comes from the _____.
   - **a.** ocean
   - **b.** sun
   - **c.** clouds
   - **d.** groundwater

3. The process in which a gas changes to a liquid is _____.
   - **a.** condensation
   - **b.** evaporation
   - **c.** precipitation
   - **d.** dissolution

4. The Mississippi River began as _____.
   - **a.** a delta
   - **b.** groundwater
   - **c.** runoff
   - **d.** none of these

5. Streams _____ sediments.
   - **a.** erode
   - **b.** deposit
   - **c.** both a and b
   - **d.** none of these

6. A _____ is a fan-shaped river deposit.
   - **a.** delta
   - **b.** bar
   - **c.** flood plain
   - **d.** levee

7. Groundwater is found _____.
   - **a.** on Earth's surface
   - **b.** below Earth's surface
   - **c.** only in oceans
   - **d.** only as runoff

8. _____ glaciers presently cover most of Greenland and Antarctica.
   - **a.** Alpine
   - **b.** Moraine
   - **c.** Continental
   - **d.** None of these

9. Permeable rocks filled with water are _____.
   - **a.** aquifers
   - **b.** stalactites
   - **c.** stalagmites
   - **d.** none of these

10. Groundwater is important to _____.
   - **a.** people
   - **b.** livestock
   - **c.** plants
   - **d.** all of these

11. _____ are gouges made by glaciers.
   - **a.** Ground moraines
   - **b.** Striations
   - **c.** Terminal moraines
   - **d.** Tills

12. A _____ is a sheetlike deposit of till.
   - **a.** terminal moraine
   - **b.** ground moraine
   - **c.** valley glacier
   - **d.** continental glacier

13. Global temperatures during the last ice age were about _____ lower than present-day temperatures.
   - **a.** 25°C
   - **b.** 10°C
   - **c.** 4°C
   - **d.** 40°C

14. Ice ages are caused by _____.
   - **a.** Earth's tilt on its axis
   - **b.** the shape of Earth's orbit
   - **c.** the wobble of Earth's axis
   - **d.** all of these

15. The most recent ice age began about _____ million years ago.
   - **a.** 8
   - **b.** 10
   - **c.** 12
   - **d.** 14

B. Understanding Concepts

Answer the following questions using complete sentences.

16. Explain the movement of water in the water cycle.
17. What is the hydrosphere?
18. How do rivers form?
19. How are some drainage patterns like a "tree?"
20. What is a floodplain?
21. How does a delta form?
22. What is a spring?
23. Compare and contrast stalactites and stalagmites.

24. How can the removal of excessive volumes of groundwater affect the surface of the land?
25. Describe ice wedging.

C. Applying Concepts

Answer the following questions using complete sentences.

26. How would replacing an empty grass lot with a parking lot affect runoff?
27. What two things determine the type of drainage pattern that will develop in an area?
28. Explain why it is possible to find alpine glaciers but not continental glaciers in the tropics today.
29. Explain why some areas of land have been rising since the end of the last ice age.
30. How are ice ages related to the tilt of Earth's axis?

SKILL REVIEW

If you need help, refer to the Skill Handbook, pages 526 to 537.

1. Suppose you are constructing a map of Earth's surface. Your map has a total area of 100 cm². How many square centimeters will you use to represent water?
2. You decide to graph Earth's water resources. You wish to show the percentages of water in Earth's oceans, ice, streams, lakes, ground, and atmosphere. What type of graph should you use?
3. Earth wobbles on its axis, varies in its tilt, and shifts in its orbit over long periods of time. What effect does this seem to have on the climate?
4. Suppose you're traveling and you discover large grooves in the local rocks. You observe that the local soils are unlayered and contain rocks and grains of many sizes. Make an inference: What made the large grooves in the rocks? Explain how they were formed.
5. Give the sequence of events that occur in the water cycle.

PROJECTS

1. Have an adult accompany you to a local stream. Use a camera to obtain photographs over a period of two or three months. Try to take pictures during rainy periods as well as dry periods. Use your photographs to show how the water flowing in a stream changes and affects the erosion of the stream bed.
2. Research what is meant by hard water. Then, test water from your home, school, a nearby river, and a public swimming pool for hardness.

READINGS

1. Milne, Lorus J. and Milne, Margery. *A Shovelful of Earth.* New York, NY: H. Holt and Co., 1987.
2. Palmer, Joy. *The World's Water.* North Pomfret, VT: David and Charles, 1988.
3. Ralaver, Ruth and Gitkin, Lisa. *The Power of Ice.* Chicago, IL: Childrens Press, 1985.

FUN WITH

Earth forms.

4.5 B.Y.A.

1759

Roller skates are invented in Belgium.

The Erie Canal opens.

1825

1901

A Texas oil field produces 80 000 barrels of oil a day.

Did you know that if you leave the water running as you brush your teeth, you use about 4 L of water?

You have probably seen many worms on the ground during or after a heavy rain. Why? Worms breathe air through their skins. If they remain in the soil during a heavy rain, they might drown.

QUESTION AND ANSWER

Mix 3 teaspoons of salt in 1 cup of water. Pour the salt water into a flat pan or dish to a depth of about 1 cm. Place the pan or dish on a shelf where it will not be disturbed. Observe the dish once in the morning and once in the evening until all of the water has evaporated. **What is the mineral that forms as the water evaporates? How might the Bonneville Salt Flats in the western United States have formed?**
Salt forms as the water evaporates. The salt flats formed when an ancient sea evaporated.

Riddle

Q. What kind of field is sometimes plowed but never planted? **A.** a snow field

TEASER

FUN RECIPE
ROCK CANDY

Mix 1 3/4 cups of white sugar, 1/2 cup light corn syrup, and 1/2 cup water in a large pan. Stir and place a candy thermometer in the pan. Place the pan over high heat until the temperature reaches 155°C. Remove the pan from the stove. Stir in 1/2 teaspoon of a flavoring oil and add food coloring. Pour onto a pan lined with confectioners' sugar. Cool and break into pieces.

SCIENCE

1908

Coffee filters invented by Mrs. Bentz.

A dog named Laika is first living space traveler.

1957

1966

Gemini 12 circles Earth 59 times before returning.

Swatch™ watch invented by Swiss engineers.

1982

QUIZ

The discharge of a river is the amount of water that flows past a certain point in a given amount of time. Discharge = channel width x channel depth x speed. The width of the Mississippi River at St. Louis is about 533 m, depth is about 10 m, and speed is 0.6 m/s. What is the discharge of the Mississippi River at St. Louis?

How did the Grand Canyon form? The spectacular gorge called the Grand Canyon exposes over a billion years of Earth's history. The canyon is the result of the erosive action of the Colorado River.

Maria and Lucia found a piece of coal near Maria's house. They examined it closely with a magnifying glass, and Maria saw what she thought was a piece of coral. Lucia thought it was a small twig. Who's correct?

JOKE

Q. What did the ground say to the rain cloud?
A. Stop it or my name will be mud!

Calvin and Hobbes

EVERYTHING FLOATS RANDOMLY IN THE ROOM! THERE'S NO GRAVITY!

CALVIN PUSHES OFF THE CEILING AT A SHARP ANGLE, AIMING FOR THE HALLWAY!

HE GLIDES WITH UNCHECKED MOMENTUM, TURNING HIMSELF TO BE ABLE TO PUSH OFF THE NEXT STATIONARY SURFACE.

C'MON, YOU! OUTSIDE! YOU'RE REALLY BOUNCING OFF THE WALLS TODAY.

AW, MOM.

253

Answers
Quiz: 3198 m/s
Teaser: Lucia is correct. Coal formed from plant remains.
Corals are animals.

UNIT 4

Earth's Air and Water

Heat from the sun, air, and moisture combine in Earth's atmosphere to form a variety of weather conditions. When two extremely different kinds of air masses collide, severe weather can result. What kinds of forces work together to make tornadoes? Tornadoes have a motion similar to a spinning top. How are the forces in a spinning top similar to the forces in tornadoes?

Air

Career: Pilot

Sarah had always wanted to be a pilot. Finally, on her sixteenth birthday she was allowed to take flying lessons. Sarah's first lessons were ground school classes. Every pilot must meet certain minimum requirements set up by the Federal Aviation Agency. First, she had to learn the importance of basic safety. Then Sarah had to learn how to check the engine, the wheels, and the radio. Next, she had to learn how to operate the instrument panel. Instruments help in the basic fundamentals of flying—holding the plane straight and level, turning and climbing at the correct angle, and keeping airspeed and altitude under control. Last and most important, Sarah learned how to get a weather briefing and file a flight plan. A pilot must know the weather before taking off. If the air is very warm, the plane will perform as if it were at a higher altitude. Bad weather may mean that the pilot has to adjust altitude or speed or use an alternate route. Extreme weather may cause flights to be cancelled.

Sarah did very well in ground school. Now she was ready to take to the air and practice what she had learned.

Air and wind affect the flight of a plane just as they affect activity on the ground. In this chapter, you will learn about the composition and structure of air, the factors that affect air, and global wind systems.

F.Y.I. Air Line Pilots Association International, 1625 Massachusetts Avenue, Washington, DC 20036

GOALS
You will study . . .
1. the composition of Earth's atmosphere.
2. the layers of the atmosphere.
3. how heat is transferred by the atmosphere.

What gases were given off by early volcanoes?

Why did oxygen begin accumulating in the atmosphere?

F.Y.I. The scattering of light by particles in the atmosphere gives the sky its blue color.

13:1 Earth's Atmosphere

You are protected from sun, cold, and severe storms by your home. Just as your home provides shelter for you, Earth's atmosphere provides shelter for the planet. The **atmosphere** is the blanket of air that surrounds Earth. Earth's atmosphere is a mixture of gases, solids, and liquids.

Scientists have hypothesized that shortly after Earth formed, large amounts of gas were given off by volcanoes. The gases given off included methane, ammonia, hydrogen, water vapor, and carbon dioxide. As time passed, the methane was replaced by carbon dioxide. Ammonia changed to nitrogen. Water vapor was added. Early forms of life could use the energy from the sun to make food. They used carbon dioxide and water and gave off oxygen as a waste product. Oxygen began accumulating in the air.

Take a deep breath. What have you "pulled" into your lungs? When asked what the air we breathe is made of, many people say oxygen. Oxygen, however, makes up only about 21 percent of Earth's atmosphere. Table 13–1 lists the gases that make up Earth's present atmosphere. As you can see, the largest part of the air you breathe is nitrogen. Dry air is 78 percent nitrogen, 21 percent oxygen, and one percent other gases.

FIGURE 13–1. Volcanoes contributed large amounts of gas to Earth's early atmosphere.

Table 13-1

Gases in Earth's Atmosphere		
Gas	Symbol	Percent by Volume
Nitrogen	N_2	78.08
Oxygen	O_2	20.95
Argon	Ar	0.93
Carbon Dioxide	CO_2	0.04
Water Vapor	H_2O	0.00 to 4.00
Neon	Ne	trace
Helium	He	trace
Methane	CH_4	trace
Krypton	Kr	trace
Xenon	Xe	trace
Hydrogen	H	trace
Ozone	O_3	trace

The gases in the atmosphere are used by organisms for their life processes. Nitrogen from the air is fixed in soil by bacteria. Plants use this nitrogen as a nutrient. When animals eat plants, they take in nitrogen. Animal wastes and decaying plants and animals eventually return nitrogen to the soil. Plants and animals use oxygen to release energy during respiration. Without oxygen, life as we know it could not survive on Earth. Carbon dioxide is used by plants and other green organisms to produce food.

SKILL BUILDER

Graphing

Construct a pie graph of the percentages by volume of gases in the air as given in Table 13-1. Because of the small amounts of argon through ozone, combine these gases as one percent of the total volume of the atmosphere. (Hint: Round off the percentages given for nitrogen and oxygen so that the total of the components equals 100 percent.) If you need help, refer to Graphing on page 532.

Questions

1. Is a pie graph more useful for interpreting the data than a table? Explain.
2. Would a line graph be useful in studying the composition of Earth's atmosphere? Explain.

13:2 Up, Up, and Away

Suppose you were sitting at your grandparents' house watching slides of their summer vacation out west. Your grandmother flips to the next slide. You gaze in wonder at the snow-covered peaks of the Rocky Mountains. For a moment, you're confused. How can there be snow in the middle of July?

The temperature of Earth's atmosphere changes with height. The changes that occur allow the atmosphere to be divided into four layers. The lowest layer of Earth's atmosphere is the **troposphere** (TROP uh sfihr). You live in this layer. The troposphere contains 75 percent of all gases in the atmosphere. It extends to a height of 8 km at the poles and 18 km at the equator. Nearly all weather forms in the troposphere. Air temperature slowly decreases with height in the troposphere. The **tropopause** is the boundary that separates the troposphere from the next layer. The tropopause acts as a ceiling to the weather zone.

Directly above the tropopause is the **stratosphere** (STRAT uh sfihr), the second layer of the atmosphere. It extends to a height of 50 km. Air temperature is

Name the atmospheric layer that you live in.

In which layer does weather form?

F.Y.I. Because of fairly constant temperatures in the lower stratosphere, material emitted by volcanic eruptions can remain in this layer for months or even years.

FIGURE 13–2. The temperature of Earth's atmosphere changes with height.

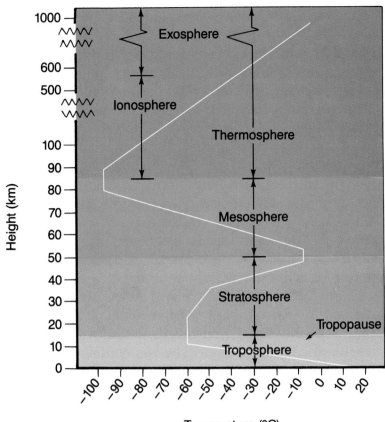

Temperature (°C)

FIGURE 13–3. The atmosphere can be divided into four main layers based on temperature.

fairly constant and low in the stratosphere, but it does increase with height. This increase in temperature is due to absorption of solar energy by ozone (OH zohn). Ozone is a form of oxygen. The ozone layer protects us from most of the ultraviolet radiation from the sun.

The third layer of the atmosphere is the **mesosphere** (MEZ uh sfihr), which extends from 50 to 85 km above Earth's surface. Air temperatures decrease with height in this layer. Thus, it is the coldest layer of Earth's atmosphere. Temperatures reach −100°C at the top of the mesosphere.

The **thermosphere** (THUR muh sfihr) extends from about 85 km above Earth's surface upward into space. Oxygen molecules in this layer absorb energy from the sun. This causes temperature to increase with height in this layer. The lower part of the thermosphere is called the ionosphere (i AHN uh sfihr). A large part of the air in the ionosphere is made of charged particles, or ions, and free electrons. Above about 550 km is the upper part of the thermosphere, the exosphere. Gas molecules in this layer are very far apart.

F.Y.I. When gases in Earth's ionosphere are excited by solar radiation, the gases give off light and glow in the sky. These lights are called the aurora borealis in the Northern Hemisphere and the aurora australis in the Southern Hemisphere.

What is ozone and why is it important to us?

F.Y.I. Gas particles in the exosphere are so far apart that a molecule can travel hundreds of kilometers before hitting another molecule.

What Is Air? 261

F.Y.I. Ninety-nine percent of Earth's atmosphere is below 32 km.

Gases in Earth's atmosphere, like all matter, have mass. The weight of the gases produced by gravitational forces between the gases and Earth can be measured. The measure of the weight of air molecules pressing down on a specific point on Earth is called **atmospheric pressure,** or air pressure. Air pressure decreases with height. As you go higher in the atmosphere, there are fewer gas molecules to press down on you.

Air pressure can also vary from one place to another at the same height due to temperature differences. Warm air molecules are farther apart than cool ones. Thus, warm air is less dense than cool air. This lower density, in turn, creates a lower air pressure in warm air than in cool air.

A barometer is an instrument used to measure air pressure. An aneroid barometer is a metal container from which most of the air has been removed. As air pressure increases or decreases, the container bends. A needle attached to the container shows the amount of pressure exerted by the air. With a mercury barometer, air pressure is measured as mercury moves up and down a long tube. High atmospheric pressure forces the mercury to rise. Low pressure makes the mercury drop in the tube.

FIGURE 13–4. In an aneroid barometer (a), air pressure pushing on a container causes a needle to move. In a mercury barometer (b), air pushing on mercury in a dish causes the mercury to rise and fall in a tube.

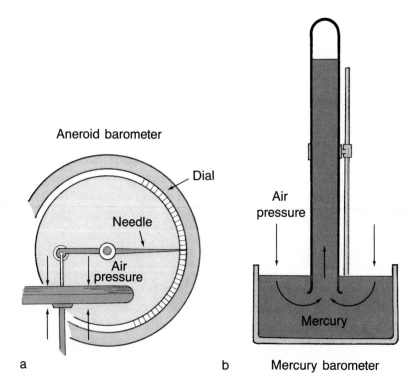

Problem: What are some properties of air?

Materties

aquarium   scissors
water   graduated cylinder
baby food jar   soft drink can
paper towels   hot plate
plastic coffee can lid   thermal mitt

Procedure

Part A

1. Half fill the aquarium with water.
2. Crumple a paper towel and place it in the baby food jar so that it will not fall out when the jar is inverted.
3. Hypothesize what will happen when the inverted jar is submerged. Record your hypothesis.
4. Keeping the inverted jar vertical, push it to the bottom of the aquarium. Remove the jar. Record your observations in your table.

Part B

5. Use the scissors to cut a circle from the coffee can lid larger than the diameter of the baby food jar.
6. Half fill the jar with water. Dip the plastic circle into some water. Place it over the mouth of the jar.
7. Record a hypothesis about what will happen when the jar is inverted.
8. Hold the jar with one hand. Place the fingers of your other hand over the plastic circle. Invert the jar over the aquarium. Carefully remove your fingers from the plastic circle. Record your observations.

Part C

9. Add 30 mL of water to the can.

10. Place the can on the hot plate for several minutes until the water boils. **CAUTION:** *Steam escaping from the opening in the can can cause burns.*
11. Hypothesize what will happen when the can is inverted in the aquarium. Record your hypothesis.
12. With the thermal mitt, carefully remove the can from the hot plate. As you turn it upside down over the aquarium, quickly place the rim and hole just below the level of water. Record your observations.

Data and Observations

Part	Hypotheses	Observations
A		
B		
C		

Questions and Conclusions

1. In Part A, what did you observe when the jar was placed under water? Explain.
2. What did you hypothesize would happen in Part B?
3. What did you observe when you removed your hand from the plastic lid? Explain.
4. What did you hypothesize would happen in Part C?
5. Using what you have learned about air pressure, explain why the soft drink can collapsed.
6. What are some properties of air?

13:3 Heat Transfer

Energy is transferred in Earth's atmosphere in three ways. Earth gets most of its energy from the sun in the form of waves. The transfer of energy by waves is **radiation.** Have you ever sat around a campfire toasting marshmallows? Did you feel warm when facing the fire? A campfire gives off radiant energy that you feel as heat.

Have you ever been to the beach or swimming pool and decided to go for a cold drink at the snack bar? When you stepped on the hot sand or cement, thermal energy was transferred by conduction from the sand or cement to your feet. **Conduction** is the transfer of thermal energy through matter by actual contact of molecules.

Have you ever watched a pot of boiling rice? Pieces of rice move around in the pot due to convection currents. **Convection** is the transfer of thermal energy due to density differences. As the stove burner heats the pot by conduction, the water molecules at the

FIGURE 13–5. Heat can be transferred by radiation (a), conduction (b), and convection (c).

a

b

c

bottom of the pot absorb energy. These warm water molecules move faster and farther apart, making the warm water less dense. Cold, denser water from the top of the pot sinks, forcing the warm, less dense water upward. Thermal energy is transferred from the bottom of the pot of water to the top. Convection currents transport the pieces of rice.

Convection currents in Earth's atmosphere transfer energy from place to place in much the same way. Air near Earth's surface is heated by radiation and conduction. Warm air molecules are less dense and thus develop a low pressure area. Cool molecules of air are more dense and thus create a high pressure area. Cold air will flow toward the low pressure area and force the warmer air aloft. The warmer air then cools, becomes more dense, and sinks.

Most of the energy Earth receives comes from the sun. Some of this energy is absorbed by the atmosphere, and some energy is reflected or scattered. Most of the energy that reaches Earth's surface is absorbed by land and water. In general, light-colored surfaces, such as snow and ice, reflect a large amount of energy. Darker surfaces, such as asphalt and vegetation, tend to absorb energy.

PROBLEM SOLVING

The New Bedroom

Sandra was happy that her sister had finally gone away to college. It meant that Sandra no longer had to share a bedroom with her younger sister.

Sandra's new bedroom was smaller than her old room, but it was nicely decorated. The room had two windows facing west. Each window had dark rose colored blinds and dark blue and rose printed curtains.

Sandra never recalled her old room being too warm or too cool. Her new room was comfortable during the morning, but early in the afternoon, it started to get warm. The room seemed to get even warmer as dinner approached. The room finally felt cooler near bedtime. Explain why Sandra's new bedroom felt too warm in the afternooon. What can Sandra do to make it more comfortable?

Problem: How do different materials absorb and release thermal energy?

Materials

paper cups (3)
sand
soil
water
metric ruler
colored pencils (3)
graph paper

Celsius thermometers
(3)
masking tape
clock or watch
gooseneck lamp with
75-watt bulb

Procedure

1. Two-thirds fill one cup with sand. Place the thermometer into the sand so that the bulb is covered to a depth of 1 cm. Use masking tape to secure the thermometer to the side of the cup.
2. Two-thirds fill another cup with soil. Two-thirds fill the last cup with water. Follow the procedure in Step 1 to attach the thermometers to each cup.
3. Observe and record the temperatures of each thermometer in a data table similar to the one shown.
4. Hypothesize what will happen to the temperature in each cup when placed under a light source. Hypothesize what will happen to the temperature in each cup when the light source is removed.

5. Place the cups 2 cm apart, directly below the gooseneck lamp.
6. Take and record temperature readings every two minutes for ten minutes.
7. Turn off the lamp.
8. Take and record temperature readings every two minutes for ten minutes.
9. Graph the temperature reading from each cup. Put the number of minutes on the *x*-axis, and temperature on the *y*-axis. Plot the data from each cup using a different color pencil.

Questions and Conclusions

1. Which material had the highest final thermometer reading in light?
2. When the light was on, which material absorbed energy fastest? Slowest?
3. When the light was off, which material lost energy fastest? Slowest?
4. What is the transfer of energy by waves?
5. What is the transfer of energy by actual contact of molecules?
6. Were your hypotheses about energy transfer supported? Explain.

Data and Observations

	IN LIGHT			OUT OF LIGHT		
Minutes	Thermometer reading (°C)			Thermometer reading (°C)		
	Sand	Soil	Water	Sand	Soil	Water
Initial						
2						
4						
6						
8						
10						

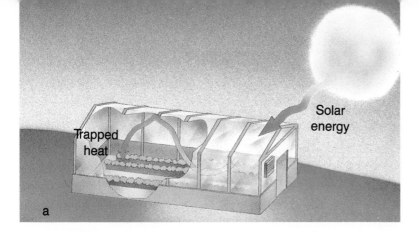

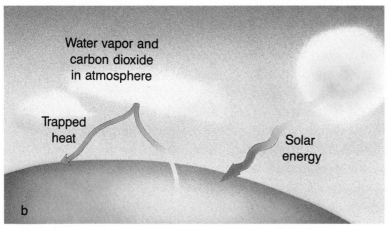

FIGURE 13–6. Both a greenhouse (a) and the atmosphere (b) trap solar energy.

If you've ever been to a greenhouse, you may have noticed that it was very warm inside. The glass or plastic windows and roof allow solar energy to enter the greenhouse. At the same time, however, the glass or plastic prevents thermal energy from escaping from the interior. Like the glass or plastic, water vapor and carbon dioxide in the atmosphere absorb energy from the sun. They also block the direct escape of energy given off by Earth's surface. This process by which heat is trapped by gases in Earth's atmosphere is called the **greenhouse effect.**

F.Y.I. The amount of carbon dioxide in the atmosphere has increased by nearly 15 percent since 1900 due to the burning of fossil fuels. Scientists hypothesize that this may increase the greenhouse effect.

REVIEW

1. Define atmosphere.
2. In which layer of the atmosphere does most weather occur?
3. What percentage of the air you breathe is oxygen?
4. What is atmospheric pressure?
5. What would happen to Earth's polar ice caps if the carbon dioxide in the atmosphere were greatly increased?

How Does Air Move?

GOALS

You will study . . .

1. what wind is and how it is measured.
2. how air circulates over Earth.
3. how wind can be used as an energy resource.

How are winds named?

What does an anemometer measure?

FIGURE 13–7. A wind vane indicates wind direction (a). An anemometer indicates wind speed (b).

13:4 Wind

Have you ever walked to school and felt a big gust of wind? It may have grabbed your homework out of your hand and blown it away. What is wind? **Wind** is the movement of air from one area to another. Wind is caused by differences in air pressure. Wind blows from high pressure areas to low pressure areas.

Perhaps you have driven through the countryside and noticed wind vanes on some of the roofs. A wind vane is an instrument used to measure wind direction. Most wind vanes have an arrow. The tail of the arrow resists the wind more than the pointed end. Thus, the pointed end points in the direction from which the wind is blowing. Winds are named for the direction from which they blow. For example, an east wind blows from the east.

Wind speed is measured with an anemometer. This instrument has three or four cups attached to a rod. When wind hits the concave side of the cups, the instrument rotates. The number of rotations per unit of time is a measure of wind speed.

a

b

13:5 The Coriolis Effect

If Earth did not rotate, heated air at the equator would be forced upward by cooler, denser air. The warm, rising air would spread out and move toward the poles. There the air would cool, become denser, and sink. This cooler air would flow from the high pressure at the poles across Earth's surface directly toward the low pressure areas at the equator. Earth's rotation keeps this direct flow of air from occurring.

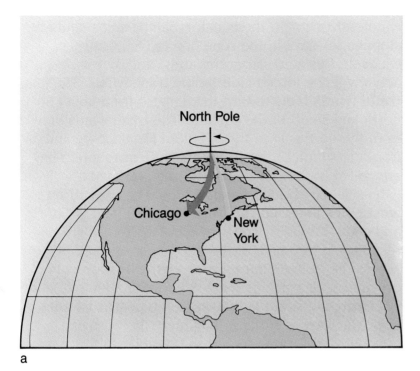

a

b

Earth rotates on its axis once every 24 hours. Earth's rotation can be compared to a spinning turntable on a record player. Place a sheet of paper on the spinning turntable. What would happen if you tried to draw a straight line from the center to the outer edge of the spinning turntable? Would you draw a straight line relative to the surface of the turntable? No, the line would be curved.

Due to Earth's rotation, wind moving from the poles is turned from its original path. In the Northern Hemisphere, winds are turned to the right. In the Southern Hemisphere, they are turned to the left. The **Coriolis** (kor ee OH lus) **effect** is an apparent force caused by Earth's rotation. It causes the deflection or turning of wind. All moving objects near the surface are deflected because Earth is rotating under them.

13:6 Global Wind Systems

The deflection or turning of wind due to Earth's rotation and the unequal heating of Earth's surface create complex global wind systems. Areas near the equator receive more energy that they lose. Polar areas lose more energy than they receive. How are these energy losses and gains balanced?

FIGURE 13–8. The Coriolis effect deflects air moving at Earth's surface (a) in the same way that a line drawn from the center to the edge of a piece of paper on a record player will be curved (b).

Name two causes of Earth's global wind systems.

Look at Figure 13–9. The **doldrums** are a nearly windless zone near the equator. Sailing ships could be stopped for days in the zone due to lack of surface winds. In this zone, air seems to be still, but it is actually being forced aloft by the trade winds. The **trade winds** blow toward the equator from about 30° north and south of the equator. The trade winds blow from the northeast in the Northern Hemisphere and from the southeast in the Southern Hemisphere. They are called trade winds because they were used extensively by trading sailing ships. The **prevailing westerlies** are winds between about 30° and 60° north and south latitudes. The prevailing westerlies are responsible for much of the movement of weather across the United States. **Polar easterlies** are cold, dry, dense air currents located between about 60° and 90° north and south latitudes. As the polar easterlies flow over Earth's surface, they meet the warmer prevailing westerlies. As a result, a polar front forms.

Very fast moving streams of air can develop near the tropopause. These jet streams of air blow from west to east. Two jet streams can occur in each hemisphere. Wind speeds in the jet streams range between 8 and 200 km/h. The latitude and height of the jet streams can change daily and with the seasons.

FIGURE 13–9. Global wind systems are affected by the unequal heating of Earth's surface and the Coriolis effect (a). Jet streams are very fast moving streams of air (b).

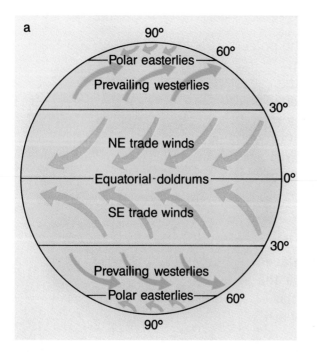

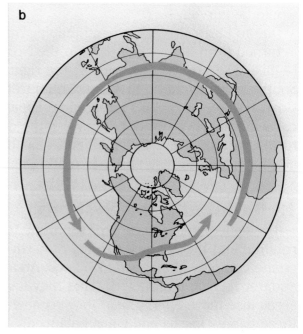

SCIENCE AND SOCIETY

13:7 Wind Power

People have used wind power for centuries to sail ships, pump water, and generate electricity. Due to the rising costs of producing electricity with fossil fuels, research is being done on windmills as an energy alternative.

Modern windmills, called wind turbines, are of two basic designs. The most common design consists of a propeller blade attached to the top of a high tower. Gears connected to a drive shaft use the spinning propeller to produce electrical energy. The propeller must be moved around so that it points into the wind. A second type of wind turbine looks like an eggbeater. Large blades are attached directly to a vertical shaft. The shaft runs a generator and produces electricity. An advantage of the eggbeater design is that it does not have to be pointed into the wind. In both designs, wind speed and the size of the blades determine the amount of energy produced.

Use of wind power can be large or small scale. In certain windy areas, large numbers of turbines are clustered in **wind farms.** These farms can generate large amounts of electricity. The best locations for wind farms are where the wind has a steady, constant speed. In the United States, these locations include the Great Plains and the east and west coasts. Single wind turbines can be installed by individual families as a supplemental energy source.

F.Y.I. In 1934, winds of 372 km/h were recorded at the top of Mount Washington, NH.

What type of usable energy would wind farms generate?

FIGURE 13-10. Wind turbines can be used to produce electricity.

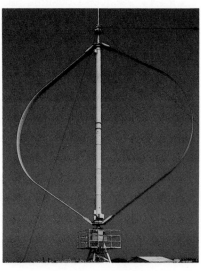

TECHNOLOGY

Kites

Kites have been around for centuries. They may have first been used as early as 206 B.C. by the Chinese. Since then, people have flown kites both for scientific uses and for fun. Ben Franklin used a kite in his electricity experiment. Kites were used for weather forecasting in the 1800s. New kite designs have been devised by people who view kite flying as a year-round sport.

All kites work the same way. A line attached to a kite is used to pull it into the wind. Air moves faster over the back of the kite than the front. This difference in pressure creates lift, which makes the kite rise into the air. Tension from the line attached to it keeps the kite at the right height.

ADVANCE

Kites are now being considered as an energy resource. One design, called a gyromill, combines helicopter-type rotors and a kite. The rotors drive a generator and produce electricity. The gyromill is landed during long periods of calm wind and for repairs.

F.Y.I. Jacques Cousteau has a ship that uses a solid windfoil in place of sails.

Wind is a renewable energy resource. There is very little air or water pollution associated with wind power. Once the wind turbines are installed, operating costs are low. Land surrounding wind turbines is usable for farming or grazing.

On the other hand, wind turbines must be very large to produce enough energy. In order for the turbines to operate properly, winds with fairly constant speeds between 16 and 40 km/h are needed. Also, what happens when there is no wind? Wind turbines tend to be noisy and can disrupt television reception. How might wind farms affect flocks of migrating birds? What are the advantages and disadvantages of using wind as an energy resource?

REVIEW

6. What is wind?
7. What instrument is used to measure wind speed?
8. What are doldrums?
9. Describe polar easterly winds.
10. Explain how a pilot could use the jet streams on a flight from San Francisco, CA to Boston, MA.

CHAPTER 13 REVIEW

SUMMARY

1. The blanket of air surrounding Earth is the atmosphere. Earth's atmosphere is composed of 78 percent nitrogen, 21 percent oxygen, and 1 percent other gases. 13:1
2. Temperature changes with height in the atmosphere. Based on changes in temperature, Earth's atmosphere can be divided into four layers: troposphere, stratosphere, mesosphere, and thermosphere. 13:2
3. Energy is transferred in Earth's atmosphere in three ways: radiation, conduction, and convection. 13:3
4. Wind is movement of air from one area to another. Wind is caused by differences in air pressure. 13:4
5. Due to Earth's rotation, moving objects are turned from their original paths. This turning or deflection is called the Coriolis effect. 13:5
6. The nearly windless zone at the equator is the doldrums. Other global wind systems include the trade winds, the prevailing westerlies, and the polar easterlies. 13:6
7. Wind turbines are modern windmills that can be used to produce electricity. Groups of wind turbines are called wind farms. 13:7

VOCABULARY

a. atmosphere
b. atmospheric pressure
c. conduction
d. convection
e. Coriolis effect
f. doldrums
g. greenhouse effect
h. mesosphere
i. polar easterlies
j. prevailing westerlies
k. radiation
l. stratosphere
m. thermosphere
n. trade winds
o. tropopause
p. troposphere
q. wind
r. wind farms

Match each description with the correct vocabulary word from the list above.

1. movement of air from one area to another
2. blanket of air surrounding Earth
3. nearly windless zone near the equator
4. layer of Earth's atmosphere that contains the ionosphere
5. layer of Earth's atmosphere where most weather forms
6. measure of the weight of air molecules pressing down on a specific point on Earth
7. transfer of energy by waves
8. winds blowing toward the equator that force air in the doldrums aloft
9. transfer of heat caused by differences in density
10. an apparent force caused by Earth's rotation

CHAPTER 13 REVIEW

MAIN IDEAS

A. Reviewing Concepts

Choose the word or phrase that correctly completes each of the following sentences.

1. The _____ marks the top of the weather zone.
   - **a.** stratopause
   - **b.** exosphere
   - **c.** tropopause
   - **d.** ionosphere
2. Which layer of Earth's atmosphere contains 75 percent of all the gases in the atmosphere?
   - **a.** mesosphere
   - **b.** tropopause
   - **c.** stratosphere
   - **d.** troposphere
3. The second most abundant gas in Earth's atmosphere is _____.
   - **a.** nitrogen
   - **b.** oxygen
   - **c.** argon
   - **d.** neon
4. _____ is the transfer of heat through matter by actual contact of molecules.
   - **a.** Radiation
   - **b.** Conduction
   - **c.** Convection
   - **d.** Reflection
5. A(n) _____ measures atmospheric pressure.
   - **a.** barometer
   - **b.** anemometer
   - **c.** wind vane
   - **d.** thermometer
6. Which of the following instruments measures wind direction?
   - **a.** wind vane
   - **b.** barometer
   - **c.** anemometer
   - **d.** thermometer
7. The process by which heat is trapped by the atmosphere is the _____.
   - **a.** Coriolis effect
   - **b.** radiation effect
   - **c.** greenhouse effect
   - **d.** revolution of Earth
8. The _____ are responsible for moving most weather across the U.S.
   - **a.** trade winds
   - **b.** doldrums
   - **c.** prevailing westerlies
   - **d.** polar easterlies
9. The _____ protects Earth from most of the ultraviolet radiation that enters the atmosphere.
   - **a.** ozone layer
   - **b.** mesosphere
   - **c.** stratosphere
   - **d.** tropopause
10. Due to Earth's rotation, winds in the Northern Hemisphere are deflected to the _____.
    - **a.** left
    - **b.** right
    - **c.** north
    - **d.** south
11. The _____ contains the ionosphere and exosphere.
    - **a.** mesosphere
    - **b.** troposphere
    - **c.** stratosphere
    - **d.** thermosphere
12. A polar front forms when the prevailing westerlies meet the _____.
    - **a.** jet streams
    - **b.** polar easterlies
    - **c.** trade winds
    - **d.** doldrums
13. Carbon dioxde and _____ trap heat in the atmosphere.
    - **a.** water vapor
    - **b.** nitrogen
    - **c.** oxygen
    - **d.** argon
14. In which layer of Earth's atmosphere are air temperatures lowest?
    - **a.** stratosphere
    - **b.** troposphere
    - **c.** thermosphere
    - **d.** mesosphere
15. _____ is fixed by bacteria and used by plants as a nutrient.
    - **a.** Water vapor
    - **b.** Methane
    - **c.** Nitrogen
    - **d.** Oxygen

B. Understanding Concepts

Answer the following questions using complete sentences.

16. List the five most common gases in Earth's atmosphere.
17. How is nitrogen used by plants?
18. Describe Earth's troposphere.
19. What is the ionosphere?
20. Explain how atmospheric pressure changes with height.

21. Explain the greenhouse effect.
22. Explain how a convection current forms in Earth's atmosphere.
23. Describe how an anemometer works.
24. From which direction do the trade winds blow in the Northern Hemisphere?
25. How are wind turbines used to generate electricity?

C. Applying Concepts

Answer the following questions using complete sentences.

26. Why are most solar collectors painted black?
27. On a hot summer day, Carla noticed her front bike tire was a little low. Since she was already late, she decided to add air when she got to her sister's house. When Carla arrived, she noticed that the tire was a little firmer than it had been earlier. What happened?
28. Why wouldn't wind farms be a good source of energy for all areas?
29. Why is it better to wear light-colored clothing in the summer?
30. By what process does a space heater heat a room?

SKILL REVIEW

If you need help, refer to the Skill Handbook, pages 526 to 537.

1. Make a pie graph to represent Earth's atmosphere. Label the portion of the graph that represents the troposphere. How should you label the remaining area of the graph?
2. Make a table to record the daily weather for one week. Your table should include the temperature, wind speed, and wind direction.

3. Suppose you decide to compare the temperatures from day to day. List three things you should keep constant when taking your measurements.
4. Complete the table below. Give the appropriate cause or effect.

Cause	Effect
	Coriolis effect
polar easterlies and prevailing westerlies meet	
	wind

5. Suppose you hear on the radio that a west wind is blowing. If you looked at a weather vane, in which direction would the arrow be pointing?

PROJECTS

1. Construct a wind vane and anemometer. Make and record daily observations of the direction and speed of the wind. Report on the winds in your area and on the working of your equipment.
2. Build a working model of a wind turbine. You may wish to try different blade sizes and shapes to see which work better in a steady wind. The wind can be supplied by a fan.

READINGS

1. Brandt, Keith. *Air.* Mahwah, NJ: Troll Assoc., 1985
2. Gay, Kathlyn. *The Greenhouse Effect.* New York, NY: Franklin Watts, 1986
3. Lemonick, Michael D. "Putting on Ancient Airs." *Time.* November 9, 1987, pg. 82.

Weather and Climate

Career: Meteorologist

Mandy's favorite weather person, Jim Brooks, was going to be the speaker at the next assembly. Her family watched his weather forecast each evening at the end of the local news. Mandy liked the maps he used and the way he marked weather systems and explained the weather.

At the assembly, it was obvious that Jim Brooks was popular. He told the students that he was actually a meteorologist with over 20 hours of credit in meteorology and a background in physics and math. He showed students how he plotted weather data such as air pressure and temperature and wind speed and direction on a large station map. He then drew lines called isobars along points of equal air pressure. Using this data, he could prepare a forecast. He said that as new data arrives through the computer from central weather stations, the forecast may change, especially the long-range forecast. Jim explained to the students how local conditions, such as hills, coastlines, and large industrial areas, affect the weather.

Mandy and her friends thought that it was one of the best assemblies of the year. Everyone agreed that one of the first questions most people ask each morning is "What's the weather going to be today?"

In this chapter, you will study weather and how it changes. You will also study how climatic conditions and people affect weather.

F.Y.I. American Meteorological Society, 45 Beacon Street, Boston, MA 02108

GOALS

You will study . . .

1. weather and the factors that control it.
2. cloud types and the kinds of weather associated with them.
3. acid precipitation and its effects on the environment.

14:1 Weather

Have you ever gone to a baseball game only to have it called off because of rain? Has your school ever been closed because of snow or ice storms? Have you ever planted a garden and had no rain for weeks? These events are all the results of changes in weather. **Weather** is the condition of the atmosphere over a short period of time. It results from variations in air pressure, wind, temperature, and moisture. In Chapter 13, you studied a number of factors about the atmosphere. Recall that air pressure is the downward force exerted on a surface by a column of air. Wind is movement of air from one area to another. Temperature in Earth's atmosphere changes with height.

How does moisture interact with these other factors to cause weather? Moisture in the atmosphere is called **humidity. Relative humidity** is the amount of water vapor in a certain volume of air compared with the maximum amount of water vapor this air could hold at a given temperature. It is expressed as a percent. For example, at 20°C, 1 m^3 of air can hold up to 12 g of water vapor. If only 4 g of water vapor are present, the relative humidity is 33 percent. What is the relative humidity of the air if 1 m^3 of air at 20°C holds 6 g of water vapor?

FIGURE 14–1. Thunderstorms (a), snowstorms (b), and droughts (c) result from changes in air pressure, wind temperature, and moisture in the atmosphere.

a

b

c

When air holds all the moisture it can at a given temperature, it is saturated (SACH uh rayt id). When this occurs, the relative humidity is 100 percent. At 100 percent relative humidity, water vapor may condense, or change from a gas to a liquid. The temperature at which condensation occurs is the **dew point.** If the temperature is below freezing, the water vapor changes directly to a solid, forming frost.

FIGURE 14–2. Frost forms when the dew point is below freezing.

14:2 Clouds

Have you ever been outside on a partly cloudy day and looked at the clouds? Some look soft and fluffy. Others look dark and gloomy. Some clouds are big and thick, while others are thin and wispy. What are clouds? How do they form?

Clouds are collections of tiny droplets of water suspended in air. Clouds form when the temperature of air at a certain altitude decreases to a point where it becomes saturated. At this temperature, water condenses around dust and other particles in the air. Tiny water droplets remain suspended in the air as clouds.

What are clouds?

Clouds are grouped into three major types based on form. The three basic forms of clouds are stratus, cumulus, and cirrus. Stratus clouds occur in layers and often cover the entire sky. They are not very thick. A light drizzle may be associated with stratus clouds. When a stratus cloud forms close to Earth's surface, it is called fog.

Cumulus clouds are thick, puffy masses that resemble pieces of popped corn. Cumulus clouds form as rising columns of warm, moist air cool to the dew point. Small cumulus clouds are usually associated with fair weather.

FIGURE 14–3. Stratus clouds occur in layers and often cover the entire sky (a). Cumulus clouds are thick and puffy (b).

a

b

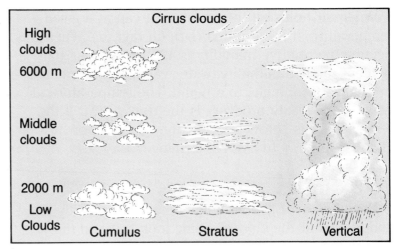

a

b

FIGURE 14–4. Cirrus clouds are thin, white, and feathery (a). Clouds can be grouped by height and form (b).

F.Y.I. A cumulus cloud often lasts only about 15 minutes.

Cirrus clouds are high, white, feathery clouds. They are made of ice crystals or supercooled water. Cirrus clouds are usually associated with fair weather but may also indicate that bad weather is on the way.

Clouds also can be grouped by the height at which they occur. High clouds occur above 6000 m. Middle clouds form between 2000 and 6000 m above Earth's surface. Low clouds are those below 2000 m. Vertical clouds are clouds that have their bottoms below 2000 m but can extend as high as 18 000 m.

Clouds that produce precipitation are nimbus clouds. Nimbus clouds are dark gray and have ragged edges. Rain or snow falls continuously from the bottoms of nimbus clouds. Cloud names are often a combination of these types. Cumulus clouds that develop vertically and produce rain are called cumulonimbus.

SKILL BUILDER

Outlining
Outline the information on clouds given in Section 14:2. If you need help, refer to Outlining on page 527.

Questions
1. What is the main idea of the second paragraph in the section?
2. How many headings are in your outline?
3. What are clouds that produce precipitation called?

Problem: What is the effect of temperature on cloud formation?

Materials

large clear plastic bottle with cap
   (2-L soft drink bottle)
graduated cylinder   hot water
cold water   matches

Procedure

1. Copy the data table.
2. Measure and pour 60 mL of cold water into the plastic bottle.
3. Replace the cap. Shake the bottle quickly back and forth for about 10 s. Place the bottle on a flat surface.
4. Remove the cap. Light a match and drop it into the mouth of the bottle. **CAUTION:** *Handle matches carefully. Close the matchbook cover before striking.*
5. Replace the cap. Squeeze the bottle with two hands to increase pressure. Then, release the pressure. Squeeze the bottle again and release.
6. Record your observations.
7. Empty the plastic bottle. Measure and pour 60 mL of hot water into the plastic bottle.
8. Hypothesize how a "cloud" formed by hot water will differ from the "cloud" formed by cold water.
9. Repeat steps 3 through 6.

Questions and Conclusions

1. What did you observe when the plastic bottle was squeezed?
2. What happened when the pressure in the plastic bottle was released?
3. What happened when you squeezed the bottle the second time?
4. What was the purpose of dropping the match into the bottle?
5. Why did releasing the pressure on the bottle cause a "cloud" to form?
6. How did the "clouds" formed by cold water and hot water compare? Explain.
7. How does your hypothesis compare with the results of the activity? Explain your answer.
8. How do clouds form?

Data and Observations

OBSERVATIONS			
Water Temperature	When match dropped in	When pressure increased	When pressure decreased

14:3 Precipitation

Recall from Chapter 12 that precipitation is an important process in the water cycle. **Precipitation** is rain, snow, sleet, or hail that falls from the atmosphere to Earth.

Raindrops are not all the same size. When you look out the window on a rainy day, you probably notice small drops rolling down the window and joining to form larger drops. Rain forms in a cloud in a similar way. Small and large drops of water collide and join to form raindrops large enough to fall to Earth as rain. Raindrops usually form in very thick or vertical clouds.

Did you know that during any season, most rain starts out as snow? This is because at high altitudes, the air temperature is below freezing (0°C), so it is too cold for rain to form. Snow forms when water vapor changes directly to a solid. Snow may fall as single ice crystals or ice crystal combinations called snowflakes.

Sleet forms when raindrops fall through a layer of air that has a temperature below −3°C. As the water droplets fall from the warmer layer through the colder layer, they freeze. They reach Earth's surface as sleet. Sleet is common in the winter.

Hail forms when droplets of water freeze in layers around a small nucleus of ice. Hailstones grow larger as they are tossed up and down by rising and falling air currents. The hailstones eventually escape the air currents and fall to the ground. Large hailstones can cause severe damage to crops, homes, and cars.

Explain why most rain starts as snow.

F.Y.I. When water droplets smaller than 2.0 mm fall, the precipitation is called drizzle.

FIGURE 14–5. Sleet forms when rain falls through a cold layer of air near the surface (a). Hail can damage property and crops (b).

a

b

SCIENCE AND SOCIETY

14:4 Acid Precipitation

The pH of a substance is a measure of how acidic or basic the substance is. The pH scale ranges from 0 to 14. A pH of 7 is neutral. A pH lower than 7 indicates an acid. A pH greater than 7 indicates a base. Acids in the air collect in water droplets of clouds and eventually fall to Earth with rain, snow, sleet, or hail. This kind of precipitation with a pH of about 5 or less is called **acid precipitation.**

What causes acid precipitation? Generally Earth's atmosphere can clean out nitrogen oxides and sulfur oxides produced by nature. Problems occur when large concentrations of these oxides are produced in one area. When fossil fuels are burned, nitrogen oxides and sulfur oxides are released into the air. These compounds react with moisture to form nitric and sulfuric acids. For example, bituminous coal often contains the mineral pyrite, an iron sulfide. As the coal is burned, the sulfur in the pyrite reacts with oxygen in the air to form sulfur dioxide. The sulfur dioxide, in turn, reacts with moisture in the air to form sulfuric acid.

Acid precipitation does not occur just around the industry burning the fossil fuel. The tall smoke stacks at most plants send the nitrogen oxides and sulfur oxides high into the air. Areas hundreds of kilometers downwind can be affected by acid precipitation. Pollutants in the air in one state or country can produce acid precipitation in another.

Define acid precipitation.

F.Y.I. Fossil fuels include oil, natural gas, and coal.

FIGURE 14–7. Acid precipitation has caused the pH of this Adirondack lake to fall from about 6.4 in 1932 to about 4.7 in 1972. As a result, the lake no longer supports fish and other wildlife.

Acid precipitation falls into lakes and streams and causes the pH of the water to fall below 4.5 to 5.0. Most fish die at this pH level. In southern Canada and the Adirondack Mountains of New York, several hundred lakes have become acidic. Almost all life has been destroyed in many of these lakes.

Acid precipitation affects other areas of the environment, too. Soils on which the precipitation falls can become acidic, harming vegetation. Buildings can be damaged by acid precipitation. Buildings made of limestone are easily damaged as the acid dissolves the limestone.

How are buildings damaged by acid precipitation?

What can be done to stop or control acid precipitation? Gases given off by coal-burning power plants would contain less sulfur if scrubbers were used to clean the gases before they were released into the air. Scrubbers are devices that remove impurities from gases before they are released into the atmosphere. Burning coal that has less pyrite in it will also reduce the amount of sulfur released. In addition, reducing the amount of fossil fuels used to generate energy could reduce the amounts of pollutants released.

REVIEW

1. How is temperature related to relative humidity?
2. How do clouds form?
3. What are nimbus clouds?
4. Describe a cirrus cloud.
5. If 1 m^3 of air at 20°C is holding 9 g of water vapor, what is the relative humidity of the air?

14:5 Air Masses and Fronts

Have you ever used vinegar and oil as a salad dressing? You may have noticed that sometimes one bite of salad may have oil on it, and the next bite, only vinegar. Since the two liquids have different properties, they tend not to mix. When you pour vinegar into a glass containing oil, the less dense oil is forced up over the denser vinegar. Large bodies of air behave in much the same way. Denser bodies of air force less dense bodies of air upward. A large body of air in which the temperature and moisture content stay about the same is an **air mass.**

Air masses usually have properties similar to the area over which they formed. Air masses are classified according to their moisture content and temperature. Dry air masses develop over continental regions and are identified by "c" for continental. Moist air masses develop over oceans and are indicated by an "m" for maritime. Cool air masses develop over high latitudes and are labeled "P" for polar. Low latitude air masses are warm and are labeled "T" for tropical. On a weather map, two symbols are used in combination to describe the temperature and moisture content of an air mass. For example, a cold, moist air mass would be designated as "mP." It would have formed over an ocean at high latitudes.

How are air masses classified?

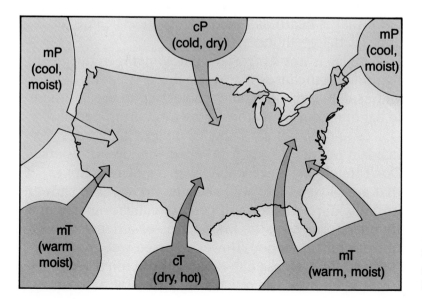

FIGURE 14–8. Two symbols are used to describe the temperature and moisture content of an air mass. What does cP mean?

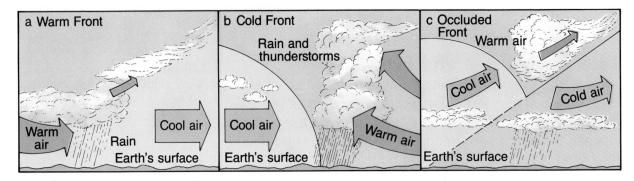

a Warm Front

b Cold Front

Rain and thunderstorms

c Occluded Front

Warm air

Warm air

Rain

Cool air

Earth's surface

Cool air

Warm air

Earth's surface

Cool air

Cold air

Earth's surface

FIGURE 14–9. Fronts form where air masses meet. Shown are a warm front (a), a cold front (b), and an occluded front (c).

A boundary between two air masses is called a front. When a warm air mass moves into the area of a cold air mass, the boundary is called a **warm front.** Because the warm air is less dense, the warm air mass slides up over the cold air mass. A **cold front** forms when a cold air mass invades a warm air mass, forcing the less dense warm air upward over the advancing cold air. If the air masses are not moving, a stationary front develops. An occluded front forms when two cold air masses merge. Less dense warm air between the two fronts is forced aloft.

14:6 Severe Weather

Thunderstorms occur when warm, moist masses of air move rapidly upward into colder, dryer layers of air. During this uplift, electric charges build in the clouds. A flow of electrons develops. The flow is seen as a lightning bolt. The extreme temperature of a bolt of lightning causes air in the path of the lightning to heat and expand. The expanding air forms a pressure wave that is heard as thunder. A thunderhead often appears before thunderstorms.

Thunder is not dangerous, but sometimes the lightning that causes it reaches the ground. Lightning will usually strike the tallest object in an area. If there is lightning during a storm, stay away from open spaces and do not seek shelter under single trees. Go inside a building, away from open windows or doors. Don't touch any electrical appliances or telephones that are plugged into wall sockets. Do not take showers or baths during a storm. If you are caught outside in a thunderstorm, seek the lowest area or a dense grove of trees for protection. However, avoid wet ground because the wetness can conduct ground currents toward you even when lightning strikes at a distance.

F.Y.I. Temperatures inside a lightning bolt can reach 28 000°C.

What causes thunder?

FIGURE 14–10. Seek shelter away from open spaces and single trees when thunderstorms threaten.

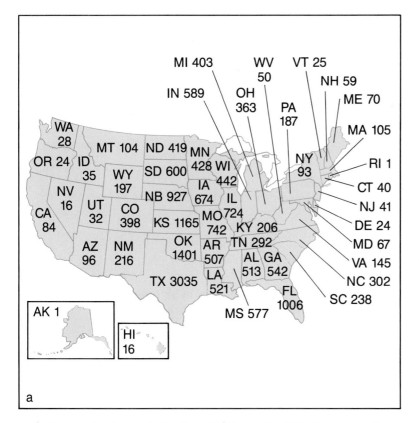

b

FIGURE 14–11. The map shows the number of tornadoes that occurred in each state over a 25-year period (a). Tornadoes form during severe thunderstorms (b).

A **tornado** is a violent, whirling wind that moves in a narrow path over land. Tornadoes form during severe thunderstorms. Tornadoes are funnel-shaped clouds that can cause severe damage when they touch the ground. During a tornado, go to the basement or to some other well-supported area of the building such as the bathroom. Stay away from windows.

Hurricanes are tropical storms that form over oceans. They usually form in latitudes between 5° and 20°. Wind speeds often exceed 120 km/h during a hurricane. Prepare for a hurricane by having plenty of food in the house. Have flashlights, batteries, portable radios, and blankets readily available. Stay on high ground. If you live near a coast, you may need to move inland to higher ground.

FIGURE 14–12. Hurricanes can be spotted and tracked by satellites.

When severe weather could occur, advisories are issued by the National Weather Service and are broadcast on radio and TV. When a **watch** is issued, severe weather conditions are expected to occur soon. During a watch, be prepared for what might happen. A **warning** is issued when severe weather is approaching or has been spotted in an area. During a warning, take immediate shelter.

How Does Weather Change? 287

14:7 Forecasting Weather

You have probably watched a local weather forecast on TV. The forecaster probably mentioned factors such as temperature, air pressure, wind speed and direction, humidity, and so on. How is weather forecast?

FIGURE 14-13. The atmospheric conditions at a reporting station are plotted on a station model.

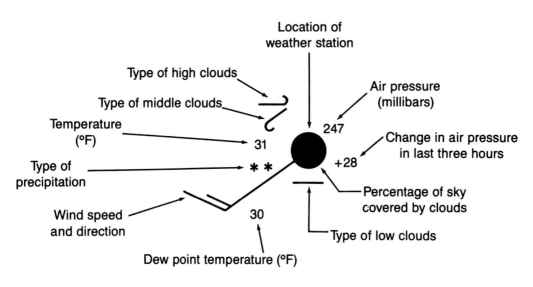

Station Model

Symbols Used in Plotting Station Model				
Precipitation	**Wind speed (knots)**	**Sky coverage**	**Some types of clouds**	**Fronts and pressure systems**
Fog	0	No Cover	Scattered cirrus	(H) or High — Center of pressure system
Snow	1–2	1/10 or less		(L) or Low
Rain	3–7	2/10 to 3/10	Thin stratus layer	Cold front
	8–12	4/10		
Thunder-storm	13–17	1/2		Warm front
	18–22	6/10	Cumulus of fair weather	
Drizzle	23–27	7/10		Occluded front
	48–52	Overcast with openings		
Showers	1 knot = 1.85 km/h	Completely overcast	Stratus of fair weather	Stationary front

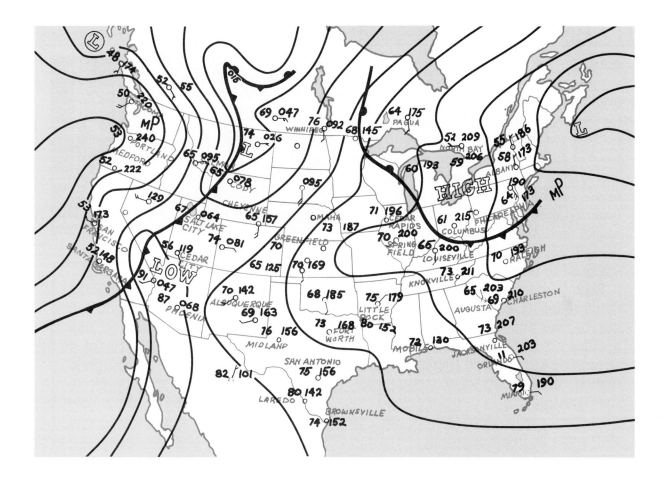

A **meteorologist** is a scientist who studies the weather. In order to forecast the weather, a meteorologist records and compares air temperature, air pressure, wind speed and direction, and humidity at many weather stations. Often, these factors are entered into a computer that draws the weather map. Forecasts for as little as 12 hours ahead require comparisons over an area as large as the United States. Forecasts for a few days require comparisons over an entire hemisphere!

Meteorologists often plot the positions of high and low pressure areas on a weather map. Air spirals outward from a high pressure area. This creates an anticyclone, which sets up fair weather conditions. Air spiraling outward from an anticyclone flows into a cyclone or low pressure area. Cyclones often are areas of stormy weather. The change in barometric readings over a period of time are used to make forecasts. A rising barometer usually indicates fair weather. A falling barometer usually indicates stormy weather.

FIGURE 14–14. Station models are compiled on a weather map. Lines of equal air pressure are drawn, and high and low pressure areas are indicated.

TECHNOLOGY

Radar

There is a speed limit on all U.S. highways. Many speeding drivers are caught by highway patrols using radar. How is radar used to detect speeding cars or trucks? Radar devices emit microwaves. The radar device determines the distance to the object by measuring the time it takes the waves to travel to the object and back. Variations in the reflected waves caused by moving objects are used to determine speed.

Radar can be used in a similar way by meteorologists. Particles of water reflect microwaves and thus become visible on a radar screen. Larger raindrops reflect stronger radar signals. Using this information, the severity of a storm, where the storm center is located, and the movement and development of the storm can be monitored.

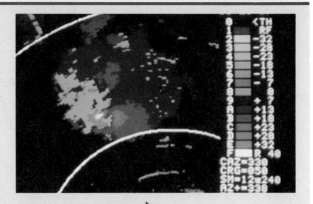

ADVANCE

Doppler radar shows not only the storm's distance and strength, but also determines the relative motions of air in various parts of a storm. Doppler radar holds great promise for spotting tornado circulations in clouds before the funnel touches down.

In the early 1900s, only surface weather conditions were studied. Today, weather balloons and satellites radio various readings back to Earth. Balloons rise as high as 30 km into the stratosphere. Many balloons carry radar reflectors to record certain weather conditions. Satellites are used to study the effect of the jet streams on weather. They also track the paths of severe thunderstorms and hurricanes. Daily, satellites send back data on cloud cover, precipitation, and other weather conditions.

REVIEW

6. How are air masses classified?
7. What is a front?
8. What precautions should you take during a thunderstorm?
9. What is a weather watch?
10. Why should you avoid beach areas during a hurricane warning?

ACTIVITY 14–2   Recording Weather Data

Problem: How can you record and predict the weather?

Materials

thermometer (1)   large rubber balloon
rubber band   drinking straw
masking tape   piece of cardboard
petroleum jelly   small jar
scissors

Procedure

Part A

1. Cut a circle larger than the mouth of the jar from the rubber balloon.
2. Place a thin coating of petroleum jelly on the rim of the jar. Stretch the circle cut from the balloon over the mouth of the jar and secure it with a rubber band.
3. Use the scissors to make a point on one end of the straw. Tape the other end of the straw to the center of the balloon.
4. Place the jar away from sources of heat. Tape the piece of cardboard to the wall behind the pointer. Draw a horizontal line on the cardboard to mark the position of the straw. Above the line write "High." Below the line write "Low." This instrument is a barometer.
5. Record the movements of the straw.

Part B

6. Observe weather conditions over a period of a week. Record the type of clouds, amount of cloud cover, and precipitation under "Weather conditions" in a data table. Record air temperature and pressure.
7. Predict what the weather will be like on the 8th day based on your analysis of the information gathered.

Data and Observations

Date/Time	Weather conditions	Air temperature	Air pressure

Questions and Conclusions

1. What type of weather is usually associated with a rising barometer? With a falling barometer?
2. Explain how your barometer works.
3. How does a weather forecaster use barometric pressure to help make a forecast?
4. How accurate were your weather predictions? Explain why your predictions were accurate or inaccurate.
5. How can you record and predict the weather?

How Does Weather Change?   291

GOALS

You will study . . .
1. Earth's three major climate zones.
2. how cities, mountains, and lakes affect climate.

14:8 Climate

Climate is the average of all weather conditions of an area over a period of about 30 years. Climate can be grouped into three major zones based on the amount of solar energy received. These climate zones are tropical, temperate, and polar. Figure 14-15 shows the climate zones of Earth.

Tropical climates exist in a zone near Earth's equator. The tropics extend from 23.5°N latitude to 23.5°S latitude. The Tropic of Cancer is the northern limit of the tropics. The Tropic of Capricorn is the southern limit of this zone. The sun's rays hit Earth's surface most directly in these latitudes. Thus, in a tropical climate, temperatures are fairly high all year long except at high elevations.

North and south of the tropics are the temperate zones. The temperate zones extend from 23.5° to 66.5° north and south of the equator. The angle at which the sun's rays strike Earth in the temperate zones varies greatly from winter to summer. Less solar energy reaches Earth's surface during the winter in the temperate zones. During the summer, more solar radiation reaches Earth's surface. Thus, changes in weather occur as the seasons change. Winter is colder, summer is hotter, and moderate temperatures occur during spring and fall. Most of North America is located in the temperate zone.

F.Y.I. Changes in global climate may have been responsible for the extinction of the dinosaurs.

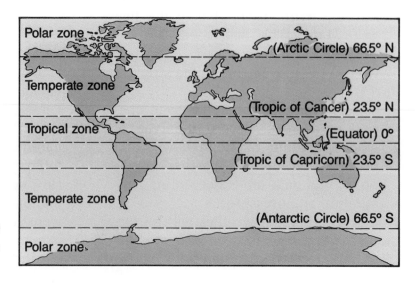

FIGURE 14–15. Earth has three types of climate zones—polar, temperate, and tropical.

The polar zones occur between 66.5° north and south latitudes and Earth's poles. In the polar regions, the sun's rays strike Earth at a very low angle. Thus, the solar energy is spread over a much larger area and doesn't warm the surface as much. During the winter, the polar zones have 24 hours of darkness. The low angle at which the sun's rays strike the polar zones and the reflection of solar energy by ice and snow cause polar zones to be cold at all times.

14:9 Microclimates

Microclimates are climates that involve small areas of Earth's surface. Small-scale changes in the climate of a region are affected by surface features. These features include mountains, valleys, bodies of water, vegetation cover, and the location of cities.

Mountains can block the flow of wind, keeping cold winds from blowing over the land. Mountains also cause wind to lose moisture. As air rises up the side of a mountain, it cools, and thus can't hold as much moisture. Precipitation then falls from clouds and supplies moisture to the vegetation that grows on this side of the mountain. Wind that flows over the mountain and descends on the other side is dry. As the wind descends, it becomes warmer, and the warm, dry air causes a desert climate to form.

BIOGRAPHY

E. Lucy Braun
1889–1971
Dr. Braun studied and taught geology, botany, and plant ecology at the University of Cincinnati. She studied and described climates during and after the ice ages and showed how North American forests changed and evolved in response to these changes.

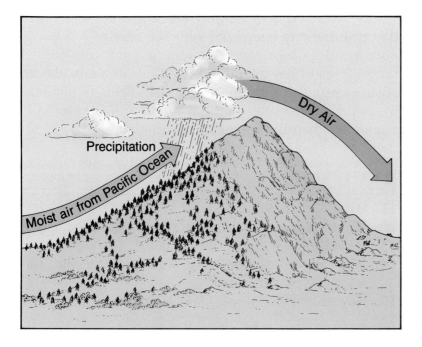

FIGURE 14–16. Along the West Coast, warm moist air moving up the mountains cools and forms rain. Deserts form on the east sides of the mountains as dry air warms and descends to the surface.

What Is Climate? 293

PROBLEM SOLVING

Cooler in the Country?

When Janet's class was studying weather, the teacher had the class record weather data from the newspaper. Janet's teacher had told the class the information came from a weather station located downtown.

Janet lived in a rural area 24 km east of the city. Janet recorded the temperature at her house and compared it with the temperature at the city weather station. The temperature at Janet's home differed from that in the paper. The temperature at her house was usually cooler than that reported in the city. She noticed a greater difference on sunny days than on cloudy days. Explain why the temperature was higher in the city. What can Janet do to determine if the temperature is really higher in the city?

In winter, oceans cause coastal areas to be warmer than areas farther inland. In summer, coastal areas are cooler than inland areas. Lakes can moderate temperatures on a small scale in much the same manner as oceans do along coastal areas. Winds that blow over large lakes, such as Lake Erie, pick up moisture that then falls as precipitation on the lakeshore.

Vegetation helps keep an area cooler in the summer. Trees and other plants absorb solar energy. Water produced during their life processes is released by the plants. Evaporation of this water further cools the area.

Have you ever noticed how much warmer a summer day is in the city compared with the nearby countryside? Cities have an effect on microclimates. Large areas of pavement and buildings in a city absorb solar energy and retain it longer than fields of plants. Thus, cities are hotter in the summer and warmer in the winter than the surrounding countryside.

REVIEW

11. What is climate?
12. What are the three climate zones called?
13. Why are polar zones always cold?
14. Why are cities generally warmer than the surrounding countryside?
15. How might building a dam affect the climate of a small area?

CHAPTER 14 REVIEW

SUMMARY

1. Weather is the condition of the atmosphere in terms of air pressure, wind, temperature, and moisture.   14:1
2. Clouds are groups of tiny water droplets suspended in air. Clouds can be classified by form and the altitude at which they occur.   14:2
3. Precipitation can be in the form of rain, snow, sleet, or hail.   14:3
4. Acid precipitation has a pH of about 5 or less. It can harm bodies of water, vegetation, animal life, and buildings.   14:4
5. An air mass is a body of air in which temperature and moisture content are constant. A boundary between two air masses is a front.   14:5
6. Severe storms include thunderstorms, tornadoes, and hurricanes.   14:6
7. A meteorologist uses data from many surface stations as well as computer data to forecast the weather.   14:7
8. Climates can be grouped into three major zones based on the amount of solar energy received.   14:8
9. Microclimates are caused by mountains and valleys, bodies of water, and the location of cities.   14:9

VOCABULARY

a. acid precipitation
b. air mass
c. climate
d. clouds
e. cold front
f. dew point
g. humidity
h. hurricanes
i. meteorologist
j. microclimates
k. precipitation
l. relative humidity
m. thunderstorms
n. tornado
o. warm front
p. warning
q. watch
r. weather

Match each description with the correct vocabulary word from the list above.
1. storms that occur when warm, moist masses of air are forced rapidly upward into colder air
2. a front that forms when a cold air mass invades a warm air mass
3. condition of the atmosphere over a short period of time
4. the average of all weather conditions of an area over 30 years
5. issued when severe weather is approaching or has been spotted
6. a scientist who studies the weather
7. a violent, whirling wind that moves in a narrow path
8. the amount of moisture contained in a certain volume of air compared with how much water vapor that same volume of air can hold at a given temperature
9. the temperature at which condensation occurs
10. body of air in which the temperature and moisture content are constant

CHAPTER 14 REVIEW

MAIN IDEAS

A. Reviewing Concepts
Choose the word or phrase that correctly completes each of the following sentences.

1. The weather changes between seasons are more obvious in the _____.
   a. polar zones
   b. temperate zones
   c. tropics
   d. all of these

2. Saturated air has a relative humidity of _____ percent.
   a. 0
   b. 25
   c. 50
   d. 100

3. _____ clouds are layered and often cover most of the sky.
   a. Stratus
   b. Cirrus
   c. Nimbus
   d. Cumulus

4. _____ clouds are dark gray, have ragged edges, and produce precipitation.
   a. Stratus
   b. Cirrus
   c. Nimbus
   d. Cumulus

5. _____ forms when water vapor changes directly to a solid.
   a. Frost
   b. Rain
   c. Humidity
   d. Acid precipitation

6. Acid precipitation has a pH of _____.
   a. 5
   b. 7
   c. 10
   d. 14

7. A(n) _____ is a dry, warm air mass.
   a. mT
   b. cT
   c. cP
   d. mP

8. A(n) _____ front forms when air masses meet and do not move.
   a. warm
   b. cold
   c. occluded
   d. stationary

9. If there is lightning during a storm, you should _____.
   a. stay away from single trees
   b. avoid windows
   c. avoid wet ground
   d. follow all of these

10. During a tornado, you should _____.
    a. run outdoors
    b. stay near a window
    c. go to a well-supported area of the building
    d. seek shelter under a single tree

11. Precipitation includes _____.
    a. snow
    b. sleet
    c. rain
    d. all of these

12. A(n) _____ is a high pressure area in which air spirals outward.
    a. thunderstorm
    b. nimbus
    c. cyclone
    d. anticyclone

13. The Tropic of Cancer is the northern limit of the _____ zone.
    a. tropical
    b. temperate
    c. polar
    d. none of these

14. Mountains can affect the climate of an area by _____.
    a. absorbing solar energy
    b. increasing circulation
    c. blocking the flow of wind
    d. increasing temperature

15. Cities affect a climate by _____.
    a. increasing moisture
    b. absorbing more solar energy than vegetated areas
    c. reflecting solar energy
    d. none of these

B. Understanding Concepts
Answer the following questions using complete sentences.

16. Suppose 1 m^3 of air at 20°C can hold 30 g of water. If the air is holding only 15 g, what is the relative humidity?

17. How should you react to a severe weather watch?

18. Describe stratus clouds.

19. Describe cirrus clouds.

20. How do hailstones form?
21. How does acid precipitation affect a lake?
22. How does an occluded front form?
23. How should you prepare for a hurricane?
24. How do meteorologists forecast the weather?
25. Describe a polar climate zone.

C. Applying Concepts

Answer the following questions using complete sentences.

26. How might cutting down trees affect the climate of an area?
27. An air mass is designated by "mT". Where did it originate?
28. Suppose 1m³ of air at 20°C can hold up to 12 g of water vapor. At 15°C it can hold up to 9 g. If the humidity on two days at these temperatures was the same, which had the higher humidity? Explain.
29. How could spreading volcanic dust on the north polar ice cap affect global temperatures?
30. Suppose you look at a weather map of the United States. A cold front and a low pressure area are just west of where you live. What can you forecast about future weather conditions in your area?

SKILL REVIEW

If you need help, refer to the Skill Handbook, pages 526 to 537.

1. Sequence the formation of acid precipitation.
2. Outline the precautions you should take during thunderstorms, tornadoes, and hurricanes.

3. Make a line graph, plotting the air temperatures you observed in Activity 14–2.
4. You observe that the sky is full of cumulonimbus clouds. The barometer is dropping. What can you infer about the weather?
5. What is the cause of the warm summer climate in Earth's temperature zones?

PROJECTS

1. Obtain local weather maps and information from a local TV station or from the newspaper. Study a week's worth of weather maps to see how weather patterns change. After the first week, forecast the weather for the following week. Compare your forecast with what actually happens. Write a report on how accurate your forecast was.
2. Collect samples of rain or snow from various locations in your area over a two week period. Use pH paper and a pH scale to determine how acidic the rain or snow is. Would it be classified as acid precipitation? Hypothesize what causes acid precipitation, if it is in your area.

READINGS

1. Alper, Joseph. "Mostly Sunny and Cooler . . . with a Chance of Flurries." *Science 86,* January/February 1986, pp. 66–73.
2. Bramwell, Martyn. *Weather.* New York: Franklin Watts, 1988.
3. Sabin, Louis. *Weather.* Mahwah, NJ: Troll Associates, 1985.

Water in Oceans

CHAPTER 15

Career: Desalination Technician

Bryan's scout troop had worked many hours in the community to raise money for a trip to Bermuda. When they arrived, they noticed how white all the buildings were. Bryan also noticed that several rooftops were so clean that they seemed to sparkle in the sun.

When they got to the hotel, Bryan asked the manager about the sparkling roofs. The manager of the hotel told them that water was in short supply, so as a result, people kept their rooftops clean so they could catch the rainwater. Bryan wondered whether the hotel swimming pool was rainwater. The manager said that it was filled with filtered salt water from the ocean. He added that the hotel drinking water was ocean water that went through their own desalination plant. Desalination is the removal of salt and other materials from ocean water. The scouts decided to tour the plant.

The desalination technician showed them the huge equipment and described how seawater is heated in a low-pressure chamber where the water boils and turns to steam. The steam is then condensed into fresh water by cool sea water that flows through coils.

In this chapter you will study the composition, temperature, and density of ocean water and how ocean water moves. You will also discuss how some minerals that are extracted from the ocean are used commercially.

F.Y.I. International Desalination Association, P.O. Box 387, Topsfield, MA 01983

GOALS

You will study . . .

1. the composition of ocean water.
2. how temperatures vary in the oceans.

What elements make up pure water?

15:1 Composition

Have you ever gone swimming in the ocean? You may have swallowed some ocean water when the waves crashed over you. Although a swallow or two of ocean water may not hurt you, it can't be used in place of fresh water for drinking. What is in ocean water that gives it an unpleasant taste and makes it undrinkable? You probably know that ocean water contains salt, which gives it a salty taste.

Pure water is a combination of the elements hydrogen and oxygen. These two elements make up about 96.5 percent of ocean water. The remaining portion is made up of dissolved solids. A measure of the dissolved solids in ocean water is the water's **salinity.** Ocean water salinity varies from place to place, but averages about 35 parts of dissolved solids per thousand parts of water. In other words, every 1000 g of ocean water contains 35 g of dissolved solids such as salt.

Sodium chloride, also known as common table salt, formed in the ocean when sodium and chlorine combined. Over time, sodium has been dissolved by water on land and carried to the oceans by rivers. Underwater volcanoes have released chlorine during eruptions. Sodium chloride makes up about 78 percent of the dissolved solids in ocean water. The salt you use on your french fries may have come from the ocean!

FIGURE 15–1. More than 97 percent of all the water on Earth is in the oceans.

FIGURE 15–2. Salt can be harvested from evaporation pools.

F.Y.I. Water expands slightly when it freezes, unlike most other substances. Because of this, ice floats on water and keeps lower layers from freezing. If ice did not expand, a body of water would freeze solid from the bottom up and life could not survive.

Some dissolved solids such as magnesium, bromine, and sodium chloride can be removed from ocean water for industrial or home use. Magnesium is a metal used in making chemicals. Bromine is used in gasoline, and salt is used for many purposes from melting ice to flavoring food. Salt can be removed from ocean water by evaporation. Ocean water is placed in large shallow pools. As the water evaporates, the solids are left behind. The salt can then be collected and processed.

15:2 Temperature

It's true that swimming in the ocean isn't always an enjoyable experience. Besides tasting salty, ocean water can also feel very cold. You may have noticed when swimming that the water is warmer at the surface than it is down by your feet. Why is this so? Water near the surface is warm because it's heated by the sun.

Most water in the oceans is very cold. Below the surface layer, temperatures decrease rapidly. Temperatures for most of the deep ocean are less than 4°C. Temperature ranges for the oceans also vary with latitude. Surface water temperatures near the equator are about 28°C. Near the poles, surface temperatures can drop to −2°C. Because this is below the freezing point of ocean water, huge sheets of ice form at the poles. The ice acts as insulation, keeping the ocean water under it from freezing.

What are the surface water temperatures at the equator and poles?

Based on the temperature changes that occur with water depth, the ocean can be divided into three temperature zones. These zones include a surface layer of relatively warm water, a middle section with a rapid temperature change, and a deep area of very cold water.

Where do most livings things live in the ocean?

The warm, surface layer where wind and waves mix the water is called the **mixed layer.** Most living things grow in the mixed layer because they need the sunlight and warmth found there. The mixed layer can vary between 100 to 300 meters in depth.

The second layer of ocean water is called the **thermocline.** Here, the lack of solar energy results in a rapid drop in temperature. The thermocline extends from the bottom of the mixed layer to a depth of about 1000 meters.

Why is there a rapid drop of temperature in the thermocline?

Below the thermocline, water temperatures are very cold and continue to decrease very slowly to the ocean floor. Temperatures range from about 4°C to less than 1°C in the deepest part of the ocean.

FIGURE 15–4. Most living things live in the mixed layer because of the warmth and light found there.

SCIENCE AND SOCIETY

15:3 Desalination

Fresh water is a very important resource that often gets taken for granted. Many people think there is an unlimited supply of fresh water. As the world's population continues to grow, more and more of our freshwater resources are being used. For centuries, people have been trying to make use of ocean water. Over 97 percent of Earth's surface water is in the oceans, but the salinity level of ocean water is too high for most uses. **Desalination** is the removal of salts and other dissolved solids from ocean water. Desalination is usually done using one of three processes—distillation, filtration, or freezing.

What is desalination?

FIGURE 15–5. Dissolved solids can be removed from ocean water in desalination plants.

Distillation is the oldest and most common method of desalination. In the most basic form of distillation, water is heated until it evaporates, leaving the salts behind. The water vapor is then turned back into a liquid, which is fresh water.

F.Y.I. One cubic kilometer of seawater contains over 36 metric tons (36 000 kg) of dissolved solids.

How is fresh water produced by distillation?

The second type of desalination uses a membrane, which is a thin plastic sheet that acts as a filter. The membrane allows water, but not salt, to pass through it. Wave action can be used to force the salt water into the membrane. Salt is retained on one side of the membrane and fresh water is produced.

The third type of desalination involves freezing. When salt water freezes, only the water itself forms ice crystals. The salt gets trapped between the ice crystals as they form. The ice crystals are then washed to rinse away the salt and melted to form fresh water.

The need for more fresh water is increasing. Desalination could fulfill this ever-increasing need. The benefits of desalination are obvious. Desalination uses an abundant resource, ocean water, and creates a limited resource, fresh water. The salts and other by-products of desalination could be sold to industries for a profit. This money would help lower the high cost of desalination and make it more affordable.

Although desalination of ocean water is an important and useful technology, its use in solving worldwide water shortages is limited. The cost of building desalination plants and the energy required to run them make it a very expensive process. Large amounts of money are needed for research to lower the price of desalination. At the present time, desalinated water costs about twice as much per liter as water obtained from fresh sources. Another drawback is the limited geographic area where it can be used. Most desalination plants are found only near coastlines where salt water is abundant. Transporting salt water to inland plants would be very expensive. Should more money be invested in desalination research? Are there other alternatives that could effectively increase the freshwater supply?

What are the benefits of desalination?

F.Y.I. Even though ocean water contains only 35 parts per 1000 of dissolved solid particles, a layer of salt 60 meters thick would form if all ocean water would evaporate.

REVIEW

1. Where did the salt in ocean water originate?
2. List three dissolved solids found in ocean water that are used in industry.
3. Why is ocean water usually warmer near the surface?
4. How is distillation desalination different from filtration desalination?
5. Why do ocean temperatures vary with latitude?

Is the Ocean in Motion?

15:4 Surface Currents

Have you ever been fishing or canoeing in a stream? You may have noticed that parts of the stream move faster than others. If your canoe is in the current, it will move faster. Currents also exist in the ocean.

Ocean **surface currents** are parts of the upper layer of the ocean that move continuously in a certain direction. Surface currents are like large rivers that flow through the surrounding water. They are caused by winds, thus surface current patterns are similar to wind patterns. In tropical areas, for example, currents are formed by trade winds.

Surface currents are classified by temperature. If a current has a higher temperature than the surrounding water, it is called a warm current. Currents colder than the surrounding water are cold currents. Most warm currents originate near the equator. These warm currents distribute warm water to higher latitudes, where they cool. Likewise, cold currents originate in polar areas and are warmed as they move toward the equator.

GOALS

You will study . . .
1. the difference between surface and density currents.
2. the temperatures and causes of currents.

What causes surface currents?

FIGURE 15-6. Many major surface currents exist on Earth's oceans.

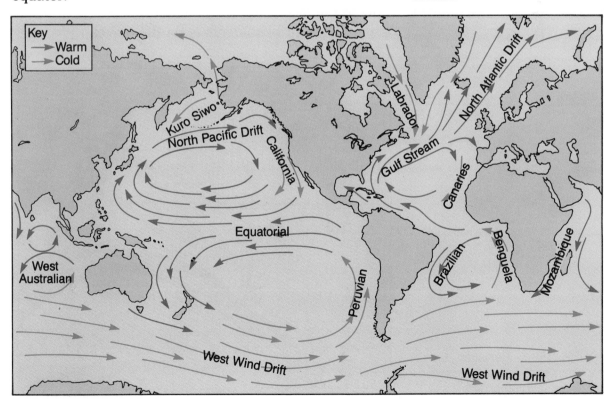

Surface currents are not controlled by wind alone. Landmasses also determine the direction of currents. Many currents flow toward land where they are bent and forced to change direction. The Gulf Stream is a warm current in the Atlantic Ocean whose direction is changed by the East Coast of the United States. It carries warm water from the equator to the northern parts of the Atlantic Ocean. The current crosses the North Atlantic Ocean and is bent south along the coast of Europe and Africa. The current then heads west to complete the cycle. This circulation pattern forms a relatively calm and warm area in the middle of the Atlantic Ocean called the Sargasso Sea.

15:5 Density Currents

  The water found near the bottom of oceans is not only the coldest, it is also usually the most dense. When a density difference exists in the ocean, water tends to flow from the denser area to the less dense area. Currents that flow because of a difference in the density of ocean water are **density currents.** You are probably in a kind of density current every day at school. When the last bell rings, what happens at your school? Students leave the densely packed school and flow to the less dense area outside the school. A density current of students is on the move!

FIGURE 15–7. Benjamin Franklin's chart of the Gulf Stream was completed in 1769 or 1770.

BENJAMIN FRANKLIN'S MAP OF THE GULF STREAM

SKILL BUILDER

Let's take a look at the two main factors that can influence the density of ocean water and cause density currents. One factor is salinity. Water with a higher salinity is more dense than water with a lower salinity. Ocean water that has a salinity different from the surrounding water may form a density current.

FIGURE 15–8. This hallway becomes very dense when students are leaving school at the end of a day.

Several factors can change the salinity of ocean water. Large amounts of rainfall can reduce the salinity of ocean water, making it less dense. Locations where rivers empty into the ocean may also reduce the salinity of ocean water. When water freezes in polar areas, salt is concentrated in a smaller volume of ocean water. The water around the ice will then have higher salinity and greater density. Density currents may result from changes in the salinity of ocean water.

Another factor that affects density is temperature. When water cools, its molecules move closer together, making it more dense. Because cold water is more dense than warm water, a density current forms as cold water sinks to the ocean floor. Since water near the poles is the coldest, it is also the most dense. Dense, cold water deep in the polar oceans flows toward the less dense regions near the equator. These slow moving density currents are responsible for all deep-water circulation.

PROBLEM SOLVING

The Fishing Expedition

Tom enjoyed spending his free time fishing. His father had a small bass boat with a motor that could take them places where shore fishermen could not go. Every Saturday morning they would gather their gear, hitch the boat, and head for the lake.

On Friday evening, Tom's father told him they would be going to the bay to fish on Saturday. Tom was so excited he could hardly go to sleep. The next morning they left earlier than usual for the ocean.

It wasn't long before they found a quiet cove and started fishing. Tom caught the first fish. As he was placing the fish into the net, he noticed that the brown water line on the boat was above the water. He remembered that the line was always in the water at the lake. Tom was confused. They had brought the same gear as they did for lake fishing. He wondered what caused the boat to float higher in the bay than in the lake. What caused the boat to float higher? How would you explain to Tom why a boat floats higher in salt water than in fresh water?

Problem: How do temperature and salinity affect ocean currents?

Materials

small plastic vials (4)
small jars (5)
food coloring
tap water
salt
spoon
ice water

hot tap water
thermal mitt
dropper
paper towels
labels

Procedure

1. Use the table and label the jars A, B, C, D, and E.
2. Fill the vials and Jar A three-quarters full with tap water. Place them on a paper towel.
3. Half fill Jar B with hot water. Add several drops of red food coloring. **CAUTION:** *Jar B may be too hot to touch. Use the thermal mitt to handle the jar.*
4. Half fill Jar C with ice water. Add blue food coloring.
5. Half fill Jars D and E with tap water. Add a spoonful of salt and several drops of green food coloring to Jar D.

Add several drops of yellow food coloring only, to Jar E.

6. Hypothesize what will happen when each of the four colored liquids is added to tap water.
7. Fill the dropper one-quarter full of the red colored water from Jar B. Carefully place the dropper on the inside surface of the fist vial of tap water. Slowly squeeze the dropper and allow the hot, red water to trickle down the inside of the vial.
8. Record observations in the table.
9. Rinse the dropper in Jar A.
10. Repeat steps 7 through 9 using water from Jars C, D, and E. Use a different vial for each liquid.

Questions and Conclusions

1. Which liquid was least dense? Explain.
2. Which liquids were most dense? Explain.
3. Describe what the vial to which hot water was added looked like at the end of the activity.
4. Describe what the vial to which cold water was added looked like at the end of the activity.
5. What was the purpose of adding tap water to tap water in the final step?
6. How do the results of the activity compare with your hypotheses?
7. Why does warm water rise in the ocean?
8. Why does cold water sink in the ocean?
9. How does temperature affect ocean currents?
10. How does salinity affect ocean currents?

Data and Observations

Liquid	Observations
Hot water Jar B	
Ice water Jar C	
Salt water Jar D	
Tap water Jar E	

FIGURE 15-9. Penquins benefit from upwellings because they feed upon living things that feed upon the nutrients in upwellings.

What causes waves to form?

How do seismic sea waves form?

F.Y.I. Seismic sea waves are also known as tsunamis.

At times, this cold, dense water moves upward toward the surface as **upwellings.** They are caused by blowing winds pushing surface water away from an area. When this happens, large amounts of cold, dense water from deep in the ocean rise to the surface. Upwellings carry nutrient-rich water into the mixed layer. Living things are abundant in upwellings because they feed upon these nutrients.

15:6 Waves

If you have ever been on a rubber raft floating in a wave pool, a large lake, or the ocean, you have experienced the movments of waves. Water waves are the alternating rising and falling of water. Most waves are formed by wind. Wind blowing over the surface of the ocean transfers energy to the water and causes waves to form. Waves are also caused by earthquakes on the ocean floor. A wave formed by an earthquake is called a **seismic sea wave.** Seismic sea waves can be very destructive because they can reach heights over 30 m near shore. Columbus's sailing ship, the *Santa Maria*, was about 29 m tall. Imagine being on its deck near shore and seeing a seismic sea wave coming toward you!

FIGURE 15-10. Seismic sea waves can be very destructive.

Waves are described using several important terms. The highest point of a wave is called the **crest.** The lowest point of a wave is called the **trough.** The vertical distance between the crest and the trough is called the **wave height.** The distance between the crests of two successive waves is the **wavelength.** The time between the passing of two successive wave crests is called the **wave period.**

TECHNOLOGY

Studying the Oceans from Space

Early studies of oceans relied mostly on information gathered from ships and from the shore. One problem was that information could be gathered only in one location at a time. It was very time-consuming and expensive for a ship to make many voyages back and forth across the oceans. As a result, each piece of information obtained was not up to date. It was difficult to study current flow and wave conditions because large areas of the ocean could not be studied at one time.

Satellite technology has improved ocean study. Some weather satellites have been used to measure the temperature of water on the ocean's surface. The pattern of ocean currents can be determined from temperature data.

ADVANCE

The success of weather satellites led to the placement of Seasat into orbit. Seasat was the first satellite to be used only for studying the oceans. Radar instruments on Seasat are able to measure ocean surface conditions related to wind such as wave height. One radar study shows that gravitational effects cause sea level to rise over undersea mountains, and fall over deep valleys. Seasat does have some limitations. It can only provide information about the surface of the ocean.

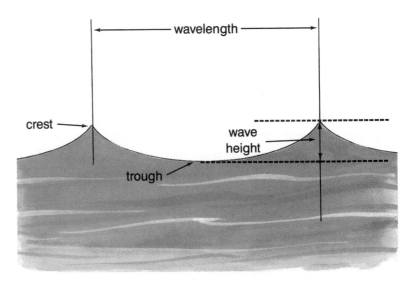

You may have seen the crest or the trough of a wave when you were at the beach. When you see crests and troughs approach the shore, it appears that the water in each wave is actually moving all the way to shore. Waves don't work this way. In deep water, water particles move in circles. The energy in the moving wave is transferred from one circle to the next. Thus, as the wave moves forward, the water stays in relatively the same place. Only the energy of the wave motion is transferred through the water. Water energy is transferred like the falling dominoes in Figure 15–12.

F.Y.I. Seismic sea waves occur when sections of the ocean floor undergo vertical movement during an earthquake. They may reach speeds of 800 km/h. As they approach shore, the water quickly withdraws from the beach. A few minutes later a surge of ocean water up to 30 m high can hit the beach. These waves cause extensive damage hundreds of meters inland. Large ocean vessels can even be picked up and deposited on shore.

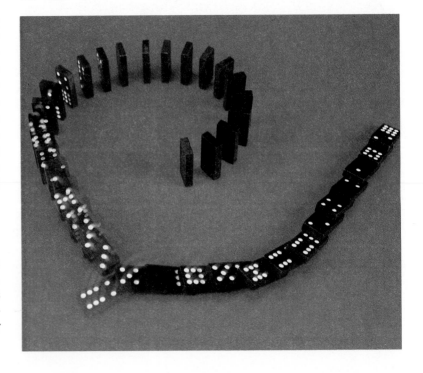

FIGURE 15–12. Wave energy is transferred like falling dominoes. As the dominoes fall, the energy is transferred down the line. Each individual domino remains near where it was standing.

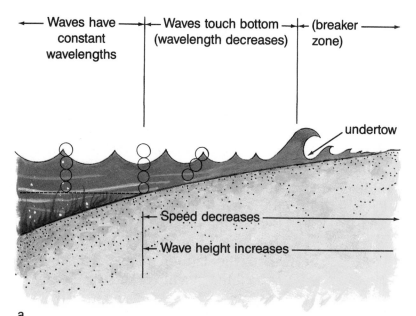

Waves have constant wavelengths — Waves touch bottom (wavelength decreases) — (breaker zone)

undertow

Speed decreases

Wave height increases

a

b

FIGURE 15–13. Wavelength decreases and wave height increases as waves become breakers (a). Surfers make use of breaking waves (b).

The motion and shape of waves change near the shore. As waves approach the shore, the depth of the water decreases. The circles of water particles that come in contact with the ocean bottom are slowed by friction. The slowing of the wave causes the wavelength to decrease and the wave height to increase. As the wave is being slowed even more from contact with the bottom, the crest of the wave keeps moving. Eventually the crest of the wave forms a sharp peak and falls forward, becoming a **breaker.** As a wave breaks, its energy is transferred in the direction it falls.

After a wave breaks in shallow water, the water from the wave runs back into the ocean. **Undertow** is a current formed when the water from breaking waves flows back into the ocean under incoming waves. Undertow also helps to slow the lower parts of incoming waves, helping to form new breakers.

What is undertow?

REVIEW

6. What causes surface currents?
7. How do landmasses affect surface currents?
8. What happens to the density of ocean water where a freshwater river empties into it? Explain.
9. What causes breakers?
10. Why are upwellings economically important?

Is the Ocean in Motion? 313

Problem: What variables affect wave height?

Materials

clear plastic box
water
three-speed electric
   adjustable fan
metric ruler

watch with
   second hand

Procedure

1. Pour water into the clear plastic box until it is about two-thirds full.
2. Place the fan at one end of the plastic box 8 cm from the end of the box. Adjust the fan blades so they are angled toward the water. **CAUTION:** *Do not let any part of the fan come in contact with the water.*
3. You will observe wave heights with the fan on low, medium, and high. Write a hypothesis stating how this wind will affect the height of the waves.
4. You will also observe the wave height at each fan speed after one minute and after three minutes. Write a hypothesis stating how wind duration will affect the height of waves.

5. Turn the fan on low. Hold the metric ruler in the box to measure the height of waves after one minute. Measure the waves again after three minutes. Record the heights.
6. Turn the fan on medium. Repeat step 5.
7. Turn the fan on high. Measure and record the heights of the waves as you did in step 5. Turn off the fan.

Data and Observations

Fan speed	Wave height	
	1 minute	3 minutes
Low		
Medium		
High		

Questions and Conclusions

1. How is wave height affected by the force of the wind? Explain.
2. How does your hypothesis about how wind forces affect the height of waves compare with the activity results?
3. How is wave height affected by the duration of the wind?
4. How does your hypothesis about how the duration of the wind affects the height of waves compare with the results of the activity?
5. What variables affect wave height?

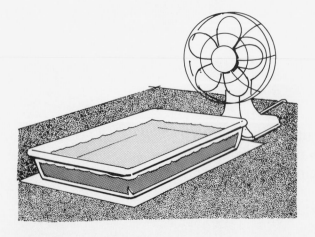

CHAPTER 15 REVIEW

SUMMARY

1. Salinity is a measure of the solids dissolved in ocean water. The most common substance dissolved in ocean water is salt.   15:1
2. Oceans are divided into three main temperature zones: the mixed layer, the thermocline, and the deepest area with very cold water.   15:2
3. Removing salt and other dissolved solids from seawater is called desalination.   15:3
4. Surface currents are like rivers flowing through the oceans. Surface currents are controlled by winds and the locations of continents.   15:4
5. A density current flows from a dense area to a less dense area. An upwelling is cold, dense water that rises to the surface. Salinity and temperature affect density.   15:5
6. The energy of waves is transferred through water by the circular motion of water particles. Crest, trough, wave height, wavelength, and wave period are terms used to describe waves.   15:6

VOCABULARY

a. breaker
b. crest
c. density currents
d. desalination
e. mixed layer
f. salinity
g. seismic sea wave
h. surface currents
i. thermocline
j. trough
k. undertow
l. upwellings
m. wave height
n. wavelength
o. wave period

Match each description with the correct vocabulary word from the list above.
1. parts of the upper layer of ocean that move continuously in one direction
2. vertical distance between the crest and the trough of a wave
3. crest of a wave that falls forward near the shore
4. layer of the ocean where temperatures drop rapidly
5. the measure of the dissolved solids in the ocean
6. the highest part of a wave
7. the removal of salt and other dissolved solids from ocean water
8. currents that flow in the ocean because of differences in density
9. distance from the crest of one wave to the crest of the next wave
10. cold, dense currents that rise toward the surface

CHAPTER 15 REVIEW

MAIN IDEAS

A. Reviewing Concepts

Choose the word or phrase that correctly completes each of the following sentences.

1. _____ is the most common salt in ocean water.
   a. Magnesium sulfate
   b. Sodium chloride
   c. Calcium carbonate
   d. Calcium sulfate

2. The average salinity of ocean water is _____ parts per thousand.
   a. 35   c. 25
   b. 40   d. 95

3. The process of removing salts from ocean water by boiling it is called _____.
   a. distillation   c. membrane
   b. freezing   d. filtration

4. _____ is commonly removed from seawater and used to make chemicals.
   a. Magnesium   c. Silver
   b. Gold   d. Potassium

5. A warm layer of the ocean that receives direct solar energy is the _____.
   a. thermocline   c. mixed layer
   b. deep layer   d. density layer

6. _____ will cause ocean water density to decrease.
   a. Increasing salinity   c. Rainfall
   b. Evaporation   d. Lowering the temperature

7. Temperature ranges for ocean water vary with _____.
   a. wave height   c. longitude
   b. latitude   d. wind

8. Surface currents are caused by _____.
   a. winds   c. density changes
   b. land masses   d. temperature

9. Upwellings are caused by _____.
   a. density differences   c. land masses
   b. wind   d. waves

10. Deep ocean water circulation is caused by _____ currents.
    a. surface   c. equatorial
    b. warm   d. density

11. Waves form _____ when they reach shallow water.
    a. upwellings   c. wavelengths
    b. breakers   d. undertow

12. Waves can be caused by _____.
    a. undertow   c. density differences
    b. earthquakes on the ocean bottom   d. land masses

13. Breakers are caused by _____.
    a. undertow   c. shallow water
    b. a wave forming a sharp peak   d. all of these

14. The time it takes for two waves in a row to pass by is known as _____.
    a. crest   c. wave height
    b. trough   d. wave period

15. _____ particle movement transmits wave energy through the water.
    a. Up and down   c. Circular
    b. Back and forth d. Side to side

B. Understanding Concepts

Answer the following questions using complete sentences.

16. How did the oceans become salty?
17. What causes water to become more dense?
18. What is the difference between wavelength and wave height?
19. Why do temperatures drop rapidly in the thermocline?
20. Why doesn't desalination solve the world's freshwater shortages?

21. What determines whether a current is a cold current or a warm current?
22. What happens to water in high latitudes?
23. What happens to the Gulf Stream when it reaches the North Atlantic Ocean?
24. What three factors can change the salinity of ocean water?
25. How can a landmass affect a surface current?

C. Applying Concepts

Answer the following questions using complete sentences.

26. Why does the density of ocean water vary?
27. Why do waves break in shallow water?
28. What happens to cold ocean currents when they meet warm ocean currents?
29. How can a current such as the Gulf Stream follow a definite path within another body of water?
30. If icebergs were towed from the North Pole to the equator, what would happen to the water around them?

SKILL REVIEW

If you need help, refer to the Skill Handbook, pages 526 to 537.

1. The thermocline receives little solar energy. What effect does this have on the temperature? Most living things are found in the mixed layer. What is the cause of this?
2. Make a bar graph to compare the surface temperatures of the ocean at the equator and at the poles.

3. You have a beaker of seawater. You decide to measure its salinity. What SI unit will you use to express your answer?
4. Outline Section 15:6 of this chapter.
5. A news report states that an ocean wave 30 m high was sighted. The news report also said that the wave was not caused by a storm. Make an inference to explain the wave. What other observations might be made to support your ideas?

PROJECTS

1. Use filters to desalinate salt water. Use four or five different types of filters such as coffee filters, pieces of cloth, balls of cotton, or paper. Mix up about 2 liters of salt water. Perform the filtration and determine by tasting which filter worked the best. Use tables or graphs to report your results. Follow the scientific method described in Chapter 1.
2. Design an experiment to show how varying amounts of salinity will affect the density of water. Test your solutions at different temperatures to see if temperature affects density.

READINGS

1. Bramwell, Martin. *The Oceans.* Danbury, CT: Watts, 1987.
2. Sandek, Cass R. *The World's Oceans.* Danbury, CT: Watts, 1987.
3. Wolkomeir, R. "The Mechanics of Waves and the Art of Surfing." *Oceans.* May-June, 1988, pp. 36–41.

Oceanography

CHAPTER 16

Career: Oceanographer

Alex and his family vacationed in Massachusetts at the ocean last summer. On the day they arrived, they learned that there had been an oil spill at sea. Using his binoculars, Alex could see the oil tanker. A team of oceanographers had arrived to study the problem. An oceanographer is a scientist who studies the ocean. The first thing the oceanographers did was to take aerial photographs of the spill. Then they studied water and sediment samples in areas where they predicted that the current would take the oil. They collected all the information they could about the movement of the oil. If the oil headed for the beach, steps would be taken to warn people and to protect organisms that live on the beach.

The lifeguard told everyone on the beach that they could help the oceanographers. They could watch for oil appearing on the beach and notify the oceanographers if any was found. People could also clean oil from the feathers of any birds that may have come in contact with the oil.

Ocean pollution is a major problem because it can affect all living things in and around the ocean. An oceanographer's knowledge is needed in cases such as oil spills because they are experts in ocean science. In this chapter, you will study the oceans and some of the things that oceanographers do.

F.Y.I. Office of Oceanography and Marine Assessment, National Ocean Service, NOAA, 6001 Executive Boulevard, Rockville, MD 20852.

How Deep Is the Ocean?

GOALS

You will study . . .

1. how oceanographers study the oceans.
2. features of the ocean floor.
3. different forms of ocean life.

Why must oceanographers know physics?

16:1 Studying the Oceans

Have you ever been boating or sailing? If you have, you probably went out on a lake or a river and returned a few hours later. Think what it would be like to stay at sea for months or years at a time. Oceanographers often spend large amounts of time at sea.

As stated in Chapter 9, oceanography is the study of the oceans. Oceanographers use knowledge from many sciences. The laws of physics are used in the study of waves. A knowledge of chemistry is useful for determining the composition of ocean water. Geology is used in understanding features near the beach and on the ocean floor. Biology is used to study life in the oceans.

As the science of oceanography developed, researchers developed special ships and instruments to help them. *H.M.S. Challenger* was the first ship whose main purpose was studying oceans. In 1872, the *Challenger* expedition began one of the most complete studies of the oceans ever done. The expedition lasted nearly four years. During that time, scientists on the *Challenger* did everything from measure water depth to collect samples of ocean life.

A well-known modern ship used for studying the oceans is the *Glomar Challenger*. This ship could drill into the ocean floor. Samples of rock and sediment were brought to the surface for study. Using these samples, scientists were able to determine the age and composition of the ocean floor where they drilled.

FIGURE 16–1. The methods of studying the oceans have changed since the days of *H.M.S Challenger* (a). The *Glomar Challenger* could drill hundreds of meters into the ocean floor while floating in water thousands of meters deep (b).

a

b

Studying the ocean from the surface has limitations. Scientists cannot observe actual features of the ocean from the surface. Submersibles allow scientists to travel beneath its surface of oceans. A **submersible** is a small, deep-diving submarine. Some submersibles can dive to a depth of 4000 m. They usually carry one to three scientists. Submersibles allow scientists to take pictures, collect samples, and record temperatures in oceans.

How are submersibles used by scientists?

TECHNOLOGY

Submersibles

Submersibles enable oceanographers to observe the sea floor. These small submarines are usually carried to a diving site by a larger ship called the mother ship. Once the submersible is lowered into the water, it can explore the depths on its own. The submersible *Alvin* is probably the most famous submersible, having completed more than 1700 dives. In 1985, *Alvin* was used to observe the wreck of the *Titanic,* a huge cruise ship that sank in 1912. *Alvin* carried three scientists to a depth of nearly 4000 m to photograph and explore the wreck.

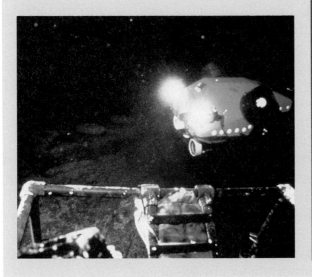

Even though *Alvin* was very useful in the dive, it still had some disadvantages. Whenever people dive to great depths in the ocean, some danger is involved. Exploring ship wrecks can be especially dangerous because the wreck may be unstable, endangering the crew. The relatively large size of *Alvin* prevented the exploration of small areas.

ADVANCE

Scientists exploring the *Titanic* developed a small robot submersible to explore the wreck in places that *Alvin* could not reach. The robot, called *Jason Jr.,* was attached to *Alvin* with a long cable. *Jason Jr.* has three small propellers, a video camera, and a still camera. Once *Alvin* arrived at the *Titanic, Jason Jr.* was launched by scientists in *Alvin* who guided the robot with a remote control. *Jason Jr.* was guided down a stairwell in the *Titanic* to get pictures of the interior of the ship where *Alvin* could not go. Robot submersibles may replace crewed submersibles for some dives in the future.

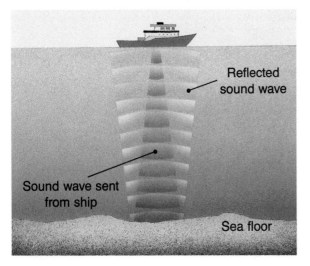
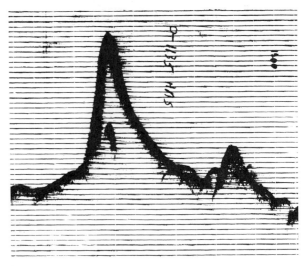

a

b

FIGURE 16-2. Echo sounding is used to determine ocean depth (a). Reflected sound waves received at the ship create a profile of the ocean floor (b).

How did early oceanographers measure ocean depths?

Scientists make maps of the ocean floor in order to organize and record information about the oceans. A profile map is a map that shows a side view or a cross section of something. A profile map of the ocean floor is made using measurements of ocean depth. Repeated ocean depth measurements are taken from a ship as it travels in a straight line. The changes in depth are then plotted on a graph where they create a profile of the ocean floor.

Early oceanographers used a weighted rope to measure ocean depth. They would drop the weight overboard and measure the depth of the water on the rope when the weight stopped sinking. This process was slow. Can you imagine pulling hundreds of meters of rope up from the ocean bottom by hand?

Scientists have developed a faster way to measure ocean depth. **Echo sounding** is a method of measuring ocean depth using reflected sound waves. The echo sounding device sends sound waves to the ocean floor. The waves bounce off the ocean floor and are received by the echo sounder. The echo sounder measures the amount of time that a wave takes to travel to the bottom and back to the ship. Scientists know that the speed of sound in water is 1454 m/s. If a sound wave takes two seconds to travel to the bottom and back, it takes only one second to reach the bottom. Therefore the depth of the ocean at that spot is 1454 m. Echo sounding has been used to create detailed maps of the ocean floor and can also be used to detect other objects in the ocean.

16:2 Ocean Basins

What does the ocean floor look like? Submersibles and echo sounding have helped oceanographers learn a great deal about the ocean floor. The ocean floor has many of the same features found on land. The ocean floor has mountains, plains, and canyons. Oceanographers have named different parts of the ocean floor according to their structure. The three main parts of the ocean floor are the continental shelf, the continental slope, and the abyssal plain.

What are some of the features found on the ocean floor?

FIGURE 16–3. The ocean basin has mountains, valleys, and plains.

The **continental shelf** is the gently sloping part of the continent that is covered with water. The **continental slope** is the steeply sloping area that connects the continental shelf and the ocean floor. The boundary between the continental slope and the ocean basin floor is the edge of a continent. The **abyssal** (uh BIHS ul) **plains** are the flat, level parts of the ocean floor. Currents carrying mud and sand down the continental slope deposit this material on the abyssal plains.

Forces within Earth are responsible for some features on the ocean floor. A seamount is an undersea volcano. Some seamounts grow tall enough to reach the surface and become islands. The Hawaiian Islands are a row of huge volcanoes. The forces that cause volcanoes also make other features on the ocean floor.

Mid-ocean ridges are undersea mountain chains that are found near the middle of some oceans. These ridges form where forces within Earth cause the sea-floor to spread apart. The mid-ocean ridge that runs down the center of the Atlantic Ocean is called the Mid-Atlantic ridge. It is larger than any mountain range on land.

If the ocean floor spreads apart in one place, it collides with ocean floor or a continent someplace else. An ocean trench is a long, narrow trough formed where a section of ocean floor collides with another section of ocean floor or a continent. The deepest trench is the Marianas Trench in the Pacific Ocean. It is about 11 km deep. If you could take the elevator in the Empire State Building to the bottom of the Marianas Trench, it would take more than 30 minutes to reach the bottom!

How do seamounts form islands?

Where do mid-ocean ridges form?

F.Y.I. Ooze is a common deposit on the abyssal plains. It is composed of at least 30% organic material and covers about 40% of the ocean floor.

FIGURE 16–4. This illustration shows some of the major features found on the ocean floor.

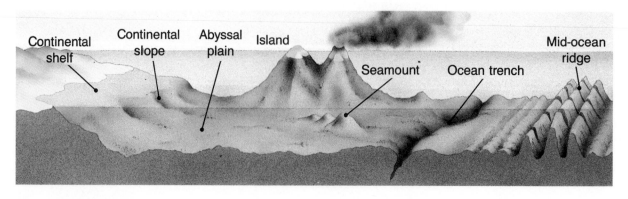

Continental shelf · Continental slope · Abyssal plain · Island · Seamount · Ocean trench · Mid-ocean ridge

Problem: How can you make a profile map of a surface that you can't directly observe?

Materials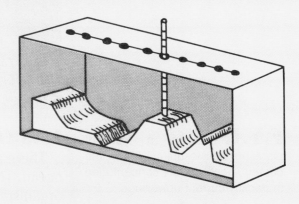

small shoe box with lid
modeling clay
rubber bands (2)
soda straw
metric ruler
scissors

Procedure

1. Copy the graph and measure the width of the box. (Note: Your graph should extend to this measurement.)
2. Place the shoe box on its side. Starting at the left, use scissors to punch ten holes 3 cm apart along a line down the middle of the box. **CAUTION:** *Be careful with the scissors.* Number the holes 1 to 10 starting at the left.
3. Use the clay to build a model of the ocean floor. Include a continental shelf and slope, a trench, an abyssal plain, a seamount, and a mid-ocean ridge.
4. When the model is complete, fasten the lid to the box with the rubber bands.
5. Place the straw next to the ruler and let one end of the straw be zero. Use a pen to mark the straw at 0.5-cm intervals. Label each centimeter mark.
6. Insert the zero marked end of the straw into hole 1 until it touches the model ocean floor. Record this measurement on your graph by placing a dot on the first vertical line at the centimeter depth you measured. Repeat this for the remaining nine holes.
7. Connect the points with a line to make a profile of your model ocean floor.

Data and Observations

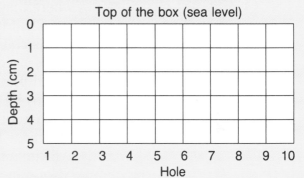

Questions and Conclusions

1. In the activity, the length of the straw beneath the lid of the box was used to represent the depth of the water. How does a ship use echo sounding to measure the depth of water?
2. Why doesn't the vertical axis of the graph have zero at the bottom like other graphs you have made?
3. How did the profile map you made compare with your clay model?
4. What feature of your model was at the greatest depth? The highest elevation?
5. How can you make a profile of a surface you can't directly observe?

FIGURE 16–5. Microscopic plankton are a major food source for other life in the ocean.

F.Y.I. Diatoms, a type of plankton vital to animal life in the oceans, become very concentrated in density current upwellings.

Where do most organisms live in the ocean?

16:3 Ocean Life

There are thousands of species of organisms in the ocean. They range from microscopic one-celled organisms to huge blue whales that can reach 24 to 30 m in length. Most organisms live in the mixed layer, where they can receive sunlight. Ocean life can be classified into different categories according to its habits and characteristics.

Microscopic organisms that drift in the oceans are called **plankton.** Plankton are carried through the oceans by currents. These organisms have characteristics of both plants and animals. Plankton is the major food source for all other life in the ocean.

Swimming animals are called **nekton** (NEK tun). Nekton include animals such as fish, dolphins, and whales. Nekton differ from plankton in that they are larger and can move freely through the water.

FIGURE 16–6. Swimming animals in the ocean are called nekton.

Organisms that live on the ocean floor are called **benthos** (BEN thahs). Examples of benthos include shallow water plants, clams, snails, and coral. Benthos often obtain food by filtering it from seawater or by catching nearby animals.

What are some examples of benthos?

Coral is a benthos that lives attached to the floor of the warm oceans found near the equator. This small, tube-like animal uses the mineral calcite it gets from seawater to build a hard outer structure. Corals live in groups and attach their outer structures together forming coral reefs.

FIGURE 16–7. Benthos live on the ocean floor.

REVIEW

1. What is the unique capability of the *Glomar Challenger?*
2. What is the difference between a continental shelf and a continental slope?
3. What is a seamount called if it breaks through the surface of the ocean?
4. What happens to the seafloor at the mid-ocean ridges?
5. How could an echo-sounding device be used in the fishing industry?

GOALS

You will study . . .
1. how beaches form.
2. how shoreline features are shaped by water.
3. how pollution affects shores.

16:4 Visiting the Beach

Have you ever been to a sandy beach? What exactly is sand? You studied the composition of sand in Chapter 10. Most sand is made of the mineral quartz. Some beaches are made of tiny pieces of coral. Some beaches in Hawaii are made of the volcanic rock basalt.

How do beaches form? Small pieces of rock that are eroded on land are carried to the oceans by rivers where they are deposited. Wave action at the shore also breaks rocks and coral into small fragments. When these fragments are deposited near the shore, a beach forms.

One of the most common features found at a beach is a sand bar. A sand bar is a ridge of sand below the surface of the water. Sand bars are formed when a current carrying sand slows down. This loss of energy causes the sand to drop out of the current and pile up. At places where breaks occur in the sand bars, water can flow outward from the beach forming rip currents. Rip currents can be very dangerous to swimmers and should always be avoided.

How do rip currents form?

PROBLEM SOLVING

The Practical Joker

Heidi was waiting at the airport for her friend Wendy to arrive from Hawaii. It seemed like forever, but Wendy's plane finally arrived.

The next day Heidi took Wendy to the seashore. Both girls enjoyed walking along the beach looking for shells and ocean debris in the white sand. At the beach Wendy told Heidi that Hawaii had beautiful white beaches and even some black sand beaches. Since Wendy was known for her practical jokes, Heidi thought she was joking about the black sand beaches. Heidi thought that all beaches had white sand. Wendy insisted that Hawaii really had black sand

beaches. How can Wendy convince her friend that she is not joking? How can Wendy explain the black sand making up the Hawaiian beach?

F.Y.I. The Cape Hatteras lighthouse stood about 457 m back from the beach on a barrier island when it was built in 1870. At present, it is only about 30 m from the beach. Eventually, it will be on an island of its own situated offshore.

A **longshore current** is a current of water flowing parallel to the shore. These currents are formed by waves that hit the shore at an angle. If a longshore current flows past the mouth of an inlet or bay, sand can be deposited in long narrow ridges called **spits.** Spits are connected to the beach at one end and stick out across the mouth of the bay. If the currents curve as they enter the bay, the spit may develop into a feature called a hook. If a spit continues across the mouth of a bay, it closes the bay off from the open ocean and forms a baymouth bar.

A barrier island is a sand bar that forms offshore and parallel to the coast. These islands form a natural barrier between the beach and the open ocean. Figure 16–9 shows the barrier islands that form the Outer Banks of North Carolina. Between the beach and the barrier island is a calm, shallow area called a lagoon. Lagoons provide a quiet water zone that small boats use in coastal areas.

The headlands of a shore are the areas that extend out into the ocean. Because waves hit the headlands first, they are eroded the most. Sometimes as waves crash against headlands, waves erode a notch in the rock. The upper layers of rock will fall as the lower layers are eroded away. This process forms a wall of rock called a sea cliff. When the upper layers of rock do not fall, the notch will enlarge and form a sea cave. If waves continue to erode through the walls of a sea cave, an opening can develop, forming a sea arch. A **stack** is an island of rock that forms if the top of a sea arch falls.

How does a baymouth bar form?

FIGURE 16–9. Ocean waves carve interesting features in shorelines.

Problem: How do currents affect a beach?

Materials

clear plastic box   metric ruler
clock or watch   water
  with second hand   sand

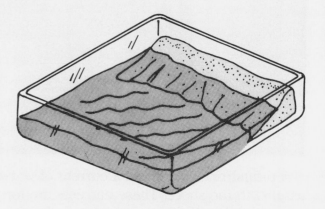

Procedure

1. Copy the table.
2. Make a sloping beach of sand at one end of the plastic box. The edge of the beach should be parallel to the end of the box.
3. Write a hypothesis stating how waves striking a beach affect it.
4. Pour water to a depth of 1 cm into the empty end of the plastic box.
5. Make waves by lifting the end of the box opposite the beach about 3 cm off the table and quickly returning it to its starting position. Repeat this every five seconds for one minute. The waves should be parallel to the beach.
6. Record your observations.
7. Rebuild the sloping beach.
8. Make waves again. This time lift either corner of the box opposite the beach about 3 cm off the table and quickly return it to its starting position. Repeat this every five seconds for one minute. The waves should hit the beach at an angle.
9. Record your observations.
10. Rebuild the beach and include a bay.
11. Write a hypothesis stating how waves striking an irregular beach directly and at an angle affect it.
12. Repeat steps 4, 5, and 6.
13. Rebuild the beach with the bay.
14. Repeat steps 8 and 9.

Data and Observations

Beach	Observations	
	Parallel Waves	Angular Waves
straight		
with bay		

Questions and Conclusions

1. What are the effects of parallel waves on a sandy beach?
2. Where do parallel waves deposit and erode sand on an irregular coast?
3. What are the effects of waves striking a beach at an angle?
4. What shoreline features began to develop when a longshore current moved along an irregular coast?
5. What causes a longshore current?
6. How do your hypotheses compare with the results of the activity?
7. How do currents affect a beach?

FIGURE 16–10. When the land sinks or the water level rises, river valleys are flooded.

16:5 Types of Shorelines

Shorelines are classified three ways according to the way they were formed. The three types of shorelines are submerged, emergent, and neutral.

How are shorelines classified?

A **submerged shoreline** occurs when sea level has risen or the land has sunk. If the submerged area is hilly, river valleys become bays, ridges become headlands, and hills become islands. The northeast coast of the United States is a good example of a submerged shoreline.

An **emergent shoreline** occurs when sea level falls or the land rises. Areas that were once submerged are now exposed. If the overall shore is steep, many sea cliffs, sea caves, and sea arches form. If the gently sloping continental shelf is exposed, long, wide beaches can form. Much of the west coast of the United States is an emergent shoreline.

A neutral shoreline does not show the features of a submerged or an emergent shoreline. This type of shore zone usually has a flat, broad beach.

FIGURE 16–11. When the land rises, or the water level drops, the shoreline emerges.

How Do Shores Change? 331

FIGURE 16–12. Jetties control sand movement on a beach.

FIGURE 16–12. Jetties control sand movement on a beach.

What can be done to alter beach erosion?

16:6 Jetties and Seawalls

In many coastal areas, beach erosion is a growing problem. Houses and other buildings close to beaches are sometimes affected by beach erosion. In an attempt to stop or alter beach erosion, jetties and seawalls are constructed.

Jetties are long structures built near harbors or bays to control the effects of longshore currents. Longshore currents carry sand and deposit it in bays and harbors, preventing the passage of boats and ships. Jetties disrupt the normal flow of longshore currents that carry sand. This disruption in the normal flow of longshore currents causes some beaches near bays or harbors to build up and some to become thinner.

A **seawall** is a barrier, usually made of rock, constructed to protect beaches from wave erosion. Seawalls absorb the force of waves and slow them down, reducing erosion. They are sometimes built on barrier islands to protect buildings located close to the beach.

FIGURE 16–13. Seawalls protect beaches from erosion.

SCIENCE AND SOCIETY

16:7 Ocean Pollution

In Sections 16:4 and 16:5, you studied how shores and beaches are changed by waves and currents. How else are shores changed? Humans have a powerful impact on shores and the water near the shores, especially when coastal populations are growing rapidly. The oceans are often used as garbage dumps. **Ocean pollution** is the introduction into the oceans of substances that produce a harmful change. Both ocean life and humans are affected by ocean pollution.

What kind of pollution is in the oceans? Many major coastal cities dump sewage directly into the ocean. Some sewage is hauled by ships offshore, where it is then unloaded. Many dangerous chemicals are also seeping into the oceans. Rain falling on land washes chemicals into storm drains or rivers and eventually into the ocean. Oil spills have harmed oceans many times in the past and continue to be a threat to ocean life. Trash and garbage are also common in the oceans. Many ships and oil drilling platforms dump their trash overboard. Much of this trash floats and ends up on beaches.

Ocean pollution can cause problems for ocean life. Some pollution causes algae to grow. This algae is called a red or brown tide because of its color. This algae takes oxygen out of the water. It also blocks sunlight. Large numbers of fish have been killed because of a lack of oxygen and sunlight in water where algae has grown. Other fish have died from diseases caused by pollution. Fish have even been found tangled in pieces of plastic and in old fishing nets.

How does a red or brown tide affect water?

FIGURE 16–14. Ocean pollution originates from many sources.

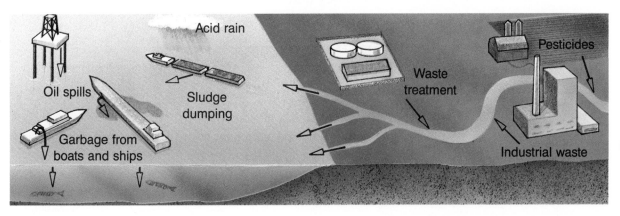

Acid rain

Oil spills

Sludge dumping

Garbage from boats and ships

Waste treatment

Pesticides

Industrial waste

FIGURE 16–15. Some trash dumped into the ocean ends up on beaches.

How can the amount of sewage being pumped into the ocean be reduced?

Humans are also affected by ocean pollution. Jobs in the fishing industry are lost when there are no fish to be caught. This also reduces the amount of fish available to people and causes the price of fish to increase. Each year, millions of people use the beaches and the oceans for recreation. Recently, many vacationers have been turned away because of pollution on the beach and in the water. People who own businesses near these closed beaches also suffer because they lose money that would have been spent by vacationers.

Ocean pollution is a severe problem that must be dealt with. In order to reduce the amount of sewage being pumped into the ocean by coastal cities, billions of dollars would be needed to improve sewage disposal facilities. Who should pay for these improvements? If cities can't dump sewage and trash in the oceans, what can they do with it? Oil spills have had harmful effects on the oceans in the past. Is there a better way to transport oil? What do you think should be done to control ocean pollution near shorelines and beaches?

REVIEW

6. How do beaches form?
7. Describe how sand bars form.
8. How does a sea arch form?
9. What is the difference between a submerged and an emergent shoreline?
10. How could a weed control chemical sprayed on a wheat field in Kansas contribute to ocean pollution?

CHAPTER 16 REVIEW

SUMMARY

1. Scientists use submersibles to study the ocean floor and use echo sounding to make profile maps.   16:1
2. The major topographic features of the ocean floor are continental shelves, continental slopes, abyssal plains, seamounts, mid-ocean ridges, and trenches.   16:2
3. Life in the oceans is classified as plankton, nekton, or benthos.   16:3
4. Currents constantly change beach areas. Waves erode many shoreline features to form sea cliffs, sea caves, sea arches, and stacks.   16:4
5. Shorelines are classified as submerged, emergent, or neutral.   16:5
6. Jetties and seawalls are constructed to control currents and to prevent erosion along coastlines.   16:6
7. Shore and ocean pollution is a serious problem and is caused by many human activities.   16:7

VOCABULARY

a. abyssal plains
b. benthos
c. continental shelf
d. continental slope
e. echo sounding
f. emergent shoreline

g. jetties
h. longshore current
i. mid-ocean ridges
j. nekton
k. ocean pollution
l. plankton

m. seawall
n. spits
o. stack
p. submerged shoreline
q. submersible

Match each description with the correct vocabulary word from the list above.
1. long, narrow ridges of sand with one end connected to the beach
2. life forms living on the ocean floor
3. large, flat areas of the ocean floor
4. small, deep-diving ship
5. shoreline where sea level has risen
6. method of using reflected sound waves to indicate ocean depth
7. an island of rock left when a sea arch falls
8. gently sloping ocean floor extending outward from the beach
9. microscopic organisms that drift in the oceans
10. a current parallel to the beach caused by waves

CHAPTER 16 REVIEW

MAIN IDEAS

A. Reviewing Concepts
Choose the word or phrase that correctly completes each of the following sentences.

1. _____ is used to measure ocean depth using sound waves.
   a. A seamount
   b. A submarine
   c. Echo sounding
   d. An ocean profile
2. A _____ is an undersea volcano.
   a. trench   c. canyon
   b. seamount   d. stack
3. All swimming animals are _____.
   a. nekton   c. fish
   b. plankton   d. benthos
4. _____ are responsible for the erosion and deposition of sand that occur along the coastline.
   a. Spits   c. Mid-ocean ridges
   b. Stacks   d. Longshore currents
5. The most common shoreline depositional feature is a _____.
   a. lagoon   c. barrier island
   b. sandbar   d. baymouth bar
6. Most ocean life is found _____.
   a. on the beach
   b. in the mixed layer
   c. on the ocean bottom
   d. none of these
7. When sea level falls or the land rises, a(n) _____ shoreline is formed.
   a. neutral   c. emergent
   b. submerged   d. none of these
8. _____ are undersea mountain chains where the seafloor is spreading.
   a. Mid-ocean ridges
   b. Ocean trenches
   c. Sea cliffs
   d. Submersibles
9. The mineral that forms the sand of most beaches is _____.
   a. feldspar   c. calcite
   b. magnetite   d. quartz
10. The type of shore zone that usually has a flat, broad beach is a(n) _____.
    a. neutral shoreline
    b. submerged shoreline
    c. emergent shoreline
    d. none of these
11. A calm, shallow area of water between a beach and a barrier island is a(n) _____.
    a. atoll   c. coral reef
    b. stack   d. lagoon
12. Features of the ocean floor include _____.
    a. plains   c. seamounts
    b. trenches   d. all of these
13. In order to study the ocean, an oceanographer must have some understanding of _____.
    a. biology   c. geology
    b. chemistry   d. all of these
14. Areas along the shore that stick out into the ocean and are first struck by the waves are _____.
    a. headlands   c. trenches
    b. seamounts   d. abyssal plains
15. Sand bars that form offshore and parallel to the coastline are _____.
    a. baymouth bars c. barrier islands
    b. spits   d. coral reefs

B. Understanding Concepts
Answer the following questions using complete sentences.

16. How is a coral reef formed?
17. How did scientists gain information about the age and composition of the seafloor?

18. What is an ocean profile and how is it made?
19. How do sandy beaches form?
20. How is a sea cliff formed?
21. What are the three main types of shorelines?
22. What are some examples of ocean pollution?
23. How does ocean pollution affect ocean life?
24. Where are the deepest parts of the ocean?
25. What causes mid-ocean ridges?

C. Applying Concepts

Answer the following questions using complete sentences.

26. In what ways have scientists been limited when studying the oceans, and what progress has been made in overcoming these limits?
27. Compare and contrast ocean trenches and mid-ocean ridges.
28. On what type of shoreline would you find most erosional features?
29. Why is ocean pollution increasing?
30. Why is it so difficult to stop polluting oceans?

SKILL REVIEW

If you need help, refer to the Skill Handbook, pages 526 to 537.

1. Seventy-one percent of Earth's surface is covered by water. Make a pie graph of Earth's surface showing the percent covered by water and the percent covered by land.
2. List the sequence of events that leads to the formation of a baymouth bar. Include the depositional features that form before a baymouth bar develops.

3. You're traveling along a coastal area. You find fossils of ancient clams, snails, and other benthic organisms. These fossils are resting in rocks 40 m above the present shoreline. Do you infer that this is an example of a submerged or emergent coast? Explain.
4. You are given two samples of beach sand. You're told that one sample came from the Hawaiian Islands and the other came from Florida. You decide to classify each sample as Hawaiian sand or as Florida sand. What characteristics of the sands will you use to classify them?
5. You study the history of a coastal region. You find that over thousands of years, the rivers became bays, the hills became islands, and the ridges became headlands. What caused these changes?

PROJECTS

1. Using modeling clay, create a model of the ocean floor between the United States and Europe.
2. Compare methods of controlling oil spills. Try to devise a new method in a bucket or small pool.

READINGS

1. Blair, Carvel. *Exploring the Sea: Oceanography Today.* New York: Random, 1986.
2. Sandok, Cass R. *The World's Oceans.* New York: Franklin Watts, 1986.
3. Yulsman, Tom. "Mapping the Seafloor." *Science Digest,* May, 1985, p. 32.

FUN WITH

500	Leonardo da Vinci invents the parachute.	1596	Ben Franklin shows lightning is electricity.
Chess is invented.	1480	Galileo invents the thermometer.	1752

Coal forms in humid, swampy regions. Coal beds have been found in Antarctica. It has a cold and dry climate. How can you explain the presence of coal there? Millions of years ago, Antarctica was near the equator and had a tropical climate during which the coal beds formed.

QUIZ

An average tuna is about 60 cm in length. A blue whale is about 2500 times larger than a deep-sea angler fish. An angler is about 10 times smaller than a tuna. How long, in meters, is the blue whale?

THE FAR SIDE

"Relax, Worthington. ... As the warm, moist air from the jungle enters the cave, the cool, denser air inside forces it to rise—resulting in turbulence that sounds not unlike heavy breathing."

338

JOKE

Q. What do you eat for lunch at the beach?
A. a *sand*wich

Jeff and his little sister Martha went to the bea[c] along North Carolina fo[r] their vacation. Martha had just graduated from "Tadpole" swimming cla[ss] and was still a beginner. Jeff assured her that sh[e] did not have to worry about swimming in the ocean if she were carefu[l] and stayed close to shor[e]. Why was Jeff so confident of his sister's swimming abilities?

SCIENCE

1783

Cavendish precisely determines the gases that compose air.

First commercial trans-Atlantic, dirigible flight.

1928

1975

The freighter *Edmund Fitzgerald* sinks in Lake Superior.

Severe drought plagues the United States.

1988

Did you know that 1 hectare of trees can remove about 13 metric tons of dust and gases from the air each year?

Riddle

Q. What did the lobster say to the chatty mussel? **A.** Clam up!

TEASER

FUN RECIPE

TUNA SALAD

Flake 1 cup of canned tuna with a fork. Add 1/4 cup of diced celery and some diced onion, if you like onions! Mix in 1/4 cup or less of mayonnaise. Add salt and pepper to taste. For a great tasting salad, add 1 tablespoon of chopped walnuts or raisins or both. Chill for about 1 hour.

QUESTION AND ANSWER

Does lightning strike more than once in the same place? Yes. Tall buildings and towers are repeatedly struck by lightning. Lightning rods are used to protect such structures from severe damage. Lightning rods are made of metals that are good conductors of electricity. The highest point of a lightning rod is kept higher than the structure so that the lightning will be attracted to the rod and not the structure. The rod is connected to the ground so that when lightning strikes, it can be conducted quickly and harmlessly to the ground.

339

UNIT 5

It's Alive!

There are millions of different living things. What is the connection between you and the nautiluses in the photograph? You are both alive. How do you know when something is alive? What do the people in the large photograph and the nautiluses in the small photograph have in common? Why do all living things need food? What else do all living things have in common?

Life and the Cell

CHAPTER 17

Career: Intensive Care Nurse

John enjoyed spending time with his grandfather, and they often went fishing together. When John learned that Grandpa was going into the hospital for heart surgery, John had some feelings of panic. Grandpa told John that heart surgery is not uncommon and that the operation would allow his heart to pump more easily.

John felt better after talking with his grandfather and asked whether he could visit him in the hospital. Grandpa explained that after the surgery, he would remain in intensive care for about five days, and that John would not be able to visit him during that time. He said that an intensive care nurse will be with him all the time. The nurse will give medications, monitor machines, and take care of any problems. The nurse will give him the best personal care so that his recovery is as rapid as possible. Grandpa said that after he leaves intensive care and is in a regular hospital room, John would be able to visit him, and they would make plans for John to help with an exercise program.

In this chapter, you will study the features of life. The intensive care nurse watches over all the life processes of the human body. All organisms have life processes. You will study cells and how they make up tissues and organs, and you will study some of the processes of life. You will find out how a system of classification is used to group organisms.

F.Y.I. American Nurses' Association, Marketing, 2420 Pershing Road, Kansas City, MO 64108

Is It Alive?

GOALS

You will study. . .
1. the features of living things.
2. viruses and how they cause diseases.

F.Y.I. The largest cell is the yolk of an ostrich egg.

Why do all living things need energy?

FIGURE 17−1. All organisms need food for energy (a) and growth (b).

17:1 Features of Life

Imagine walking along the beach of an ocean and finding a purple-colored blob. You might say, "Yuck, is it alive?" How can you find out if it is alive, dead, or just a chunk of nonliving grape jelly?

When you think of living things, you probably think of animals. You might say that something is alive if it moves around, eats, and has young. These are some features of animals. Plants, mushrooms, bacteria, and amoebas are living things, too, although they do not eat, move, or produce young the same way animals do. A definition of life must include the features that are common to all living things. Each living thing is called an **organism** (OR guh nihz um). There are six features of life that are common to all organisms.

Feature 1: *Organisms are made of cells.*

A **cell** is the basic unit of all living things. Some organisms, such as an amoeba, are just one cell. Other organisms, such as your pet dog or cat, are made up of billions of cells.

Feature 2: *Organisms need food for energy.*

All living things need energy for life processes, such as growth, movement, and reproduction. Living things use food as a source of energy.

Features 3: *Organisms grow.*

All living things grow. Growth of an organism results in an increase in size and in mass. For example, trees, people, and mice increase in size as they grow.

a

b

344   Life and the Cell

a

b

Feature 4: *Organisms respond to their environments.*
All living things are affected by changes in their surroundings. A change in the environment that affects an organism is a **stimulus** (STIHM yuh lus). The stimulus, such as a change in light, sound, or odor, may cause a response. A **response** is a change in the behavior of an organism as a result of a stimulus.

Feature 5: *Organisms reproduce.*
All living things reproduce. Reproduction is the process by which organisms produce more organisms of the same kind. Reproduction is needed in order for organisms to keep their kind on Earth.

Feature 6: *Organisms are adapted to the environment.*
When living things are adapted to their environments, they have a good chance of survival. **Adaptation** (ad ap TAY shun) is the way that the features of a living thing allow it to live successfully in its environment. For example, the features of a trout adapt it to fresh water, whereas a shark has features that adapt it to salt water.

Now, let's investigate our purple blob. How can you decide if it is living? Let's consider each feature of life. A piece of the blob can be examined under a microscope to see if it is made of cells. If it is made of cells but does not have any of the other features of life, it may be a dead organism. The blob can be carefully observed to determine if it takes in food, grows, breathes, moves, and reproduces. The blob can also be tested to see if it responds to a stimulus.

FIGURE 17–2. All organisms respond to a stimulus (a) and can adapt to their environments (b).

Why is it important for living things to adapt to their environment?

Problem: How do mealworms respond to different foods?

Materials

1-L glass jar	bran flakes (20 g)
mealworms (40)	apple slice
rubber band	oatmeal (250 g)
cheesecloth	cornflakes (20 g)
plastic box	wheat crackers (20 g)
pan balance	hand lens

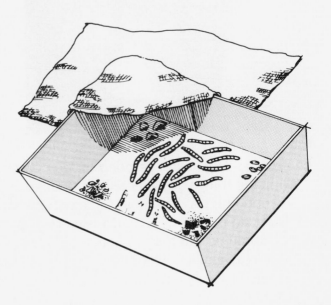

Procedure

1. Establish a mealworm colony. Add 5 cm of oatmeal to the 1-L glass jar. Place the mealworms and a slice of apple on top of the oatmeal. Cover the top of the jar with cheesecloth held in place with a rubber band.
2. Mass 20 g each of bran flakes, oatmeal, cornflakes, and wheat crackers.
3. Add the bran flakes and oatmeal to separate corners of the plastic box. Crush the cornflakes and wheat crackers, and place each in a different corner of the box. Place 20 mealworms from your colony into the center of the box. Cover the box with cheesecloth, and place in a dimly lit, warm location.
4. Make a hypothesis that states which food mealworms prefer.
5. Each day count the numbers of mealworms that have moved to each corner of the box. Record these numbers in a data table like the one shown. Return the mealworms to the center of the box. Repeat this procedure for three more days.
6. Calculate the average number of mealworms in each food substance over the four days.

Data and Observations

Test Food	Number of Mealworms			
	Day 1	Day 2	Day 3	Day 4
Oatmeal				
Cornflakes				
Wheat Crackers				
Bran flakes				

Questions and Conclusions

1. How do mealworms respond to different foods?
2. Do you accept or reject your hypothesis? Explain.
3. How did you test your hypothesis?
4. What were your conclusions?
5. How would you improve the procedure to gain more confidence in your conclusions? Explain.

17:2 Viruses

Deciding if something is living is not always as easy as testing a blob of grape jelly. Imagine a crystal that just sits in a test tube for years. A crystal is nonliving. It does not show any of the processes of life. Imagine that the crystal can be placed inside an organism where it changes its form to that of a particle and begins to reproduce. This cannot happen to a true crystal. However, viruses can form crystals, but can also reproduce. A **virus** is a complex particle that has features of both living and nonliving things. Viruses reproduce, but only inside living cells. Viruses are not made of cells. They are not visible with the unaided eye. Scientists could see viruses only after the electron microscope was invented. Viruses have one of four shapes. Viruses can look like a sphere, a rod, a many-sided sphere, or a many-sided sphere with a tail.

What shapes do viruses have?

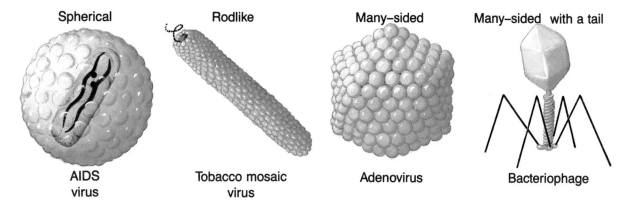

Spherical	Rodlike	Many–sided	Many–sided with a tail
AIDS virus	Tobacco mosaic virus	Adenovirus	Bacteriophage

FIGURE 17–3. There are four basic shapes of viruses.

When a virus becomes active, it changes the life processes of cells in the organism it has entered. This change in an organism often results in a disease. Viruses are known to cause diseases in bacteria, plants, and animals. Once inside a cell, a virus particle forms many new viruses. The life of the cell is destroyed and the cell bursts open. The new viruses are then released and can enter other cells. The infection spreads quickly and the disease may cause death of the organism. Viruses in humans can cause diseases such as colds, polio, measles, chicken pox, mumps, influenza, rabies, and AIDS.

When your body becomes infected with a cold virus, certain cells in the blood trap and destroy the virus particles. You will study more about how your body fights disease in Chapter 23.

F.Y.I. Warts are not caused by touching toads. Viruses cause warts.

Some viruses may be spread through air and water. If you sneeze or cough when you have a cold, thousands of viruses are thrown into the air. Some viruses may also be spread by contact with objects, such as drinking glasses, that have been used by an infected person. Other viruses are spread by the bite of fleas, mosquitoes, and ticks. Viruses that cause diseases such as AIDS, can be spread by sexual contact, by use of a needle that has first been used by someone with the virus, or by receiving a transfusion of infected blood. An infected mother can also pass the virus to her unborn child.

F.Y.I. A microbe is a microscopic organism or virus that sometimes causes disease.

What is a polio vaccine?

SCIENCE AND SOCIETY

17:3 The Helpful Use of Viruses

When you catch a cold, you know you have cold viruses in your body. Viruses can make you feel miserable. They affect many of the normal functions of your body. You may also have read about the dangers of the AIDS virus.

Then how is it possible for a virus to be useful? If you have received shots to protect you against measles or polio, you are being helped by viruses. The shots contained a vaccine. A **vaccine** is a solution of dead or weakened microbes that are injected into the body. A polio vaccine contains dead or weakened polio viruses. When you have had a shot, your body reacts to the virus by producing cells that can destroy

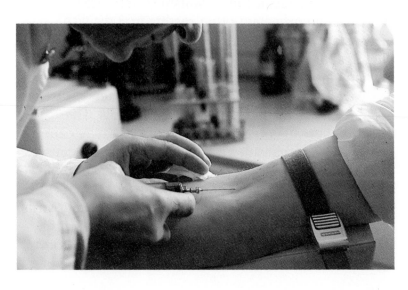

FIGURE 17–4. People can be tested for the presence of the AIDS virus at public testing stations.

the virus and any others like it that may enter the body later.

How was this use of viruses discovered? Edward Jenner was a physician in England when smallpox was a very common disease. Many people died of smallpox, but those people who survived did not get the disease a second time. It was also known that dairymaids, women who milked the cows daily, would often get cowpox, a mild disease similar to smallpox. These women did not get smallpox. In 1796, Jenner took fluid from a cowpox sore on a dairymaid's hand. He then injected this into a young boy who became ill with cowpox. Jenner later injected the smallpox virus into the boy, who did not develop this more serious disease. As a result of Jenner's bold experiment, people no longer get the smallpox disease.

How do we develop new vaccines today? You have learned that viruses can grow and reproduce only when they are inside living cells. Would a physician today carry out Jenner's experiment on a human? Would you expect your physician to ask if he could inject you with a vaccine that had not been tested?

Vaccines against viruses have been made in the laboratory by copying parts of the outer coat of the virus. These vaccines keep a virus from reproducing in the body. The problem with newly developed vaccines, as with any new medicine, is how to test that it is safe to use in humans. New drugs are often tested first on animals such as mice. In some cases, such as with new drugs against the AIDS virus, tests have been carried out on human volunteers. People who have a disease often volunteer in the hope that the new drug will work. The best test, though, is the one carried out by Jenner, to inject a healthy person with the virus to observe if the drug later protects against the disease.

What is the result of Jenner's experiment?

REVIEW

1. What are the six features of life?
2. Which feature of life do viruses lack?
3. What are two ways that viral diseases are spread?
4. Why is Edward Jenner's experiment described as bold?
5. Chemical crystals grow in solutions. Why are they not alive?

What Is a Cell?

GOALS

You will study. . .
1. the structures of cells.
2. about processes within the cell.
3. about tissues, organs, and systems.

F.Y.I. Mitochondria and chloroplasts are thought to have developed originally from bacteria.

Why is chlorophyll important to some organisms?

FIGURE 17–5. A cell of a plant (a) and an animal (b) are packed with structures that are vital to the life of the organism. Different kinds of organisms can be identified from their cell structures.

17:4 Cell Structures

You studied in Section 17:1 that the cell is the basic unit of all living things. Most cells are too small to be seen with the unaided eye. The structure of cells can be observed with a microscope. Each cell has a membrane. A **cell membrane** is a thin layer that surrounds and holds the parts of a cell together. The cell membrane controls the movement of substances into and out of the cell. In plants, the cell membrane is surrounded by a cell wall. The cell wall is a rigid layer that provides support for the plant.

The cell membrane surrounds a material called cytoplasm (SITE uh plaz um). **Cytoplasm** is the jellylike liquid material of the cell. Within the cytoplasm are several small cell parts. The activities of the cell occur mainly in these cell parts. **Mitochondria** (mite uh KAHN dree uh) are rodlike cell parts that release energy for cell processes. Some cells have chloroplasts (KLOR uh plastz). **Chloroplasts** are small, oval-shaped bodies that contain a substance called chlorophyll. Chlorophyll often gives the cell a green color. Green plants and other organisms that have chlorophyll can use the energy of sunlight to make their own food.

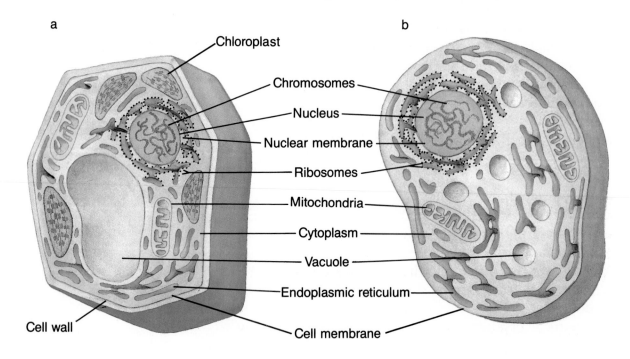

a

b

Chloroplast

Chromosomes

Nucleus

Nuclear membrane

Ribosomes

Mitochondria

Cytoplasm

Vacuole

Endoplasmic reticulum

Cell wall

Cell membrane

In most cells, the cytoplasm contains a nucleus (NEW klee us). The **nucleus** is a dense, rounded structure that controls the activities of the cell. A membrane surrounds the nucleus. The material inside the nucleus is made up of threadlike strands called **chromosomes** (KROH muh sohmz). The chromosomes carry a code that controls the processes of life.

17:5 Cell Processes

Living cells use energy to carry out many complex processes. **Metabolism** (muh TAB uh lihz um) is the sum of chemical reactions in living cells. To carry out metabolism, a cell needs many kinds of substances. Substances outside of the cell can move from one place to another by diffusion (dihf YEW zhun). **Diffusion** is the movement of particles from where they are more concentrated to where they are less concentrated. Suppose you put five drops of red food coloring into one side of a glass of water. What happens to the food coloring? It diffuses throughout the water, and soon the water has a uniform pink color. This indicates that the concentration of the food coloring is now the same throughout the solution.

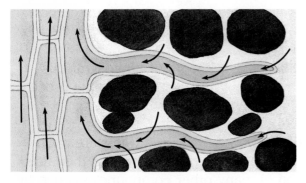

a   Water molecules enter a root

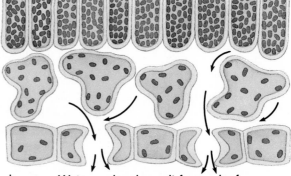

b   Water molecules exit from a leaf

The cell membrane controls the kind and amount of substances that pass into and out of a cell. Sugar, water, and oxygen diffuse through the cell membrane into a cell. Waste materials and carbon dioxide diffuse out of a cell. **Osmosis** (ahs MOH sus) is the process of diffusion of water molecules through a cell membrane. Cells contain a high concentration of substances, such as salts, but a low concentration of water molecules. Thus, water will diffuse into the cell.

FIGURE 17–6. A plant takes up water from the soil by osmosis (a). Water molecules pass through the cell membrane. A plant loses water through openings in the leaves by diffusion (b).

What materials diffuse out of a cell?

What Is a Cell?   351

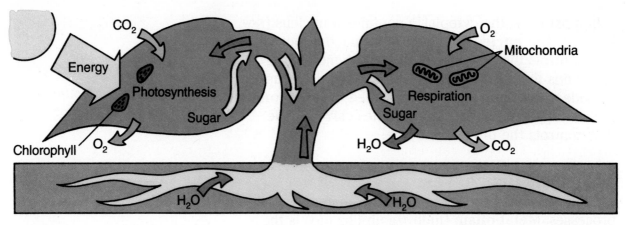

FIGURE 17–7. A plant is an organism that can make food by photosynthesis and use the energy by respiration.

Why must all cells carry on respiration?

Substances may also pass through a cell membrane from areas of low concentration to areas where the concentration is higher. This process is known as active transport. Cells always use energy to carry out active transport. In plants, nutrients (NEW tree unts) needed for growth are taken up by the roots. Many of these nutrients, such as potassium, are absorbed by active transport.

Another cell process is respiration. **Respiration** is the process by which food is broken down and energy is released. All cells carry on respiration in order to have energy for metabolism. Most cells need oxygen to carry out respiration. The oxygen combines with sugar in the cell. Sugar reacts with oxygen to form carbon dioxide and water. This chemical reaction results in a release of energy.

Cells with chloroplasts carry out photosynthesis (foht oh SIHN thuh sus). **Photosynthesis** is the process in which the energy of sunlight is trapped by chlorophyll and used to make food. During photosynthesis, carbon dioxide and water are combined to form sugars. These sugars are then used in the formation of many other compounds needed by the cell.

17:6 The Origin of Life

More than three hundred years ago, people thought that living things came from nonliving things. They said that eels came from mud. Some said that they had seen roundworms come from horsehair that had fallen into freshwater ponds. When people observed maggots crawl out of decayed meat, they thought they had seen life come from dead matter.

PROBLEM SOLVING

The Case of the Shriveling Fingers

Beth and Joan were members of the city swim team. They had decided to spend the morning at the pool practicing the crawl and backstroke. They practiced for an hour and then decided to take a short break. They sat on the edge of the pool dangling their feet in the water. Then, Beth saw that Joan had forgotten to remove her bracelet. She worried that Joan might lose it, so she suggested that Joan take it off. As Joan was removing the bracelet, she noticed that her fingers were shriveled.

"I wonder what caused my fingers to shrivel?" she said to Beth. It was then that Beth noticed her own shriveled fingers. What could the girls do to find the cause of what happened to their fingers? What do you think had happened?

In 1668, an Italian physician named Francesco Redi proved that maggots came from eggs laid by flies on the decaying meat. In 1864, the work of a French scientist, Louis Pasteur, showed that bacteria and other microscopic organisms came from living things. These discoveries caused people to wonder where the first living things came from. Scientific evidence shows that the first living things appeared on Earth about three billion years ago.

Two main hypotheses about the origin of life have been put forward. One hypothesis suggests that the early atmosphere of Earth was very different from the atmosphere today. Instead of mostly nitrogen and oxygen, it is thought that there were large amounts of carbon dioxide, water vapor, ammonia, and methane. Lightning may have caused these substances to combine, resulting in the formation of complex chemical compounds such as proteins. Over thousands of years, these compounds grouped together and formed cells that could carry on the processes of life. A second hypothesis of the origin of life is that life on Earth came from meteorites. A meteorite is a rocklike mass that has fallen to Earth from outer space. Some meteorites have been found to contain chemicals that make up proteins.

When did the first living things appear on Earth?

Problem: How does osmosis take place?

Materials

large eggs (3)
water
salt
500-mL beaker
25-mL graduated
    cylinder

baby food jars (3)
masking tape
permanent marker
table knife
watch

Procedure

1. Use the masking tape and marker to label the three jars and the three eggs A, B, and C.
2. Add 400 mL of water to the beaker. Add salt until no more will dissolve.
3. Fill jars A and C with salt water. Fill jar B with fresh water.
4. Crack the wider end of egg A with the handle of the knife. Peel the shell away from the membrane of the egg until the area is the size of a quarter. Be careful not to break the membrane. Repeat for eggs B and C.

5. Use the knife to make a hole in the narrow end of each egg. Empty each egg from its shell. Then, enlarge the holes to the size of a quarter.
6. Measure and pour 15 mL of water into eggshell A. Rest the egg in jar A so that the membrane is under water. Measure and pour 15 mL of salt water into egg-shells B and C. Place these eggshells into jars B and C.
7. Hypothesize what will happen to the level of water in the eggshells.
8. After 30 minutes, pour the water from eggshell A into the graduated cylinder and record the amount in your table. Repeat the measurement for eggshells B and C.

Data and Observations

Eggshell	Amount of Liquid		
	at start	after 30 min	water level in eggshell
A			
B			
C			

Questions and Conclusions

1. What is osmosis?
2. What evidence do you have that osmosis occurred in the activity?
3. Explain the direction of movement of water in eggshells A and B.
4. What was the purpose of eggshell C?
5. Compare your hypothesis with the results of the activity.

a

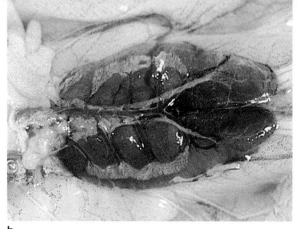

b

17:7 Tissues, Organs, and Systems

In organisms made up of many cells, different groups of cells have different functions. Think about a tree. It has a thick woody trunk, spreading branches, and green leaves. Each of these parts of a tree is made up of cells that work together and form tissues. A **tissue** is a group of cells of a similar type and function. In animals, a group of muscle cells make up muscle tissue.

Groups of tissues form an organ. An **organ** is a structure composed of groups of tissues that work together. The heart is an organ that is composed of muscle, nerve, and connective tissues. The tissues of the heart give this vital organ its strength and ability to pump blood for a lifetime. The leaf is an organ made up of several layers of tissues. The tissues of a leaf work together to make and move food from the leaf to other parts of the plant.

A group of organs that functions together is known as a **system.** The heart and the blood vessels are the organs of the circulatory (SUR kyuh luh tor ee) system. The brain, spinal cord, and sense organs make up the nervous system.

FIGURE 17–8. A leaf (a) is an organ of a plant. Kidneys (b) are organs of an animal.

What types of tissues are found in a heart?

F.Y.I. The skin is the largest organ of the human body.

REVIEW

6. What are two ways that a plant cell differs from an animal cell?
7. Give the function of these cell parts.
   (a) mitochondria (b) membrane (c) chloroplasts
8. What is the function of the cell membrane?
9. What is an organ?
10. How might life on Earth have developed if the atmosphere were carbon dioxide?

TECHNOLOGY

Growth of Blood Cells

Blood is often needed at hospitals. Supplies are kept in blood banks for emergencies. Blood is a tissue made up of red and white cells. Red cells in the blood carry oxygen to all parts of the body. White cells help the body fight infections. They destroy bacteria, viruses, and other infectious microbes. When large amounts of blood are needed after an accident or during an operation, the supply may run out.

Chemicals that cause the production of blood cells inside the body have been discovered. These chemicals are known as colony-stimulating factors (CSFs.) The CSFs can be produced in laboratories. When the chemicals are injected into the body, they cause the production of red and white blood cells. The body can then take in more oxygen and defend itself against infections.

ADVANCE

Scientists found that production of CSFs in the body is controlled by factors in the nuclei of cells. These controlling factors were made in the laboratory and placed in cultured cells. The cells formed CSFs. The CSFs were injected into people in need of new blood cells.

How Are Organisms Classified?

GOALS
You will study. . .
1. characteristics of the five kingdoms of living things.
2. organisms in each kingdom.
3. scientific naming.

17:8 The Five Kingdoms

Over one and a half million species of living things are known. How can you possibly recognize each one? It isn't possible, is it? It is possible, however, to place organisms into groups that you can study more easily. This grouping is called classifying.

Early systems of classification placed all living things into two groups. One group was made up of plants, and the other group contained animals. These two groups were called kingdoms. A **kingdom** is the largest category of organisms. Tools, such as the microscope, gave scientists new data. New organisms were discovered. Some of these did not seem to "fit" into either the plant or animal kingdoms. It was found that all organisms could be better classified into five kingdoms. The kingdoms are monerans (muh NIHR unz), protists, fungi, plants, and animals. This system of classification is the one most commonly used today.

The moneran kingdom is made up of one-celled organisms. A **moneran** is a simple, one-celled organism that has no nucleus. The material in the cell nucleus is not bounded by a nuclear membrane. Often, moneran cells are found in groups or long chains. They have a rigid cell wall. Bacteria (bak TIHR ee uh) and cyanobacteria (si uh noh bak TIHR ee uh) are two main types of monerans. Many bacteria take in food from their surroundings. Cyanobacteria have chlorophyll and can make their own food. They are sometimes known as blue-green algae.

What are two main types of monerans?

The protist kingdom is made up of organisms that are also one-celled. However, a **protist** is a simple, one-celled organism that has a nucleus. The nucleus of a protist is bounded by a membrane. Some protists have a rigid cell wall. Some contain chlorophyll. Diatoms are protists with a thick cell wall. They also contain chlorophyll and so can make their own food. Other protists include protozoans (proht uh ZOH unz). Protists are an important source of food for other organisms.

The fungus kingdom has organisms that are one-celled, or are made up of tissues with threadlike cells. Each cell has a cell wall. Some fungi have more than one nucleus in each cell. All fungi lack chlorophyll. Thus, they cannot make their own food. They must all take in their food from their environment. Mildews, molds, mushrooms, and yeasts are found in this kingdom. You will study monerans, protists, and fungi in Chapter 18.

FIGURE 17–9. An amoeba (a) is a protozoan in the protist kingdom. Bracket fungi (b) are classified in the fungus kingdom.

a
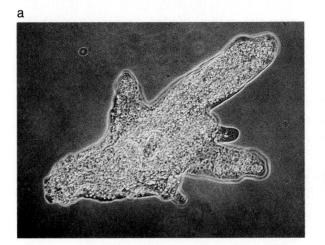

b

FIGURE 17–10. The plant and animal kingdoms contain complex organisms.

Describe the contents of a plant cell.

The green plants we see around us each day are members of the plant kingdom. Seaweeds, mosses, ferns, grasses, trees, and wildflowers are plants. The cells of plants have a nucleus, a cell wall, and usually contain chlorophyll. Green plants make their own food by photosynthesis. You will study more about plants in Chapter 19.

The animal kingdom may be the most familiar kingdom to you. Most of the creeping, crawling, swimming, flying, hopping, and running organisms you know are grouped in this kingdom. Animals have cells with a nucleus but no cell walls. Animals cannot make their own food. Main groups of animals include worms, snails, insects, fish, amphibians, reptiles, birds, and mammals. You will study this interesting group of organisms in Chapter 20.

SKILL BUILDER

Using Tables

Make a table with six horizontal rows and six vertical columns. In the top, left-hand box, write the word *characteristic*. Enter the names of the kingdoms of moneran, protist, fungus, plant, and animal in the boxes over the other five vertical columns. Write the following characteristics in the rows down the first column: nucleus, cell wall, one celled, contains chlorophyll, example. Refer to Sections 17:8 and 17:9 in the text to classify the following organisms: worms, mushroom, diatom, cyanobacteria, moss. In each box, make a + if the organism has the characteristic, or a − if it does not. Then write the name of the organism in the bottom row under the kingdom to which it belongs. Give your table a title. If you need help, refer to Using Tables on page 530.

Questions
1. Which organisms are one celled?
2. Which organism has only one of the characteristics?
3. Which organism contains all four characteristics?
4. What is the purpose of your table?

17:9 Scientific Naming

When living things are classified, they are given names. Names are important in communication. If you were explaining to your friends that a raccoon came into your yard, they would be able to picture the kind of animal you were talking about. People of different countries have their own names for common plants and animals. There may even be more than one name for the same organism in different regions of a country. In different parts of the United States, the mountain lion is known as a puma, cougar, and panther. In some cases, the same name is used to describe different organisms. The name *gopher* is used in the west for a ground squirrel, in the midwest for a pocket gopher, and in the south for a kind of turtle. All these names are called common names.

To avoid confusion with common names, scientists use a standard system for naming organisms. Each kind of living thing belongs to a group called a species (SPEE sheez). A **species** is a group of similar organisms that can mate and produce young like themselves. Species that are closely related are grouped together into a genus (JEE nus). The plural form of genus is genera (JEN uh ruh). Genera with similar characteristics are grouped into a family. Similar families are grouped into an order, and similar orders are grouped into a class. Classes of plants are grouped into a division. Classes of other organisms are grouped into a phylum (FI lum). The plural form of phylum is phyla. Divisions and phyla are grouped under one of the five kingdoms.

F.Y.I. A common weed in North America is the narrow leaf plantain, *Plantago lanceolata.* It is also known as English plantain, snake plantain, buckhorn, rib grass, and ripple grass.

What groups make up a family?

FIGURE 17–11. A deer is a *cerf* (SERF) in French, a *Hirsch* (HEERSH) in German, and a *vanado* (ven AH doh) in Spanish.

Table 17–1

Scientific Naming		
Kingdom	**Plant**	**Animal**
Division/Phylum	Tracheophyta	Chordata
Class	Angiospermae	Mammalia
Order	Polemoniales	Rodentia
Family	Convolvulaceae	Muridae
Genus	*Convolvulus*	*Mus*
Species	*arvensis*	*musculus*
Common Name	Bindweed Morning Glory	House Mouse

To what species do all humans belong?

The scientific name for an organism is made up of two parts: the genus name followed by the species name. The scientific name for bindweed is *Convolvulus arvensis* (kon VOLV yew lus • ar VEHN sus). The name for the house mouse is *Mus musculus* (MUS • MUS kyew lus). These names are used by scientists all over the world.

All members of a species have similar features. However, within a species there are small variations. For example, within a species of butterfly there might be some that are larger or smaller than others. Some butterflies might have a paler color than others. The spots on their wings might be different. All humans are of the species *Homo sapiens* (HOH moh • SAY pee unz). You have noticed that some of your classmates are taller or shorter than you. Some have different colored eyes and hair from yours. These differences are variations in the human species.

REVIEW

11. How are monerans different from protists?
12. List four members of the fungus kingdom.
13. Why are insects classified as animals?
14. Why is a standard system of naming organisms important?
15. What variations can be observed in an oak tree?

CHAPTER 17 REVIEW

SUMMARY

1. There are six features that are common to all living things—cells, need for food, growth, response to stimulus, reproduction, and adaptation. 17:1
2. Viruses are nonliving particles that can reproduce in living cells. Viruses cause diseases in bacteria, plants, and animals. 17:2
3. Viruses in vaccines can be used to help control viral diseases. 17:3
4. The cell is the basic unit of all living things. 17:4
5. Cells carry on life processes including diffusion, osmosis, respiration, and photosynthesis. 17:5
6. Living things appeared on Earth about three billion years ago. 17:6
7. Cells are organized into tissues, tissues make up organs, and organs work together in organ systems. 17:7
8. Living things are classified into one of five kingdoms—monerans, protists, fungi, plants, and animals. 17:8
9. Scientific naming is helpful in communication. 17:9

VOCABULARY

a. adaptation
b. cell
c. cell membrane
d. chloroplasts
e. chromosomes
f. cytoplasm
g. diffusion
h. kingdom
i. metabolism

j. mitochondria
k. moneran
l. nucleus
m. organ
n. organism
o. osmosis
p. photosynthesis
q. protist

r. respiration
s. response
t. species
u. stimulus
v. system
w. tissue
x. vaccine
y. virus

Match each description with the correct vocabulary word from the list above.
1. the basic unit of structure of all living things
2. part of a cell that controls the cell's activities
3. nonliving complex particle that can reproduce in cells
4. the jellylike substance within a cell
5. a feature in an organism that increases its chances of survival
6. group of cells with a similar function
7. the movement of substances from higher to lower areas of concentration
8. a group of similar organisms that can mate
9. a cell process that releases energy
10. a change in the environment that causes a response

MAIN IDEAS

A. Reviewing Concepts

Choose the word or phrase that correctly completes each of the following sentences.

1. One feature of all living things is
   _____.
   a. sunlight   c. oxygen
   b. growth   d. thinking
2. The sum of chemical reactions in living cells is _____.
   a. metabolism   c. photosynthesis
   b. respiration   d. organism
3. The _____ is the unit of structure of living things.
   a. species   c. cell
   b. name   d. chemical
4. Cell structures that release energy are the _____.
   a. membranes   c. chloroplasts
   b. chromosomes   d. mitochondria
5. _____ are cell parts found in the cytoplasm of plant cells.
   a. Bacteria   c. Chloroplasts
   b. Fibers   d. Tissues
6. A _____ is a solution of dead or weakened microbes that are injected into the body.
   a. chloroplast   c. system
   b. vaccine   d. response
7. Respiration is a cell process that releases _____ from food.
   a. cytoplasm   c. viruses
   b. energy   d. chlorophyll
8. _____ are groups of organs that function together.
   a. Systems   c. Tissues
   b. Species   d. Phyla
9. An example of an organism in the moneran kingdom is a _____.
   a. protozoan   c. bacterium
   b. yeast   d. mosquito

10. Mushrooms are classified as _____.
    a. plants   c. fungi
    b. monerans   d. animals
11. A cell can be identified as a plant cell by its _____.
    a. cell wall   c. mitochondria
    b. nucleus   d. membrane
12. Animal cells cannot carry on the process of _____.
    a. diffusion   c. respiration
    b. osmosis   d. photosynthesis
13. Related species are grouped into _____.
    a. classes   c. orders
    b. divisions   d. genera
14. The scientific name of an organism is the _____.
    a. phylum-class   c. genus-species
    b. kingdom-class   d. family-genus
15. One nonliving feature of viruses is they can form _____.
    a. mitochondria   c. cells
    b. crystals   d. chloroplasts

B. Understanding Concepts

Answer the following questions using complete sentences.

16. What are three features of a living thing?
17. Name three processes that use energy.
18. What is an adaptation?
19. How does a virus cause a disease?
20. Why is a scientific naming system necessary?
21. What are two examples of organs?
22. How can viruses help society?
23. Give an example of a stimulus.
24. What is the function of the nucleus of a cell?
25. How do diffusion and osmosis differ?

CHAPTER 17 REVIEW

C. Applying Concepts

Answer the following questions using complete sentences.

26. If the atmosphere of Earth did not contain oxygen when the first cells formed, what kind of organism may have first developed?
27. How are plant cells different from animal cells?
28. Why are mushrooms and plants classified into separate kingdoms?
29. In what way are the cell membrane and nuclear membrane alike?
30. How are cells, tissues, organs, and organ systems related?

SKILL REVIEW

If you need help, refer to the Skill Handbook, pages 526 to 537.

1. How many vertical columns are needed in a table when an animal, a plant, and a moneran are being compared?
2. What type of graph would you choose to compare the average number of mealworms that prefer each of four types of food?
3. Make an outline of Section 17:1.
4. You have three plants of the same species. Each day you give one plant sunlight and 50 mL of water, one plant incandescent light and 50 mL of water, and the third plant 50 mL of water but no light. After two weeks you measure the heights of the three plants. What is your control, your constant, your independent variable, and your dependent variable?

5. If, from the experiment in Question 4, you observe that the plant given sunlight grows the most, what can you infer?

PROJECTS

1. Prepare a display that explains the differences between living and nonliving things. Include labels that describe the features of life. Use a plant in a pot or an insect in a jar as an example of a living thing. Be sure to take proper care of the organism. A rock or piece of iron can serve as the example of the nonliving thing.
2. Find out about "spontaneous generation." Write a report about this belief of people who lived in the 1600s and how it was finally disproved. Use the library to find out about Francesco Redi, an Italian biologist.

READINGS

1. Baggett, J.A. "Winning the Battle Against the Ultimate Parasites: Viruses." *Science World.* February 23, 1987, pp. 18-21.
2. Bodanis, David. *The Secret House: 24 Hours in the Strange and Unexpected World in Which We Spend Our Nights and Days.* New York: Simon and Schuster, 1986.
3. Fichter, George S. *Cells.* Danbury, CT: Watts, 1986.

Simple Organisms

CHAPTER 18

Career: Baker

Christine and her best friend Jared were walking through the shopping mall. Suddenly, their mouths began to water. They walked faster, and the smell of freshly baked bread became stronger. In the bakery window, the baker was kneading bread and turning it every few minutes to work flour into the dough.

As they entered the bakery, they noticed that there were several pans on the counter, some with more dough than others. As Christine bought a cinnamon roll, she asked the baker why some pans had more dough than others.

The baker explained that they were seeing the results of different processes in the life of a fungus called yeast. Before kneading in the flour, he added yeast and an energy source such as sugar. When the kneaded dough was placed in a warm place, the yeast used the sugar to produce energy. During this process, called fermentation, carbon dioxide formed and made the dough swell, or rise. After the bread had risen, the baker placed it in the oven, where the yeast was killed by the heat. When you look at a piece of yeast bread, the "air" holes you see are actually the result of carbon dioxide bubbles produced by the yeast.

This is just one example of how we use simple organisms or the results of their life processes every day. In this chapter you will study other ways in which simple organisms affect your life.

F.Y.I. American Bakers Association, 1111 14th Street NW, Washington, DC 20005

GOALS

You will study . . .

1. characteristics of bacteria and cyanobacteria.
2. some helpful and harmful effects of bacteria.

18:1 Classifying Monerans

In Chapter 17 you learned that five kingdoms of organisms are recognized. Recall that organisms in the moneran kingdom are all one-celled, and in a moneran the nuclear material is not surrounded by a membrane. Monerans often have a jellylike layer around a rigid cell wall. This outer layer causes the cells to stick together. Many monerans live in clusters or chains. A group of moneran cells is known as a colony (KAHL un ee). The two kinds of monerans are bacteria and cyanobacteria (si uh noh bak TIHR ee uh). Most bacteria absorb food from their surroundings. Some bacteria and all cyanobacteria have chlorophyll that traps the sun's energy to make food.

Bacteria are microscopic organisms that are found almost everywhere. They live in the intestines of animals, in hot springs, under Antarctic ice, in deep ocean waters, or in cans of spoiled food. Bacteria have one of three shapes: sphere, rod, or spiral. Some bacteria move by means of flagella (fluh JEL uh). **Flagella** are long, thin, hairlike structures. As the flagella rotate, a bacterium moves forward. Bacteria reproduce by fission. **Fission** is the equal division of an organism into two. Bacteria divide every few minutes. Millions can be produced in a few hours.

Cyanobacteria used to be known as blue-green algae. The name *algae* now refers to organisms in the protist and plant kingdoms. Like plants, cyanobacteria contain chlorophyll. Unlike plants, the chlorophyll is not contained in chloroplasts. Cyanobacteria are found in water or in moist places on soil and tree bark.

FIGURE 18−1. Most monerans form colonies and move by flagella (a). Cyanobacteria are sometimes known as blue-green algae (b).

a

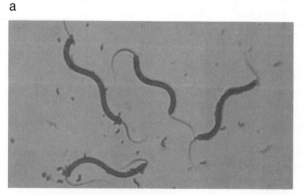

b

18:2 Activities of Monerans

Imagine what Earth would be like if all the plants and animals that die didn't decay! When organisms die, they are broken down by bacteria. Bacteria produce chemicals that cause organisms to decay. Bacteria then absorb this decayed material as food. Some of the decayed matter passes into the soil and is used as nutrients by plants. Nitrogen is a nutrient used by plants to make proteins. Plants such as beans, peas, and clover have small swellings on their roots called nodules. Bacteria that live in these nodules change nitrogen in the soil into a form that the plants can use.

People have found many uses for bacteria. Bacteria can produce flavors in foods, such as yogurt, cheese, and sauerkraut. They are also used to make vinegar, some alcohols, vitamins, and medicines. Bacteria are used in sewage treatment plants to speed up the decay of raw sewage.

Many bacteria cause diseases. Bacterial diseases can destroy crop plants, fruit trees, and decorative plants. Bacterial diseases in humans include strep throat, tetanus, diphtheria, and typhus. The shots you were given when you were an infant protect you from some bacterial diseases. There is no shot that protects you from food poisoning. Have you ever eaten something that gave you a terrible stomachache? When bacteria begin to decay food, they produce chemicals that may be poisonous to humans.

FIGURE 18–2. Bacteria that live in nodules on the roots of a pea plant provide the plant with nitrogen.

What are some bacterial diseases in humans?

FIGURE 18–3. Bacteria help keep the environment clear of dead organisms.

Cyanobacteria sometimes reproduce rapidly in lakes and water supplies. These large colonies use up most of the oxygen in the water. Other organisms, such as water plants and fish, die from a lack of oxygen. The water develops a bad odor from the decay. The rapid growth of cyanobacteria in water is often the result of pollution (puh LEW shun). **Pollution** is the effect caused by adding substances to the environment that are harmful to living organisms. For example, when chemicals are dumped into water, the natural balance of living organisms is altered. Chemicals in polluted water cause cyanobacteria to grow fast.

REVIEW

1. What are two characteristics of monerans?
2. What are the three basic shapes of bacteria?
3. How do cyanobacteria differ from bacteria?
4. How are cyanobacteria different from plants?
5. What would be the value of planting clover plants in a field low in nitrogen?

TECHNOLOGY

Frogs to the Rescue

A scientist working with frogs discovered a new chemical that kills bacteria. He observed that a wounded frog swimming in an aquarium full of bacteria did not get any infections. The scientist considered the idea that something in the skin of the frog may be preventing infection. He tested this idea and found that the frog's skin secretes a chemical that kills bacteria. He named the new chemical *magainin* (muh GAY nun).

Investigations are now underway to find if other animals, including humans, have similar kinds of chemicals. If magainins could be made in the lab, they could be used to prevent various infections. Frogs may be useful in the fight against disease.

ADVANCE

Magainins have been found to affect the balance of water in cells. Magainins cause cells to explode. A possible future use of the newly discovered chemical is to destroy viruses and cancerous cells.

What Are Protists?

18:3 Classifying Protists

Organisms that are one-celled and have a nucleus surrounded by a membrane are classified as protists. The protist kingdom is made up of three different types of organisms. Some protists were once classified as plants because they have plantlike characteristics. Plantlike protists have cell walls and chloroplasts with which they can make their own food. Other protists were classified as animals because they have characteristics like those of animals. Animal-like protists can move, have no cell wall, and cannot make their own food. A third group of protists are funguslike. They have characteristics like animals, but reproduce like fungi. Some form colonies.

Plantlike protists are an important food source for animals in lakes and oceans. A euglena (yoo GLEE nuh) is a common plantlike protist that moves with flagella.

An animal-like protist is also called a **protozoan.** There are four different kinds of protozoans. Protozoans are classified by their means of movement. Amoebas (uh MEE buz) make up one group of protozoa. An amoeba pushes out extensions of its cytoplasm to move. The extension of cytoplasm in an amoeba is called a **pseudopod** (SEWD uh pahd). After a pseudopod pushes out in the direction of movement, the rest of the amoeba flows in the same direction.

GOALS
You will study . . .
1. the characteristics of protists.
2. how protists cause diseases.

How were protists once classified?

F.Y.I. Some species of plantlike protists can produce a chemical light. This can cause the water to seem to be on fire or full of stars when seen at night.

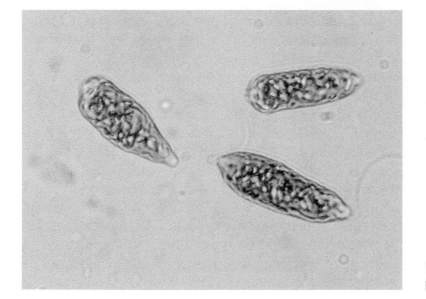

FIGURE 18–4. Some plantlike protists move by flagella.

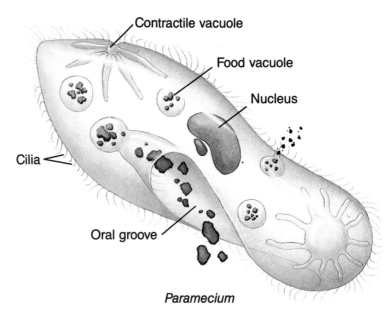

FIGURE 18–5. A ciliate uses cilia to move through water and to take in food.

Contractile vacuole

Food vacuole

Nucleus

Cilia

Oral groove

Paramecium

Flagellates (FLAJ uh layts) are a second group of protozoans. They move by means of flagella. The whipping action of the flagella push or pull the organism through the fluid in which it lives. A third group is made up of ciliates (SIHL ee ayts). These protozoans have their cell surfaces covered with cilia. **Cilia** are short, hairlike structures. Movements of the cilia cause the ciliate to move. Sporozoans (spor uh ZOH unz) make up a fourth group of protozoans. Sporozoans have no means of movement. They live in other organisms and absorb food from the blood of their host. Sporozoans reproduce with spores. A **spore** is a reproductive structure that can develop into a new organism.

How do sporozoans move?

The funguslike group of protists is made up of slime molds. Imagine an organism like an amoeba that flows around in damp soil or rotting wood and feeds on bacteria. When the one-celled slime molds have eaten all the bacteria around them, they move together to form a clump of cells. The clump of cells begins to move like a new organism. It behaves like a slug crawling over the ground leaving a slimy trail. The slime mold stops and forms a thin stalk. A ball of spores forms at the top of the stalk. When conditions are right, the spores are released. Each spore develops into a new, one-celled slime mold. The process begins all over again. With this type of life cycle, you can understand why scientists have placed the slime molds in different kingdoms.

FIGURE 18–6. Slime molds are funguslike protists that also have characteristics of flagellates.

Problem: How can you classify protists?

Materials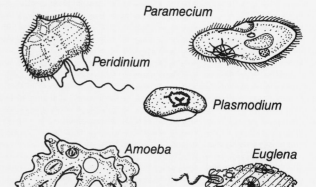

Euglena prepared slide   microscope
Peridinium prepared slide
Amoeba prepared slide
Paramecium prepared slide
Plasmodium prepared slide

Procedure

1. Make a table like the one shown.
2. Observe the prepared slide of *Euglena* under low power. Turn to higher power. Record your observations.
3. Observe the prepared slides of the other protists in the same manner. Record your observations of each in the table.

Questions and Conclusions

1. Which protist has a cell wall?
2. Which protists have chloroplasts?
3. What structure enables *Euglena* and *Peridinium* to move?

4. Which protist does not have a structure that enables it to move?
5. Which protists make their own food?
6. Which protists can't make their own food?
7. Which protists are like plants? Which are like animals?
8. What characteristics do all protists have in common?
9. What characteristics are different among protists?
10. What are two ways you can classify protists? Explain each way.

Data and Observations

Characteristics	Organism				
	Euglena	*Amoeba*	*Paramecium*	*Plasmodium*	*Peridinium*
Cell membrane					
Cell wall					
Nucleus					
Chloroplasts					
Method of movement					

Outlining

Write an outline of the information given in Section 18:3 of your text. Use **Protist Kingdom** as your heading. If you need help, refer to Outlining on page 527.

Questions

1. What is the main idea of your outline?
2. What are your major topics within this main idea?
3. What are the main points of information concerning protozoans?

How is sleeping sickness spread to humans?

BIOGRAPHY

Jessie I. Price
1930–

Jessie Price is a veterinary microbiologist. She researches how bacterial infections affect animals. She received her Ph.D. from Cornell University. She studied cholera in birds. She also studied how bacteria cause botulism, a kind of food poisoning.

18:4 Protists and Disease

Some protists are parasites. A **parasite** is an organism that lives and feeds in or on another living organism. Often the parasite harms the organism on which it feeds. Sleeping sickness, a common disease of humans in Africa, is caused by a parasitic flagellate. This parasite is passed from animals, such as cattle to humans in the bite of the tsetse fly. The parasite attacks the nervous system of the infected person.

Sporozoans are parasites that also cause diseases. Malaria is a disease caused by a sporozoan that attacks the blood cells of humans and other animals. The malaria sporozoan is passed from person to person in the bite of a species of mosquito. The parasite multiplies in the blood cells. The blood cells are destroyed, and this causes the person to develop a fever. Malaria is common in Central America and Africa where the climate is hot and moist.

Several methods are used to fight diseases caused by protists. Chemicals called insecticides (ihn SEK tuh sidez) are used to kill insects that carry the parasites. The insects can also be controlled by destroying places where they reproduce. Swamps and ponds are drained or a thin coat of oil is sprayed on the water to prevent the young stages of mosquitoes from taking in oxygen and becoming adults. Also there are many medicines that are used to treat diseases caused by protists.

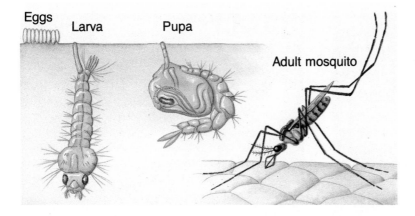

Eggs　Larva　Pupa

Adult mosquito

FIGURE 18–7. A mosquito begins life as an egg laid on water. A larva develops into a pupa, and the adult emerges to feed on the blood of animals.

REVIEW

6. Give two features of a plantlike protist.
7. What are the three stages in the life cycle of a slime mold?
8. What are the three means of movement used by protozoans?
9. Why is the malaria sporozoan a parasite?
10. The tropics have many insects. How does this relate to the great number of diseases caused by protists there?

What Is a Fungus?

18:5 Classifying Fungi

Have you ever walked through a forest in the fall? You may have noticed many different mushrooms that grow from the dead twigs of trees. Have you ever seen moldy food in the refrigerator? Mushrooms and molds are examples of fungi and are grouped in the fungus kingdom. A **fungus** is an organism that has tissues made up of long, threadlike structures. These thin, often branching, threads of fungi are called **hyphae** (HI fee).

A fungus obtains its food from material on which it grows. Masses of hyphae grow from the fungus into the material. Most fungi are saprophytes (SAP ruh fitez). A **saprophyte** is an organism that lives and feeds in or on a dead organism. The hyphae of a mushroom grow down into dead plant material. Dissolved plant material is absorbed by the mushroom. Some fungi are parasites that feed on live plants or animals.

GOALS

You will study . . .
1. four types of fungi.
2. the role of fungi in the environment.
3. how yeast cells are used in research.

Name two examples of fungi.

a

b

FIGURE 18–8. Water molds (a) and club fungi (b) are two examples of fungi.

How does a fungus reproduce?

F.Y.I. The giant puffball can grow to be 40 centimeters in diameter and have a mass of as much as 4.5 kg.

A fungus reproduces by forming spores. There are four types of fungi, and each type produces different types of spores. In sporangium (spuh RAN jee um) fungi, the spores are formed in round cases called sporangia (spuh RAN jee uh). You may have seen moldy bread. Did you notice that it seemed to be covered with black spots on short threadlike stalks? The black spots are spore cases. The threadlike stalks are hyphae. Other hyphae of the bread mold are within the bread.

Water molds are a group of fungi that have spores with flagella for swimming through the water. Water molds are parasites. The cottony fungus around the mouths of aquarium fish is caused by a water mold. The potato famine in Ireland was caused by crop failure due to the potato blight. Potato blight is a disease caused by another water mold.

Club fungi are the familiar mushrooms. The spores of club fungi are formed on the underside of an umbrella-like cap. After the spores have been released, the cap rots away. Rusts and smuts are parasitic club fungi. Rusts and smuts often appear as rust- or soot-colored powders on plants such as corn, wheat, and apples. The plants are destroyed by these fungi.

The sac fungi produce spores in a sac. Yeasts are one-celled sac fungi. Yeasts also reproduce by budding. **Budding** is a form of reproduction in which a new organism is formed by an outgrowth of the parent organism. A small budlike growth appears on the surface of the yeast cell. It grows and pulls away to live as a separate organism.

Many-celled sac fungi include cup fungi. Cup fungi look like small leathery cups on rotting logs and sticks. You may have seen cup fungi on the mulch that is used to cover flower beds in gardens. Another member of the sac fungi is the genus *Penicillium* (pen uh SIHL ee um). Penicillin, a valuable drug, is extracted from the hyphae of this fungus.

Some organisms are difficult to classify. They have characteristics that would put them in more than one kingdom. A lichen (LI kun) is classified in the fungus kingdom. It is an example of an organism with a combination of characteristics. A **lichen** is a fungus that has green algae or cyanobacteria living amongst its hyphae. The green organism makes food for the lichen. The fungus absorbs water and holds the lichen to the surface on which it is growing. Together the two organisms benefit one another. A relationship in which two organisms live together for mutual benefit is called **mutualism** (MYEW chuh lihz um).

Why are some organisms difficult to classify?

PROBLEM SOLVING

What Happened to the Bread?

Eunice arrived at her grandmother's house on Friday to visit for the weekend. Her grandmother asked if she would like to help bake some bread to use for chicken salad sandwiches for Saturday's lunch. Eunice thought that sounded like fun.

She and her grandmother gathered the following ingredients:
   1 package active dry yeast
   2 cups warm water
   1 ½ tablespoons shortening
   1 ½ teaspooons salt
   2 tablespoons sugar
   5 cups all-purpose floor

They dissolved the yeast in some of the warm water. Then, they added the rest of the water, salt, shortening, and flour. After kneading the dough for ten minutes, they placed it in a greased bowl.

Grandmother covered the bowl and put it in a warm place to rise for an hour. When they went to the kitchen to bake the dough, Eunice discovered that the dough had not risen. Did they make a mistake? What could Eunice do to find the cause of what had happened? What do you think had happened?

Problem: What is needed for yeast to grow?

Materials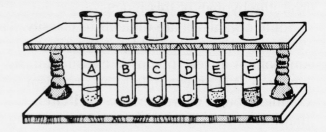

dry yeast (1 package)   dropper
table sugar   masking tape
flour   apron
water   microscope
test tubes (6)   microscope slide
test tube rack   cover slip

Procedure

1. Use the masking tape to label the test tubes A, B, C, D, E, and F.
2. Place the test tubes into the test tube rack.
3. Add the following to each test tube:
   A—pinch of yeast, 20 drops water
   B—pinch of yeast, 2 pinches sugar
   C—pinch of yeast, 2 pinches flour
   D—pinch of yeast
   E—pinch of yeast, 20 drops water, 2 pinches sugar
   F—pinch of yeast, 20 drops water, 2 pinches flour
4. Swirl each test tube to mix the ingredients.
5. Hypothesize which substances are necessary for yeast to grow.
6. After 15 minutes, observe each test tube. Record your observations in a table like the one shown.

7. After 30 minutes, observe and record your observations.
8. Observe the budding yeast cells with a microscope.

Questions and Conclusions

1. Which test tubes did not change?
2. In which test tubes did you observe a change?
3. Why was only one ingredient added to the yeast in test tubes A, B, and C?
4. Why was only yeast added to test tube D?
5. What is needed for yeast to grow?
6. What was your hypothesis? Was it supported by the activity?
7. What did you observe with the microscope?
8. How do yeast cells reproduce?
9. If a baker wants bread to rise using yeast, what other ingredients must be used?

Data and Observations

Test tube	A	B	C	D	E	F
Observations after 15 minutes						
Observation after 30 minutes						

a

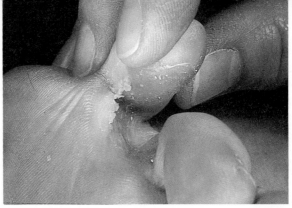
b

18:6 Activities of Fungi

Saprophytic fungi cause decay of dead organisms. These fungi are decomposers (dee kum POH zurz). A **decomposer** is an organism that breaks down complex organic compounds into simpler compounds. Decomposers are important to the health of the environment.

Some fungi have been used in making medicines, foods, and beverages. Molds are grown to produce penicillin and to flavor blue cheeses. Yeasts have been used for centuries in the making of bread, beer, and wine. Yeast cells live on the skins of most fruits and are grown commercially for baking and research.

Some fungi, such as commercial mushrooms, are good to eat. Other mushrooms are edible, and people collect them from fields and forests. Only an expert can tell which mushrooms are safe to eat. Many fungi are extremely poisonous, so it is safer never to eat wild mushrooms.

Many kinds of fungi are harmful. Molds grow on foods and on other organic material, such as leather and cotton, and cause them to decay. Molds, rusts, and smuts cause serious diseases on plants such as wheat and corn. Millions of elm trees have died from a fungus disease. Fungi sometimes infect the skin of humans.

FIGURE 18–9. Helpful fungi (a) can be used to flavor food. Harmful fungi (b) may infect a person's skin.

What is a decomposer?

F.Y.I. The Death Cap, Destroying Angel, and Fly Agaric are names for three very poisonous mushrooms that all belong to the genus *Amanita*.

SCIENCE AND SOCIETY

18:7 Yeast as a Research Tool

The yeast used as an ingredient in making bread and pizza dough is now being used in the search for a cure for diseases such as cancer and AIDS. Yeast cells are very similar in structure to human cells.

What Is a Fungus?   377

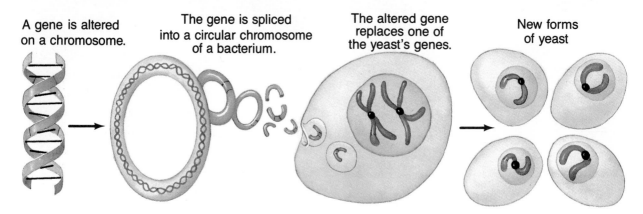

A gene is altered on a chromosome.

The gene is spliced into a circular chromosome of a bacterium.

The altered gene replaces one of the yeast's genes.

New forms of yeast

FIGURE 18–10. New forms of yeast cells can be produced by moving genes. Genes are spliced into the large yeast chromosomes.

What is gene splicing?

You learned in Chapter 17 that chromosomes carry the code for the life processes of an organism. Chromosomes are made up of genes. A **gene** is a small part of a chromosome that controls a characteristic of an organism. The nucleus of a yeast cell contains six fewer, but larger chromosomes than those of a human cell.

Scientists are now able to move sections of genes from one cell to another. **Gene splicing** is a technique that replaces a section of genes in one cell with a section of genes from a different cell. Scientists have spliced a section of genes from a human cell into the nucleus of a yeast cell.

Gene splicing can be used to find out which genes are responsible for different human birth defects. The technique is also used to develop vaccines that can fight diseases. The vaccine for hepatitis B, a serious disease in humans, was the first vaccine to be made by splicing a yeast cell with a section of genes from a human cell. Maybe this technique could be used to develop forms of yeast resistant to diseases such as cancer and AIDS. What are the risks and benefits of producing altered forms of yeast? Could experimental forms of yeast pose new health problems? Humans may not be resistant to these new organisms.

REVIEW

11. What are the four main kinds of fungi?
12. How do fungi obtain their food?
13. What are the two ways that yeasts reproduce?
14. What are three ways that fungi are useful?
15. Some fungi live in mutualism with plant roots. How does this benefit both the plant and the fungus?

CHAPTER 18 REVIEW

SUMMARY

1. Bacteria and cyanobacteria are the two kinds of monerans. Some bacteria have flagella. The chlorophyll of cyanobacteria is not contained in chloroplasts. 18:1
2. Monerans are both helpful and harmful in the environment. Bacteria help decay dead organisms and cause diseases. Rapid growth of cyanobacteria is caused by pollution. 18:2
3. Protists are one-celled organisms with a nucleus. They are plantlike, animal-like, or funguslike 18:3
4. Parasitic protists cause diseases. Insects that carry parasitic protists can be controlled. 18:4
5. The four main types of fungi are sporangium fungi, water molds, club fungi, and sac fungi. Lichens are classified as fungi. 18:5
6. Fungi are both helpful and harmful in the environment. Saprophytic fungi are decomposers of dead organisms. Some fungi cause diseases. 18:6
7. Yeast cells are being used for important genetic research. Transfer of genes from a chromosome of one organism to that of another is called gene splicing. 18:7

VOCABULARY

a. budding
b. cilia
c. decomposer
d. fission
e. flagella
f. fungus
g. gene
h. gene splicing
i. hyphae
j. lichen
k. mutualism
l. parasite
m. pollution
n. protozoan
o. pseudopod
p. saprophyte
q. spore

Match each description with the correct vocabulary word from the list above.
1. process of an organism dividing into two
2. threadlike structures of fungi
3. short, hairlike structures on some kinds of protozoans
4. an extension of cytoplasm used for movement
5. a living thing made of a green organism and a fungus
6. reproductive structure that grows into a new organism
7. long, hairlike structures used for movement
8. an organism that breaks down complex organic compounds
9. an organism that lives and feeds on a dead organism
10. an organism that lives and feeds in or on another living organism

CHAPTER 18 REVIEW

MAIN IDEAS

A. Reviewing Concepts

Choose the word or phrase that correctly completes each of the following sentences.

1. _____ are examples of monerans.
   - a. Molds
   - b. Protozoans
   - c. Bacteria
   - d. Mildews

2. An amoeba moves by _____.
   - a. flagella
   - b. hyphae
   - c. cilia
   - d. pseudopods

3. Some plants have bacteria that live on their roots in structures called _____.
   - a. nodules
   - b. spores
   - c. hyphae
   - d. lichens

4. Protozoans that have no means of movement are _____.
   - a. amoebas
   - b. pseudopods
   - c. ciliates
   - d. sporozoans

5. _____ have a jellylike layer around a rigid cell wall.
   - a. Fungi
   - b. Slime molds
   - c. Protists
   - d. Monerans

6. A _____ is a protist that moves with flagella and contains chlorophyll.
   - a. euglena
   - b. ciliate
   - c. slime mold
   - d. yeast

7. Many fungi reproduce by _____.
   - a. spores
   - b. chloroplasts
   - c. hyphae
   - d. nodules

8. _____ is a relationship that benefits two organisms living together.
   - a. Parasitism
   - b. Decomposition
   - c. Mutualism
   - d. Saphrophytism

9. A disease caused by protozoans is _____.
   - a. strep throat
   - b. tetanus
   - c. malaria
   - d. diphtheria

10. One-celled fungi are _____.
    - a. slime molds
    - b. yeasts
    - c. mushrooms
    - d. mildews

11. A _____ is an example of a club fungus.
    - a. slime mold
    - b. mushroom
    - c. yeast
    - d. bread mold

12. The cap of a _____ releases spores.
    - a. mushroom
    - b. mold
    - c. yeast
    - d. smut

13. Yeasts are one kind of _____ that produces spores in a sac.
    - a. moneran
    - b. flagellate
    - c. protist
    - d. fungus

14. A slime mold can move like a _____.
    - a. ciliate
    - b. rust
    - c. slug
    - d. yeast

15. Millions of bacteria are produced by _____ every few hours.
    - a. parasites
    - b. pseudopods
    - c. fission
    - d. budding

B. Understanding Concepts

Answer the following questions using complete sentences.

16. What are the three basic shapes of bacteria?

17. How are bacteria helpful to people and their environment?

18. What is a characteristic used to classify protozoans?

19. Name two groups of organisms that use flagella for movement.

20. What characteristics of yeast make it ideal for cell research?

21. What are the four basic types of fungi?

22. What are two club fungi that cause plant diseases?

23. What is gene splicing?

24. What type of fungus produces penicillin?

25. How do slime molds reproduce?

C. Applying Concepts

Answer the following questions using complete sentences.

26. Describe the roles of the green alga and fungus that make up a lichen.
27. What are some advantages and disadvantages of gene splicing?
28. How is a parasite, such as a fungus, different from a meat-eating animal, such as a tiger?
29. Explain how bacteria can cause food to spoil in a few hours.
30. Give reasons for classifying a slime mold as an animal and a fungus.

SKILL REVIEW

If you need help, refer to the Skill Handbook, pages 526 to 537.

1. Prepare bread dough according to a recipe. Allow one-third of the dough to rise at the temperature given in the recipe. Give each of the other thirds a higher and a lower temperature, respectively. Measure the heights of the risen dough in centimeters.
2. For Question 1, identify the constant, the controls, the independent variable, and the dependent variable.
3. List the following events in the correct order: bacteria produce chemicals that cause decay, bacterial decay releases nutrients into the soil, organism dies, bacteria absorb products of decay, plant roots absorb nutrients from the soil.
4. If the number of bacteria doubles every 15 minutes, determine how many you will have from one bacterium after 90 minutes. Plot your results on a graph similar to the one shown.

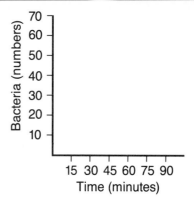

5. What is a possible cause and effect of food poisoning?

PROJECTS

1. Collect a mushroom from a field or forest. **CAUTION:** *Do not taste the mushroom.* Remove the stalk and place the cap on a piece of paper. The underside of the mushroom should be facing down on the paper. Cover the mushroom with a bowl and allow to stand overnight. **CAUTION:** *Wash your hands after handling mushrooms.* Carefully remove the bowl and mushroom cap. Observe the print made by the spores that fell onto the paper.
2. Write a report about lichens and how they can be used to detect pollution.

READINGS

1. Angier, N. "A Stupid Cell With All the Answers." *Discover.* November, 1986, pp. 70–74.
2. Hurtley, K. "A Parasite With the Guts of a Burglar." *Science News.* June 6, 1987, p. 359.
3. Sabine, Francine. *Microbes and Bacteria.* Mahwah, N.J.: Troll Associates, 1985.

Plants

CHAPTER 19

Career: Tree Farmer

Greenville had begun a beautification project, and students were invited to join a contest. Each student entry had to have a colorful drawing of Main Street showing flowers, trees, shrubs, and grass.

Trista wanted to draw a boulevard lined with colorful trees. She decided to call Tree Top Farms to ask for their help in choosing the right kinds of trees. The manager of the farm met with Trista and discussed the names, sizes, and shapes of ornamental trees that would be most suitable for a boulevard. They discussed the colors of the trees' spring flowers and their fall berries. Before Trista left, they took a tour of the farm. The manager showed her the trees that are sold to garden stores. He also pointed out the large hardwood trees that are harvested for lumber, for making paper products, and for fuel. They saw some trees being cut down. The manager explained that some smaller trees are cut and used to make fence posts and other small items, which makes room for other trees to grow larger. When those trees reach the proper size, they are cut and sold. New seedlings are planted to replace them. They also saw a field of pine trees that would be cut for holiday decorations.

In this chapter you will study different types of plants and learn why they are important. You will study spore plants, conifers, and flowering plants.

F.Y.I. American Forest Council, 1250 Connecticut Avenue NW, Suite 320, Washington, DC 20036

What Is a Plant?

GOALS
You will study . . .
1. characteristics of plants.
2. plant functions.
3. how plants are important to people.

What is cellulose?

FIGURE 19–1. Plants without chlorophyll absorb nutrients from the plants or materials on which they grow (a). Most plants are green and can make their own food (b).

19:1 Characteristics of Plants

What do you imagine when you think of plants? Most people think of trees and flowers. Some of you might think of other plants such as common garden weeds, grasses, vegetable plants, cacti, or seaweeds. What are the common characteristics of plants? You might say that plants have green leaves. However, parasitic plants are not green, and seaweeds are plants that do not have leaves. All plants contain cellulose (SEL yuh lohs). **Cellulose** is the substance that makes up most of the cell walls of plants. The fiber in your diet is largely cellulose. Most plants are green. Cells of green plants contain chlorophyll in chloroplasts. Plants that have chlorophyll can make their own food. Parasitic plants get their food from other plants on which they grow. Examples of plants include seaweeds, mosses, ferns, conifers, and flowering plants.

All plants need water. Seaweeds are plants that live in water and so can take in water from any part of their surfaces. Water passes from cell to cell by osmosis. Many plants that live on land have tissues that allow them to take up water from the soil. Just as you have a system of tubes that carries blood around your body, many land plants have a system of tubes. The tubes in plants form vascular tissues. **Vascular tissue** of a plant is a tissue that conducts water and food to all parts of the plant.

a

b

a

b

There are two types of vascular tissues: xylem (ZI lum) and phloem (FLOH em). **Xylem** tubes make up vascular tissues that conduct water and nutrients from the roots to the rest of the plant. Xylem tissues are rigid and allow a plant to grow tall. **Phloem** tubes make up vascular tissues that move food materials from the leaves to all parts of the plant. Some land plants do not have vascular tissues and therefore, cannot grow very tall. Water passes to the cells by osmosis.

Land plants such as trees or grass are held in the ground by roots. A root anchors the plant and takes in water and nutrients from the ground through root hairs. Root hairs are hairlike structures that grow from cells in the root tips. There are two main types of roots: taproots and fibrous roots. A taproot stores food. It has one main root with many small side roots. The roots of carrots and dandelions are taproots. A fibrous root is made up of many thin roots that branch and spread out. Grasses have fibrous roots.

A stem supports the leaves and connects the roots to the other parts of a plant. Leaves and reproductive organs of a plant grow from the stems. There are two main types of stems: herbaceous (hur BAY shus) stems and woody stems. Herbaceous stems are soft and green. Green stems have chlorophyll and so can make food. Herbaceous stems have many different forms. For example, dandelion stems are very short, hollyhock stems are tall, strawberry stems creep along the ground, and bindweed stems are climbers. Woody stems have xylem cells with very thick walls. Maple trees and rose bushes have woody stems. The xylem cells are surrounded by long, thick fibers. Woody stems are hard and often colored gray or brown.

FIGURE 19–2. A taproot often has stored food (a). The stem of a rose shrub is woody (b).

What are the functions of roots?

What are the two main types of roots?

F.Y.I. If a bluegrass root system were placed end to end, it would be 400 meters in length.

What Is a Plant? 385

FIGURE 19–3. The veins of a leaf are made of vascular tissue.

F.Y.I. A tulip bulb is a short, underground stem surrounded by the swollen leaf bases of the previous year's leaves.

What is a seed?

A leaf is a green plant organ that grows from the stem and makes food. A leaf has a flattened blade that traps the sunlight and a leaf stalk that connects the leaf to the stem. When you look at a leaf blade, you may see a pattern of netlike ridges. These are the veins of the leaf. The ridges are caused by long bundles of vascular tissue. A leaf is covered by a layer of cells, called the epidermis. Gases enter and leave the leaf through openings in the epidermis. The tissues between the upper and lower layers of epidemis are made up of cells that contain chloroplasts. Photosynthesis, the plant process of food production, takes place in these cells.

Herbaceous stems are killed by frosts. Many herbaceous plants survive cold winters by storing food in underground stems, roots, or leaves. A potato is a tuber. A tuber is an underground stem that stores food. Peonies have an underground storage stem called a rhizome (RI zohm). A gladiolus has a swollen underground storage stem called a corm. Tulips survive cold winters by storing food in the underground bases of their leaves. This storage organ is called a bulb. Seeds are also storage organs that allow new plants to survive the winter. A **seed** is a plant structure that contains and protects an undeveloped plant. The food stored in seeds and underground plant organs is often starch or fats.

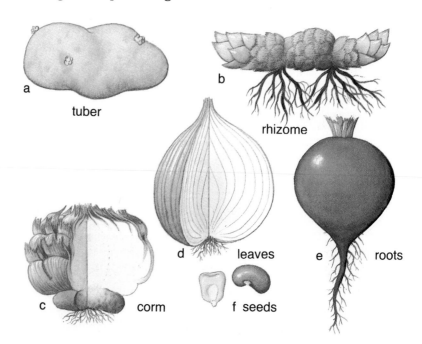

a tuber
b rhizome
c corm
d leaves
e roots
f seeds

FIGURE 19–4. Plants store food in stems (a, b, c), in leaves (d), in roots (e), and in seeds (f).

TECHNOLOGY

Yellow Jewel

Soybeans are the seeds of a flowering plant. The food stored in soybean seeds is mainly oil and protein. Protein is a compound that is rich in nitrogen. The Chinese have grown soybeans as a crop plant for nearly 3000 years. Because of its high food value, it became very popular. The Chinese gave the beans the name "yellow jewel." Soybean plants have a relationship of mutualism with bacteria in their roots. The bacteria change nitrogen in the air into a form that the plant can use. When the plants are plowed into the soil after the beans are harvested, nitrogen is returned to the soil.

Soybeans are a good source of protein and, therefore, a possible substitute for meat. A custardlike product of soybeans, called tofu, is becoming a popular food around the world. Soybean products are also used in ice cream, margarine, salad oil, and mayonnaise. The "yellow jewel" has become a valuable part of our food industry.

ADVANCE

Many people in the world do not have enough protein in their diets. Meat is not easily available or too expensive. Without protein, the body can't grow and develop. Efforts are being made to find ways to add soybean products to foods that people are more familiar with. Soybean products can be made to look like the foods we are used to eating, such as chicken or fish. Soybeans may be the plants used to solve the world's food shortage problems.

19:2 Functions of Plants

Photosynthesis is the process by which green organisms make food. An organism that makes its own food is a **producer.** Green plants are producers. Photosynthesis is the source of food for almost every other organism. When you eat a hamburger and milk shake, all the energy you gain from this meal comes from plants. Beef and milk come from cows that feed on grass. In photosynthesis, carbon dioxide and water are combined with the aid of energy from light. The products of photosynthesis are sugars and oxygen. This process is the major source of oxygen in our atmosphere. Photosynthesis can be represented by this equation.

What is photosynthesis?

$$6CO_2 + 6H_2O \xrightarrow[\text{energy from the sun}]{\text{chlorophyll}} C_6H_{12}O_6 + 6O_2$$

What gas enters through the epidermis?

What gas exits through the epidermis?

Plants take up water through their roots. The water travels along the xylem tubes to the leaves. Carbon dioxide enters the leaves through small openings in the epidermis. The chlorophyll in the cells of the leaves traps energy from the sun. This energy is used to break the molecules of water into atoms of hydrogen and oxygen. The oxygen passes out of the leaf through the openings in the epidermis. The hydrogen combines with carbon dioxide and forms a simple sugar called glucose, which provides the energy source for all of the plant's metabolism. Glucose moves around the plant through the phloem tubes. The glucose is changed into other compounds, such as more complex sugars, starches, and cellulose, that are used for the plant's growth.

Some organisms are consumers. A **consumer** is an organism that can't make its own food and must use the food made by other organisms that contain chlorophyll. Cows eat grass. You eat plants, such as corn and potatoes, and animals, such as cows that have eaten plants. Cows and people are consumers.

Respiration is another plant process. The cell process of respiration results in a release of energy from food. In respiration, the glucose from photosynthesis combines with oxygen. Energy is released. Respiration can be represented by this equation.

$$C_6H_{12}O_6 + 6O_2 \rightarrow 6H_2O + 6CO_2 + energy$$

F.Y.I. On some leaves, there are as many as 500 tiny openings, called stomata, per mm^2.

FIGURE 19–5. Producers, such as plants, supply people and other consumers with a source of energy.

a

b

The energy from respiration is used for all activities of the cell's metabolism. Carbon dioxide and water are the products of respiration. Carbon dioxide and water vapor pass out of the openings in the leaves. The movement of water vapor out of a plant is called **transpiration.** You may have seen a mist over a field on an early summer morning. The mist is caused by transpiration from the plants before the warm sun's rays evaporate the water.

Deciduous plants lose their leaves each year. In autumn, these plants stop making chlorophyll. The leaves become red, yellow, and orange. These colors are caused by molecules in the cells that are always present but are usually hidden by chlorophyll. As the weather turns colder, the leaves fall. Maple, apple, and hickory are deciduous. Evergreen plants keep their leaves for several years before they are dropped. These plants are green all year. Ivy, azalea, and pine are evergreens.

Like all living things, plants respond to stimuli. You may have noticed house plants with their leaves up against the window pane. A stem responds to light by growing longer on the side away from the light. This causes the stem to grow toward the light. As a result the leaves are in a better position to receive light from the sun. Parts of a plant also respond to changes in water pressure within cells. Water that moves out of cells by osmosis can cause leaves, such as those of the sensitive plant, to fold at night. Plants also respond to the force of gravity or to contact with a support. The movement or response of a plant to a stimulus is called a tropism. For example, gravitropism is the response of stems and roots to gravity.

FIGURE 19–6. The leaves of a sensitive plant (a) respond to touch by folding up (b).

What are deciduous plants?

F.Y.I. There are many kinds of plant tropisms.
thigmotropism-response to contact
phototropism-response to light
chemotropism-response to chemicals
hydrotropism-response to water

What Is a Plant? 389

Problem: How does gravity affect the growth of roots and stems?

Materials

soaked radish seeds (1 package)
clear plastic cup
water (50 mL)
plastic wrap
paper towels (2)

Procedure

1. Copy the data table.
2. Moisten a strip of paper towel and use it to line a plastic cup.
3. Crumple a second paper towel and push it into the center of the cup.
4. Drop several soaked radish seeds between the paper towel lining and the inside of the cup. The seeds should be spread out around the cup and about halfway down from the top.
5. Add 50 mL of water to the cup. Cover the top of the cup with plastic wrap.
6. After the radish seeds begin to grow, observe the growth of the roots and stems from the radish seeds each day for three days. Record your observations in the data table.
7. Remove the plastic wrap three days after the seeds begin to grow. Pour the water from the cup.
8. Replace the plastic wrap and place the cup on its side.
9. Predict the direction in which the roots and stems will grow. If there is a response to a stimulus, it may be positive (toward) or negative (away from). For two more days, record your observations in the table.

Data and Observations

Time	Observations
1 day	
2 days	
3 days	
4 days	
5 days	

Questions and Conclusions

1. How did roots respond to gravity?
2. How did stems respond to gravity?
3. What is the response of a plant to gravity called?
4. Why was the plastic wrap placed over the open end of the plastic cup?
5. How did roots respond to gravity when the cup was placed on its side?
6. How did stems respond to gravity when the cup was placed on its side?
7. How does gravity affect the growth of roots and stems?
8. How are the effects of gravitropism important to plants?

SCIENCE AND SOCIETY

19:3 Plants and Human Life

Before people lived in cities, they moved from place to place in search of food. Those early people ate the roots, stems, leaves, fruits, and seeds of many wild plants. They also used plants for shelter, warmth, and medicines. They hunted and trapped animals for food, clothing, and oils that they used for cooking. When the people had eaten most of the plants and animals in one area, they would move on to another place.

Eventually, people discovered that many plants could be grown from seeds. People began to grow plants for food. Each year they saved seeds and stored them for the next year's crops. The seeds were selected from the best-tasting plants. After thousands of years of selective breeding, the plants looked very different from the original weedy plants. **Selective breeding** is the selection and mating of organisms that have desirable characteristics. Other species of plants were selected for value as fibers, dyes, oils, medicines, spices, and flavorings. Today people grow grains, vegetables, and fruits that are more nutritional and are better able to resist diseases than are some wild species.

The Mayans were a society of native Americans that lived in Mexico and Central America from about 500 B.C. to 1500 A.D. Large numbers of Mayans lived in an area of hot and humid forests called tropical rain forests. Very little of the forest was cut and burned to use the land for farming. How could such large numbers of Mayan people have had enough food?

BIOGRAPHY

Eloy Rodriguez
1947-

Eloy Rodriguez is a chemist who studies chemicals in plants. Some are very useful to humans. Rubber plants grow mainly in the tropics. He is finding ways to move rubber-making plant cells into other plants that can then be grown in colder climates.

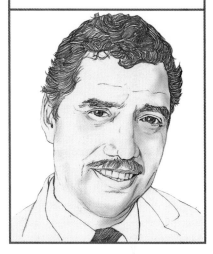

Who were the Mayans?

FIGURE 19-7. Many plants that are grown today for food are the result of hundreds of years of selective breeding.

What Is a Plant? 391

FIGURE 19–8. Plants have been a source of shelter for thousands of years.

F.Y.I. There is archaeological evidence that wheat was grown in the Middle East as early as 6000 B.C.

Why are tropical rain forests being destroyed?

Scientists found that Mayans grew plants in small gardens within the forest. The people cut down and burned trees to clear spaces for crops. Trees found useful for food, medicines, and building materials were not cut. The Mayans planted tomatoes, beans, and sweet potatoes.

Over the centuries, humans have become very dependent on plants for food, warmth, and shelter. The world's human population has increased so rapidly that more and more plants are needed to supply people with food and other important products. Large areas of tropical rain forests are being destroyed each year to provide people with homes, firewood, and furniture. Many of these areas have not yet been studied, and there is no way of knowing how many undiscovered plant species are being destroyed. Some of these plants might have been used to benefit people in one way or another.

Perhaps people should learn a lesson from the Mayans. The Mayans farmed the land but did not destroy the natural environment. Today some methods of forest clearing used by industry in tropical areas are destroying the natural vegetation.

REVIEW

1. What are the two kinds of vascular tissues and what are their functions?
2. What is the major function of a leaf?
3. What are four kinds of underground storage organs?
4. What are four major uses of plants?
5. Why is photosynthesis important to animals?

19:4 Nonvascular Spore Plants

You learned that many plants have vascular tissues with xylem and phloem tubes. Some plants are nonvascular. Nonvascular plants don't have xylem and phloem tubes. These plants include brown, red, and green algae, mosses, and liverworts. The three groups of algae are commonly known as seaweeds. Recall that the term *algae* is often used for organisms in the moneran, protist, and plant kingdoms. All algae contain chlorophyll and live in water. Seaweeds are classified as plants because they contain cellulose.

A nonvascular plant has a life cycle that includes male cells, female cells, and spores. Male and female cells are called sex cells. The male sex cell is the sperm, and the female sex cell is the egg. Yes, plants have eggs and sperm, too! A sperm joins with an egg in a process called **fertilization** (furt ul uh ZAY shun). The fertilized egg grows and develops into a stage that produces spores. The spores are blown by the wind from the parent plant. The spores of algae, however, often have flagella for swimming away from the parent plant. Each spore then grows into a new plant. Each new plant produces sex cells and the life cycle continues.

The main body of a seaweed is often formless. A seaweed may have a stemlike structure that holds it to a rock. Many seaweeds have air-filled sacs called bladders. The bladders help the seaweed to float.

GOALS

You will study . . .
1. characteristics of nonvascular plants.
2. characteristics of vascular spore plants.

What is fertilization?

F.Y.I. The Sargasso Sea in the mid-Atlantic Ocean is about 5 000 000 km^2 of floating seaweed. Sailors used to believe the seaweed trapped ships.

FIGURE 19–9. Seaweeds are nonvascular plants that reproduce by spores.

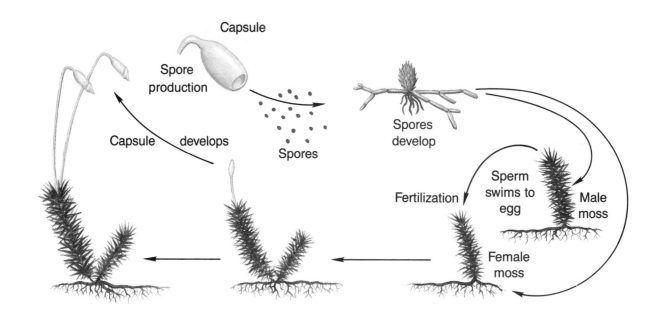

Capsule

Spore production

Capsule develops

Spores

Spores develop

Fertilization

Sperm swims to egg

Male moss

Female moss

FIGURE 19–10. The life cycle of a moss includes an alternation of the two processes of fertilization and spore production.

Just like other plants, all three kinds of algae have chlorophyll. The green color of red and brown algae is hidden by molecules that produce these other colors. You may be familiar with some common seaweeds. Sea lettuce is a green alga that floats without bladders. Its body is like a large, flat sheet. Irish moss is a red alga that lives in cooler waters. The giant kelp that lives along the Pacific Ocean coast from California to Alaska is a brown alga. Many kelp plants are over 100 meters long.

Mosses and liverworts are two other groups of nonvascular plants. They are often found on the floor of a forest and on fallen tree branches. Mosses and liverworts grow best in moist, shady areas. The plants are attached to the ground by hairlike structures that grow down from the stems. The stem of a moss is thin and grows straight up or, in some species, creeps along the ground. The body of some liverworts is a flat, formless structure. In others, there are three rows of thin leaves on a creeping stem. Mosses have very thin leaves that grow from all sides of the stem.

Eggs and sperm form in the tip of the moss stem. After an egg and sperm join, a long, hairlike stalk grows up from the tip of the stem. On the top of the stalk is a small swelling called a capsule where spores are produced. When the capsule is ripe, it breaks open and releases the spores. The spores of mosses are very light and are blown easily by the wind.

How are moss spores carried away from the parent moss plant?

SKILL BUILDER

Sequencing

All organisms have a life cycle. A life cycle is a series of events in the life of an organism. Most organisms reproduce themselves. Reproduction is either sexual or asexual.

Sexual reproduction involves a male and a female parent, each of which produces sex cells. In many plants and some animals, one parent can produce both male and female sex cells. A new organism grows and develops from a fertilized egg.

Asexual reproduction is the formation of a new organism by means other than the use of sex cells. Some organisms reproduce asexually by spores. In others, pieces of the body may break away and grow into new organisms.

The life cycles of many plants often have both kinds of reproduction that alternate. Put the following stages into a sequence that would represent the life cycle of a moss. If you need help with Sequencing, refer to page 537.

a. spores released
b. fertilization of an egg by a sperm
c. a leafy moss plant
d. capsule grows from top of a stem
e. a leafy moss plant

Questions

1. Is the leafy moss plant a male, a female, or either?
2. Where does fertilization occur in a moss plant?
3. What is produced by the capsule?
4. What grows from a moss spore?

F.Y.I. Over 12 000 species of ferns have been identified, more than any other vascular, spore plant.

FIGURE 19–11. Ferns are vascular plants that produce spores.

19:5 Vascular Spore Plants

Some vascular plants produce spores. Ferns are vascular plants that form large numbers of spores. The leaf of a fern is called a **frond** (FRAHND). Clusters of spore sacs are formed on the undersides of the fronds each year. The spores fall to the ground and begin to grow if they land where it is moist.

a

b

FIGURE 19–12. Vascular spore plants such as ferns (a) and horse-tails (b) were common on Earth long before the dinosaurs.

What is a rhizome?

Spores grow into small heart-shaped plants that look like flat liverworts. Eggs and sperm are formed in this plant. When the egg and sperm join, a new young fern develops. The young leaves are coiled like the top of a violin and are called *fiddleheads*.

Many ferns have rhizomes. Recall that a rhizome is an underground stem with stored food. Roots grow from the rhizome and take in water from the ground. Although ferns grow in all parts of the world, they are most common in tropical climates. Ferns range in size from water ferns that are about one cm across to tree ferns that grow to about 18 m tall!

Club mosses and horsetails are two more groups of vascular spore plants that live in moist places. Ferns, club mosses, and horsetails were abundant on Earth about 350 million years ago. Large, treelike forms of these plants grew in swampy places. When the plants died, they fell into the swampy water where they formed a thick, black mud. This material was rich in carbon and formed the coal beds that are mined for fuel today.

REVIEW

6. Why are seaweeds classified as plants?
7. What are the two main forms of reproductive structures that alternate in the life cycle of a non-vascular plant?
8. Name one way in which mosses and ferns are alike, and one way they are not alike.
9. What kinds of plants became today's coal beds?
10. How do mosses help to reduce loss of soil?

PROBLEM SOLVING

What Happened to the House Plants?

Terry wanted to make some extra money to buy a new tape of his favorite vocal group. Since he didn't have any ideas, he asked his father to help. His father knew that the Smiths were going on vacation. Mrs. Smith had told him she needed someone to water her plants while they were away.

Terry talked to Mrs. Smith and was given the job of watering her plants. She told him to give the fern a little water every day. The ivy and begonia were to be watered twice a week. Then, she told him not to water the cactus at all. The Smiths left the next day.

Terry was eager to water the plants. He visited the house every day and watered the plants according to what he thought were his instructions. During the

second week, the plants started to look unhealthy. The fern fronds had turned yellow, and the cactus looked sick and was leaning over. Only the ivy and begonia looked healthy. How can you explain what happened?

What Is a Seed Plant?

19:6 Conifers

Vascular plants that produce seeds are called seed plants. You probably know that peanuts, peas, beans, and corn are seeds. Much of the food you eat each day, such as cabbage, potatoes, apples, raisins, and lettuce, comes from vascular seed plants. All seed plants have a life cycle that includes the formation of pollen and ovules. **Pollen** is a small grainlike structure that contains the sperm of a seed plant. An **ovule** is a small structure that contains the egg of a seed plant. The pollen of a seed plant is carried or blown to the ovule of another seed plant. Sperm moves out of the pollen toward the ovule where the egg is fertilized by the sperm. The fertilized egg inside the ovule grows and develops into a seed. Seeds are carried away from the plant. When they land where there is enough water and the right temperature, the seeds will germinate. **Germination** is the growth of a seed to form a new plant.

GOALS
You will study . . .
1. characteristics of nonflowering seed plants.
2. characteristics of flowering seed plants.

a

b

FIGURE 19–13. A conifer (a) is a vascular seed plant that produces seeds in cones (b).

There are two main types of seed plants: conifers and flowering plants. Conifers produce seeds that are not surrounded by an outer protective wall. Conifers belong to a group of plants commonly called the gymnosperms (JIHM nuh spurmz). *Gymnosperm* means *naked seed.* A **conifer** is a seed plant that produces naked seeds in cones. Most conifers produce male and female cones. Cones are made up of overlapping scales. The male cones are small and grow in clusters at the ends of new branches. In the spring, these male cones produce large quantities of pollen. The larger, woody, and more familiar cone of the conifers is the female cone. Ovules develop on the upper side of each woody scale of a female cone. As the ovules mature into seeds, the cone scales open.

Pollen is blown away from the male cones by the wind. Early in the spring, conifer trees may be covered with yellow, powdery pollen. **Pollination** is the transfer of pollen from the male organ to the female organ of a seed plant. In conifers, some of the pollen lands on the surface of the ovules in the female cones. A short tube grows from the pollen, and the sperm passes along the tube and enters the ovule. Then the scales of the female cone close up tightly. The scales of the female cone open when the seeds are fully developed. The seeds are carried away from the tree by wind, birds, or animals. Eventually they grow into new conifer plants.

What is pollination?

F.Y.I. The cone of the west coast sugar pine can grow to almost 0.5 m long.

Examples of conifers include pine, fir, yew, redwood, spruce, and larch. The leaves of conifers are needlelike or scalelike. Many conifers are evergreen, but the great northern forests of larch trees lose their leaves each year.

Look at your pencil. Notice the light color and soft feel of the wood from which it is made. Millions of pencils are made each year from the relatively soft wood of conifers. What else do you see in your classroom that might be made from a conifer? A cupboard, a desk, or even the frame of your classroom when the school was built may have been made from a conifer. You may be familiar with the strong, pleasant smell of a pine tree. This is caused by oils in the soft wood. Pine oil is a common bathroom cleaning fluid. Many conifers are used to decorate the grounds of schools, homes, and businesses. Next time you walk around your neighborhood, see how many different conifers you notice.

Cycads are an ancient group of gymnosperms. They also existed millions of years ago in the time of the dinosaurs. Cycads have fernlike leaves and large cones at the top of a thick stem. The ginkgo is another ancient plant that is now a popular street tree all over the United States. The ginkgo is unusual because its seeds eventually grow to look like green cherries.

Do ginkgo plants exist today?

FIGURE 19–14. The soft wood of conifers is useful in the manufacture of pencils, paper, and many items of furniture.

19:7 Flowering Plants

In flowering plants, seeds are formed inside an ovary. An ovary is the part of the female reproductive organ that contains ovules. The ovules are surrounded by the protective wall of the ovary. When the ovules are fertilized, the ovary develops. The ovary with the fully grown seeds inside is called a **fruit.**

Flowering plants are also known as angiosperms (AN jee uh spurmz). *Angiosperm* means *covered seed.* The male and female reproductive organs of angiosperms are in structures called flowers. Most flowers are made up of four organs—sepals, petals, stamens, and pistils. The sepals are leaflike organs that protect the flower when it is still a bud. They are often green. When the flower bud opens, the sepals are below the petals. The petals are leaflike structures that are often very colorful and sweet smelling. The sweet smell comes from a small sac of sugary solution called nectar at the bases of the petals. The bright colors and nectar of petals attract many kinds of insects that are important for pollination. Inside the flower's petals are stamens. **Stamens** are the male reproductive organs of a seed plant. Pollen forms inside sacs on the stamens. The **pistil** is the female reproductive organ of the plant. The ovary with the ovules is at the base of the pistil. A stalk grows up from the ovary and at its tip is a sticky surface where pollen becomes trapped.

Name the male and female organs of seed plants.

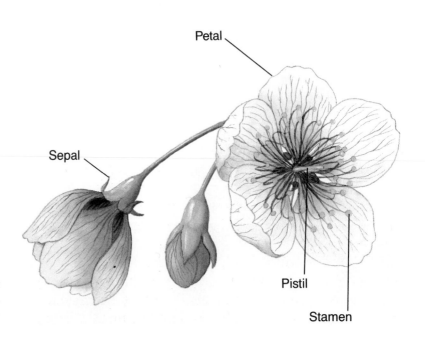

FIGURE 19–15. Bright, showy flowers attract insects for pollination.

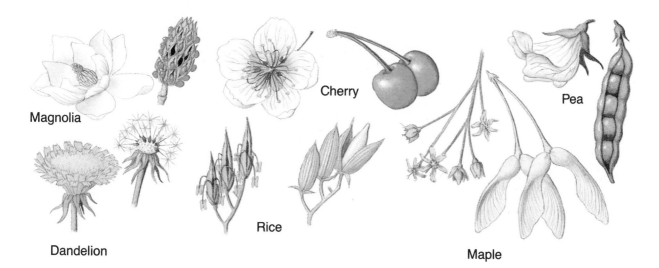

Magnolia

Cherry

Pea

Dandelion

Rice

Maple

Many showy flowers are adapted to pollination by insects such as bees or moths. Pollen is carried on the insects' bodies. Some flowers may not have showy petals. Flowering plants such as grasses and willow are pollinated by the wind. When pollen lands on a pistil, a tube grows down toward the ovary. Sperm pass down the tube and fertilize the eggs.

As the seeds grow, the ovary develops into a fruit. The petals and sepals dry up and fall from the ripening fruit. You have eaten or played with many kinds of fruits. The pea pod, grape, tomato, peach, acorn, and parachute "seeds" of a dandelion are all fruits. They all contain seeds.

There are many kinds of fruits. Some fruits, such as an orange, contain many seeds while others, such as a walnut, have only one seed. Some fruits, such as a pea pod, are dry when ripe and others, such as a melon, have a fleshy wall. Dandelion fruits are carried away by the wind. The fruits of impatiens burst open and shoot out their seeds. The fleshy fruits of raspberry plants are eaten by birds, and the seeds are then dropped away from the parent plant.

There are many kinds of seeds. The seeds of orchids are microscopic. They are carried by the wind. A coconut is a large seed up to 30 cm across. Coconuts are washed away by moving water. Maple and milkweed seeds have wings or parachutes and can be carried by the wind. Some seeds such as beggar's ticks and cockleburs have spines or hooks that catch onto hair, fur, or feathers of animals. You may have seen this seed in your socks after walking through a field.

FIGURE 19–16. There are many kinds of flowers, but they all produce seeds inside a fruit.

How is a grass flower pollinated?

F.Y.I. Some tropical moths that are adapted to pollinate orchids have a mouthpart that is 28 cm long to reach into the long tubes of the flowers.

What Is a Seed Plant? 401

Problem: How does plant food affect the growth of bean plants?

Materials

soaked lima beans (20)
potting soil
water
1-L jar
100-mL beakers (2)

pen
large plastic pots (2)
masking tape
water-soluble plant food
metric ruler

Procedure

1. Copy the data table.
2. Fill two plastic pots with equal amounts of potting soil. Moisten the soil by adding equal amounts of water.
3. In each pot, plant 10 lima bean seeds.
4. Label one pot *experimental group.* Label the other pot *control group.*
5. Place both pots in a location out of direct sunlight. Keep the soil moist in both containers by adding 25 mL of water to each pot each day.
6. After the first leaves have grown from each seed, measure the heights of the ten plants in each pot. Add these heights together and divide by ten to obtain the average height of plants for each pot.
7. Follow the directions on the package of plant food, and mix the fertilizer in a jar with water.
8. Measure 100 mL of fertilizer solution in a beaker. Water the experimental group with the solution. Measure and add 100 mL of water to the control group.
9. Hypothesize what will happen to each group of plants over the next four days.

10. Each day measure the bean plants in both pots and calculate the average heights for four days. Record the average heights in the table.

Data and Observation

Day	Average Height (mm)	
	Experimental	**Control**
Start		
Day 1		
Day 2		
Day 3		
Day 4		

Questions and Conclusions

1. What was the independent variable?
2. What was the dependent variable?
3. What was the purpose of using a control group?
4. Why did you measure the amount of liquid added to each pot?
5. Why were both pots placed in the same location?
6. What was your hypothesis? Was it supported by the experiment? Explain.
7. How does plant food affect the growth of bean plants?

a

b

The new plant inside a seed is called the embryo. The embryo has small seed leaves called cotyledons (kaht ul EED unz). Seeds that have two cotyledons are from seed plants called **dicotyledons** or dicots (DI kahts). **Monocotyledons** are plants that have only one seed leaf. They are often called monocots (MAHN uh kahts). Seeds contain stored food for the embryo's growth. In dicots, the stored food is in the two cotyledons. You may have noticed how beans and peanuts fall easily into two halves. These are the two cotyledons. In monocots, the stored food is in a tissue called endosperm. When you eat corn, you are eating mainly endosperm.

A corn plant is a typical monocot. Monocots have narrow leaves with parallel rows of veins. Their flower parts are often in groups of threes or sixes. Other monocots include grasses, orchids, bananas, lilies, and palm trees. A chrysanthemum is a typical dicot. Dicots have broad leaves with branched patterns of veins. The flower parts are usually in groups of fours or fives. Other dicots include oaks, spinach, melons, orchids, sunflowers, roses, beans, and cacti.

Seed plants live for one year, two years, or many years. Annuals are plants that grow from seeds, produce seeds, and die in one year. A common annual is a petunia. If you grow a plant in a climate colder than where it naturally grows, it will grow like an annual and die during the winter. Many garden flowers are thought to be annuals. Marigolds, coleus, and tomatoes are garden annuals that die each winter. These garden annuals live longer in the warmer climates of Africa and South America where they were originally discovered.

FIGURE 19-17. A monocot (a) has flower parts in threes. A dicot (b) has flower parts in groups of four or five.

What are annuals?

F.Y.I. The rate of growth of bamboo, a monocot, may be as much as 30 cm per day.

What Is a Seed Plant? 403

FIGURE 19–18. A garden planted with annuals, biennials, and perennials can be very attractive.

Biennials are plants that complete their life cycle in two years. In the first year, biennials produce roots, stems, and leaves. In the second year, they produce flowers and seeds. The plant then dies. Sweet clover, foxglove, hollyhock, and potato are biennials.

Perennials live for many years. Perennials produce roots, stems, leaves, flowers, and seeds all in the first year. The stem and leaves may die off during the winter, but the next spring the plants begin to grow again. Examples of perennials are violets, roses, chrysanthemums, and peonies. All the trees, such as oaks, maples, and birches are also perennial plants.

What are biennials?

F.Y.I. Lotus seeds over 400 years old found in the dried bed of an ancient Chinese lake were still able to germinate.

REVIEW

11. From which organ does a seed develop?
12. How are pine cones pollinated?
13. How are petals important to pollination?
14. How long is the life cycle of a biennial?
15. A coconut palm has leaves with parallel rows of veins and a seed with a thick layer of white endosperm. Is it a monocot or a dicot?

SUMMARY

1. Plants have cells with cellulose cell walls. All plants need water. Some plants take up water through vascular tissues. The roots, stems, and leaves of plants are adapted to life on land. 19:1
2. Photosynthesis and respiration are two important processes of plants. Plants respond to stimuli such as light and gravity. 19:2
3. Humans are dependent on plants for food, warmth, and shelter. The Mayans were an ancient society that learned to grow crops in forest areas without destroying the environment. 19:3
4. Nonvascular spore plants include mosses, liverworts, and three groups of algae. All plants have sex cells. An egg is fertilized by a sperm. Spore plants also reproduce by spores. 19:4
5. Vascular spore plants include ferns, club mosses, and horsetails. 19:5
6. All seed plants are vascular and have a life cycle that includes eggs, sperm, pollen, and ovules. Gymnosperms produce seeds that develop from unprotected ovules in cones. 19:6
7. Angiosperms produce seeds inside an ovary. The ovary ripens to form the fruit that is either dry or fleshy. Flowering plants are either annuals, biennials, or perennials. 19:7

VOCABULARY

a. cellulose
b. conifer
c. consumer
d. dicotyledons
e. fertilization
f. frond
g. fruit

h. germination
i. monocotyledons
j. ovule
k. phloem
l. pistil
m. pollen
n. pollination

o. producer
p. seed
q. selective breeding
r. stamens
s. transpiration
t. vascular tissue
u. xylem

Match each description with the correct vocabulary word from the list above.

1. a plant organ that protects the fully grown seeds
2. a plant that has seeds in cones
3. small, grainlike structure that contains sperm
4. the joining of an egg and a sperm
5. the movement of water out of a plant
6. the leaf of a fern
7. plants that have two seed leaves
8. the male reproductive organs of flowering plants
9. transfer of pollen from the stamens to the pistil
10. food conducting tubes in vascular plants

CHAPTER 19 REVIEW

MAIN IDEAS

A. Reviewing Concepts

Choose the word or phrase that correctly completes each of the following sentences.

1. The leaves of all green plants _____.
   a. produce glucose
   b. contain spores
   c. develop flowers
   d. produce seeds
2. The part of the vascular tissue that transports water is _____.
   a. chlorophyll
   b. phloem
   c. xylem
   d. epidermis
3. _____ are produced in the process of respiration.
   a. H_2O and O_2
   b. CO_2 and O_2
   c. $C_6H_{12}O_6$ and O_2
   d. H_2O and CO_2
4. The reproductive organ of a flower that produces eggs is the _____.
   a. stamen
   b. style
   c. anther
   d. pistil
5. _____ are underground storage organs.
   a. Needles
   b. Fronds
   c. Rhizomes
   d. Cotyledons
6. Early people stored _____ for the next year's crops.
   a. vegetables
   b. wood
   c. flowers
   d. seeds
7. Flowers without bright colors or nectar are pollinated by _____.
   a. spores
   b. wind
   c. water
   d. insects
8. A flowering plant with two seed leaves is a _____.
   a. dicot
   b. moss
   c. seaweed
   d. monocot
9. Conifers produce seeds in structures called _____.
   a. flowers
   b. spores
   c. cones
   d. anthers
10. Annuals live for _____.
    a. two years
    b. many years
    c. one month
    d. one year
11. _____ are plants that live for many years.
    a. Biennials
    b. Annuals
    c. Bicentennials
    d. Perennials
12. _____ are plants that produce flowers.
    a. Angiosperms
    b. Gymnosperms
    c. Conifers
    d. Ferns
13. An example of a seaweed is a _____.
    a. cycad
    b. moss
    c. brown alga
    d. liverwort
14. The food-producing process of plants is called _____.
    a. pollination
    b. photosynthesis
    c. germination
    d. respiration
15. Stems that are soft and green are _____.
    a. woody
    b. scaly
    c. herbaceous
    d. vascular

B. Understanding Concepts

Answer the following questions using complete sentences.

16. What is pollination?
17. What are the two kinds of root systems?
18. On which part of a fern are spores produced?
19. What is the main source of energy for photosynthesis?
20. What compound is the source of energy for respiration?
21. Name five plant products used by people.
22. Where do most mosses grow?
23. How are bright colors important in pollination of flowers?

24. Name three stimuli to which plants respond.

25. Where do most algae live?

C. Applying Concepts

Answer the following questions using complete sentences.

26. Describe how the process of photosynthesis affects the oxygen in our atmosphere.

27. Describe the life cycle of a moss.

28. What is the purpose of a fruit, such as a ripe tomato?

29. How are green plants like cyanobacteria? How are they different?

30. Explain the statement, "All food comes from the sun."

SKILL REVIEW

If you need help, refer to the Skill Handbook, pages 526 to 537.

1. Classify the following plants as either gymnosperms or angiosperms. Refer to Sections 19:7 and 19:8 for help.

tomato   cycads   ginkgoes
peach   dandelion

2. Put the following items in the correct sequence.

a. green color of leaves breaks down
b. leaves fall from the plant
c. the weather begins to get cold
d. leaves turn red, yellow, or orange
e. leaves stop making chlorophyll

3. You are responsible for recording the daily growth and total height of the school's bamboo plant. Unfortunately, you forgot to record all of your measurements. Now you must complete your data table using only the information you recorded. Copy and complete the data table and give it a heading.

Day	Daily Growth (cm)	Total Height (cm)
1	2	2
2	3	
3	5	
4		20
5	5	

4. You have 30 pea plants that you divide into two groups of 15. You water the soil of the first group every other day for two weeks. You water the second group at the same time but pour it only on the plants' leaves, not allowing any of it to reach the pea plants' roots. After two weeks you find the first group grew while the second group wilted. What can you infer from this experiment?

5. In the experiment described in Question 4, which group is the control group?

PROJECTS

1. Make a collection of fruits and seeds. Classify them according to whether each is dispersed by wind, water, or animals.

2. Use books from the library to find out about the history of some of our food crops such as wheat and potatoes.

READINGS

1. Carey, J. "Brave New World of Super Plants." *International Wildlife.* November-December, 1986, pages 16-18.

2. Parker, Steve. *How Plants Grow.* Danbury, CT: Watts, 1985.

3. Woods, Sylvia. *Plant Facts and Fancies.* Winchester, MA: Faber and Faber, 1985.

Animals

CHAPTER 20

Career: Guide Dog Trainer

Kristen had always wanted a dog. One of her friends told her about adopting dogs that "failed" in guide-dog training. The failures were house-trained, only about a year old, and may have failed only because they were too friendly or didn't like loud noises. Kristen's parents decided that that kind of dog might work out.

When they arrived at Guide School to pick up their dog, they were surprised at all the activity. Several people were in the yard holding harnesses that were around other people. The trainer who met them explained that the people wearing harnesses were pretending to be guide dogs. They were helping the new trainers to learn how to give commands. Later, the new trainers would work with dogs, teaching them how to be the "eyes" for blind people. Each dog is trained daily for four months, and each trainer is responsible for a particular dog. Then the trainer introduces the dog to the blind student and teaches the student to work with the dog.

The trainer introduced Kristen to her new dog, a very friendly, lop-eared retriever. She now had the responsibility of being a loving owner.

In this chapter, you will study the characteristics of animals. You will also study the differences between invertebrates and vertebrates, and between warm- and cold-blooded animals.

F.Y.I. Leader Dogs for the Blind, 1039 South Rochester Road, Rochester, MI 48063

What Is an Animal?

GOALS

You will study . . .
1. the characteristics of animals.
2. adaptations of animals.
3. how zoos help animals survive.

How does an animal obtain food?

FIGURE 20–1. The nine phyla of animals.

20:1 Characteristics of Animals

Have you ever heard someone say, "That's not an animal, it's an insect"? Many people think of animals as only those that are pets or are kept in a zoo. Sometimes people do not like to think of themselves as animals. This might be because humans seem to have control over all organisms. However, humans are also classified in the animal kingdom.

There are over one million species of animals. All animals have similar characteristics. Recall that animal cells do not have a cell wall or chloroplasts. Animals are consumers, and they must move around to find their food or to keep from being eaten.

Animals are classified into nine major phyla. Eight of the nine phyla of animals are invertebrates (in VERT uh brayts). An **invertebrate** is an animal without a backbone. *Vertebra* means "backbone" and *in-* means "without." Sponges, stinging-celled animals, flatworms, and roundworms are invertebrates that have simple body structures and systems. Invertebrates that have more complex organization of body structures are segmented worms, mollusks (MAHL usks), spiny-bodied

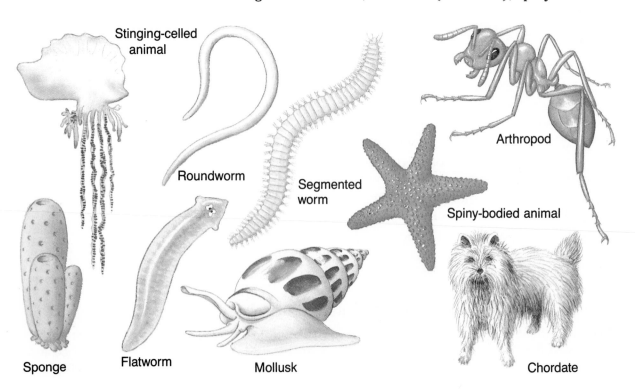

Stinging-celled animal

Roundworm

Segmented worm

Arthropod

Spiny-bodied animal

Sponge

Flatworm

Mollusk

Chordate

animals, and arthropods (AR thruh pahdz). Some invertebrate animals have an exoskeleton (EK soh skel uht uhn). An **exoskeleton** is a hard outer covering such as the shell of a crab or a beetle. *Exo-* means "outer." An exoskeleton protects the soft body of an invertebrate. Invertebrates without an exoskeleton are protected by spines, a tough skin, or cells that can sting.

What structures protect the soft body of an invertebrate?

The ninth group of animals belongs to the chordate (KOR dayt) phylum. Most chordates are vertebrates (VERT uh brayts). A **vertebrate** is an animal with a backbone. There are seven major classes of vertebrates. These classes are three kinds of fishes, amphibians, reptiles, birds, and mammals. A vertebrate has an endoskeleton (EN doh skel uht uhn). An **endoskeleton** is a skeleton on the inside of the body. *Endo-* means "inner." An endoskeleton supports the soft body of a vertebrate. You will learn more about the nine animal phyla later in this chapter.

SKILL BUILDER

Graphing

There are over one million species of animals. Use the following data to make a bar graph of different animal phyla to show how their numbers of species compare. If you need help, refer to Graphing on pages 532–533.

Phylum	Numbers of Species
Sponges	5 000
Stinging-celled animals	11 000
Three worm phyla	26 000
Mollusks	80 000
Arthropods	826 000
Spiny-bodied animals	5 000
Chordates	47 000

Questions

1. On which axis did you plot numbers of species?
2. On the bar graph, how can you recognize that two phyla have the same numbers of species?
3. Why is a bar graph useful for comparing numbers of animal species?

20:2 Animal Adaptations

As you take a walk in the park, you notice a chipmunk running into a hole in the ground. At that moment a mosquito buzzes near your ear, and as you move quickly to avoid its bite you startle a bird in a nearby bush. You sit down by a pond to watch the goldfish swimming by, and a frog leaps and lands with a plop into the water. These animals are all so different. Why do some fly, some swim, and some live underground? All these variations among animals are the result of adaptations.

Respiration

What is oxygen used for by most animals?

Most animals use oxygen for the cell process that releases energy from foods. Some animals take in oxygen from the air. Insects and spiders have a system of tiny tubes through which oxygen passes to all cells of the body. Animals such as reptiles and birds have internal saclike organs called lungs. Oxygen is breathed into the lungs where it enters the blood and is carried to the cells. Worms that live in soil or water absorb oxygen directly through the skin. Some animals such as fish take in oxygen from the water through gills. Gills are flaplike organs with many tubes through which gases can pass into and out of the body. Water enters the animal's mouth, passes over the gills where the gases are exchanged, and flows out of the openings in the sides of the body called gill slits.

FIGURE 20–2. Some animals are adapted to breathing oxygen from the air (a). Others take in oxygen from water (b).

a

b

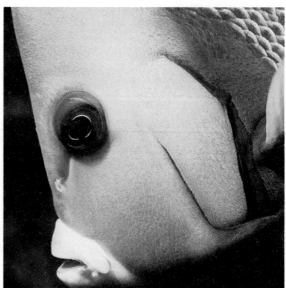

Body Temperature

Some of the energy that is released by respiration is used by vertebrates to keep their bodies warm. Different kinds of vertebrates have different body temperatures. If body temperature falls too low or rises too high, an animal may die. Birds are warm-blooded vertebrates. Warm-blooded vertebrates can keep their body temperature the same even in cold or hot weather. Your average body temperature is 37°C regardless of the changes in daily outside temperatures. You are a warm-blooded vertebrate.

The body temperature of a cold-blooded vertebrate changes as the temperature of its surroundings changes. Cold-blooded vertebrates cannot keep their body temperature the same. Fish, amphibians, and reptiles are cold-blooded vertebrates.

a

b

Reproduction

Reproduction is the process by which new individuals are produced. A large female cod fish may lay over nine million eggs in one spring. A robin lays six to ten eggs a year. Why does one kind of animal produce so many more eggs than another?

Remember the female sex cells are eggs, the male sex cells are sperm, and eggs are fertilized by sperm. Fertilization usually requires water because the sperm must swim to the egg. In many animals that live in water, fertilization is external. **External fertilization** is the uniting of an egg and sperm outside of the body.

FIGURE 20–3. Vertebrates are either warm blooded (a) or cold blooded (b).

Define external fertilization.

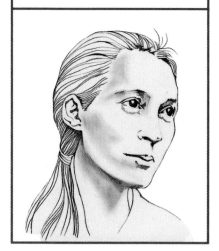
A female fish deposits large numbers of eggs in the water. The male fish swims over the eggs and releases sperm. Many sperm may be washed away so that only a few of the eggs are fertilized. In external fertilization, many eggs and sperm become food for other animals.

The eggs of animals that live on land are fertilized internally. **Internal fertilization** is the uniting of egg and sperm inside the body of the female. The male deposits sperm directly inside the body of the female. When eggs are fertilized inside the body fewer eggs are wasted. The eggs of insects are fertilized before they are laid. In reptiles and birds a protective shell forms around the fertilized eggs before they are laid. In a mammal, the fertilized eggs develop for a long time inside the body of the female before the young are born.

Communication

Communication (kuh myew nih KAY shun) is a very important adaptation for the survival and reproduction of a species. Communication is the exchange of signals or messages such as flashing lights, odors, bright colors, or sound. Animals of the same species use communication for mating. Fireflies attract mates by patterns of light flashes. The female gypsy moth gives off a scent that can be detected by a male 4.5 km away. Male frogs use croaking sounds to attract females.

FIGURE 20–4. Animals attract their mates with colors, smells, patterns of behavior, and sounds.

a

b

FIGURE 20-5. Warning colors (a) and camouflage (b) are two adaptations that protect animals from predators.

Some animal signals help to warn away predators (PRED ut urz) or hide an animal from its prey. A **predator** is an animal that captures other animals for food. The animals that are eaten by the predator are the **prey.** Some color patterns on an animal are warning colors. **Warning colors** are bright, bold color patterns on an animal that warn predators away. Warning colors are often seen on animals that can sting, bite, or have a bad taste. Once a toad has been stung by a bee with a pattern of orange and black bands of color, it will not try to eat any other insect with this color pattern.

Many animals can learn. The toad can learn to avoid the warning colors that caused it to be stung. Your pet dog will learn how to beg if it is given a reward such as food. Learning is important for the survival of many wild animals. Animals soon learn how to recognize their predators or where to find food.

The colors and patterns of some animals provide camouflage (KAM uh flahj). **Camouflage** is the natural disguise that hides an animal from its predators or its prey. Some animals have the body shape of something in their surroundings. The stick insect looks like a thin twig of a bush. This insect rests among the twigs and hardly moves. An animal with camouflage can capture prey or escape from predators without being seen.

What animals often have warning colors?

F.Y.I. A tropical grasshopper that resembles a green leaf even has markings on it that look like holes chewed by insects.

What Is an Animal? 415

PROBLEM SOLVING

The Trained Goldfish

Harvey was the proud new owner of two goldfish. Harvey had been given the goldfish by a friend who had moved away. He fed the goldfish every morning. Since Harvey wanted to watch them, he turned on the aquarium light before he fed them.

His grandparents from out of town were visiting one weekend. Since they had not seen his goldfish, he wanted to show them off. One evening they all went to Harvey's room to see the goldfish. When Harvey turned on the light, the goldfish stopped swimming and came to the surface looking for food.

What caused the behavior of the goldfish? How can Harvey be sure what caused their behavior?

SCIENCE AND SOCIETY

20:3 Zoos—Menageries or Preserves?

Zoological gardens, commonly called zoos, are collections of live animals in parks. Animals have been kept in zoos for over two thousand years. The ancient Egyptians and Chinese had large collections of exotic animals. Many of these zoos were just for show. Collections of animals for show are called menageries (muh NAJ uh rihz).

Early zoos contained collections of animals in cages and pits with as many different and unusual animals as they could display. Today, many zoos try to make the cages or enclosures look more like the places where the animals once lived. Animals are more likely to mate and breed in natural environments.

Many animals in the wild are not able to survive because their natural habitats have been destroyed. A **habitat** is the place in the environment where an organism lives. As more people need space, more habitats have been taken over for crops, houses, and highways. The panda in China, the condor in California, and the rhinoceros in Java are all endangered species. **Endangered species** are those that have so few members that they may not be able to survive.

a

b

Zoos keep family groups of endangered species on preserves. Preserves are large natural areas of protected land. Animals in preserves mate more often and have more young than those kept in cages. The protected animals are then released into the wild where the species may become reestablished. Is it wise to release animals back into the wild where there may not be any natural predators? Are zoos interfering with nature when they save rare animals from extinction?

FIGURE 20–6. Endangered species such as the red wolf (a) can be cared for by zoos and later released in a protected area (b).

REVIEW

1. What are the nine major phyla of animals?
2. How do animals obtain oxygen from water?
3. What is a warm-blooded vertebrate?
4. What two adaptations protect animals from predators?
5. How do zoos help to preserve species of animals?

What Is an Invertebrate?

20:4 Simple Invertebrates

Remember that invertebrates are animals without backbones and that there are eight major phyla. When you walk across a lawn or a field you may notice lots of small invertebrate animals jumping, flying, or crawling about. If you turn over some rocks in a shallow stream, you may notice very small wormlike animals that are attached to the rocks. These animals are also invertebrates. Simple invertebrates are animals that do not have complex tissues, organs, or organ systems. The four phyla are sponges, stinging-celled animals, flatworms, and roundworms.

GOALS

You will study . . .
1. the characteristics of simple invertebrates.
2. the characteristics of complex invertebrates.

Name the four phyla of simple invertebrates.

Sponges

The sponge phylum is made up of simple invertebrates that live at the bottom of oceans, rivers, or streams. You may have seen a natural sponge in your bathroom. Today, it is more common to use a factory-made sponge for washing and cleaning.

The body of a sponge is like a bag with two layers of cells and an opening at the top. In between these layers are spiny or soft materials from which the two layers develop. The wall of the sponge has small openings called pores. The cells on the inside of the body have flagella. The flagella move and cause water to flow in through the pores into the body cavity and out through the opening at the top. As the water is pulled into the body, tiny organisms in the water are trapped inside the sponge and used by some of the cells for food.

What is a larva?

A sponge produces both eggs and sperm. A fertilized egg forms a larva. A **larva** is an early undeveloped and active stage of some animals. The sponge larvae swim out of the body opening, settle on a hard surface, and develop into new sponges. Sponges also reproduce by budding. Pieces of a sponge's body break away into the water where they grow into new sponges.

FIGURE 20–7. A sponge (a) has a simple body structure with two layers of cells (b).

a

b

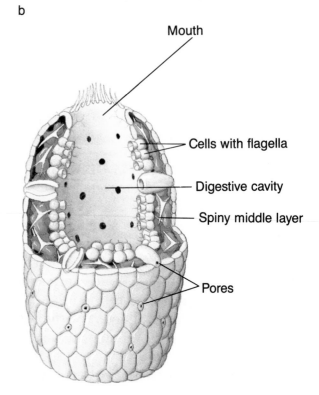

Mouth

Cells with flagella

Digestive cavity

Spiny middle layer

Pores

Stinging-celled Animals

Stinging-celled animals are simple invertebrates that live in oceans, rivers, or streams. If you have ever been stung by a coral or a jellyfish, you know why this phylum has its name. Jellyfish, hydra, sea anemones (uh NEM uh neez), and corals are all stinging-celled animals. All have armlike structures called tentacles that grow out around an opening at the top of the body. The stinging cells are found along the length of each tentacle. The tentacles and stinging cells are used by the animals to capture and paralyze prey. The opening at the top is the animal's mouth. Small organisms that swim by and touch the tentacles are stung and trapped. The tentacles push the organisms into the mouth, and they become food for the animal.

It may be difficult to believe that a rocklike coral is an animal. A piece of coral is a colony of animals. Each animal builds a small cup of limestone. The cups are held together by more limestone. The tentacles of the coral push out from the cup and wave around in the water to capture food. Many thousands of animals may live in a coral colony. When a coral dies, the cup in which it once lived remains. New coral grows on top of it, causing the mound to become larger. After thousands of years a coral reef is formed.

What is coral?

F.Y.I. Entire islands in the Pacific Ocean are made of coral.

How does a coral reef form?

FIGURE 20–8. A jellyfish (a) is a typical stinging-celled animal with a mouth surrounded by tentacles (b).

a

b

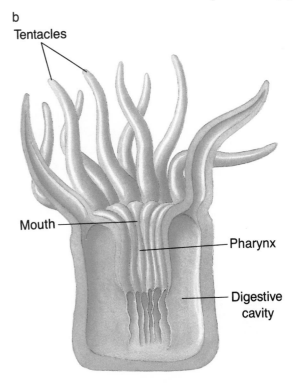

Tentacles

Mouth

Pharynx

Digestive cavity

Describe the general appearance of a flatworm.

Flatworms

When you think of a worm, you probably think of an earthworm. However, there are three phyla of worms. Flatworms and roundworms are simple invertebrates. The earthworm is a segmented worm and will be described later as a phylum of complex invertebrates.

Worms with a flattened body and three body layers of cells belong to the flatworm phylum. The solid body of a flatworm has a head end, a tail end, and only one body opening. Planarians are flatworms. On the underside of a planarian's body is a tube with a mouth at the end, by which food is sucked up.

Some flatworms are parasites. A tapeworm is a flatworm parasite of humans. The head of a tapeworm has hooks that attach it to the wall of the small intestine. Its long, ribbonlike body extends along the intestine. Tapeworms do not have a mouth or a body cavity. Food is absorbed directly into its body from the intestine. Tapeworms produce millions of eggs that pass out of a person's body within solid wastes. If these solid wastes contaminate food on which cows or pigs feed, the eggs develop and move into the muscles of the animal. People can become infected with tapeworms when they eat beef or pork that is infected and not properly cooked.

FIGURE 20–9. Flatworms such as a planarian (a) have a simple body structure (b).

a

b

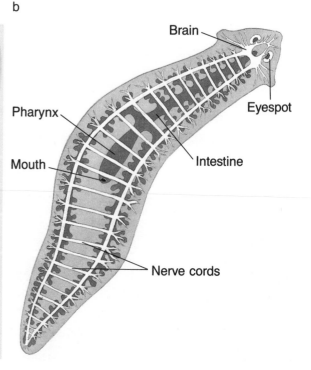

Roundworms

Worms with smooth, rounded bodies and openings at both ends belong to the roundworm phylum. Roundworms are found in soil or water, and some are parasites. A roundworm takes in food through a mouth at one end, and wastes are released at the other end. The tube through a roundworm's body is a simple digestive system.

How many body openings does a roundworm have?

Some roundworms are helpful in the environment. Soil roundworms are microscopic, threadlike organisms. A shovelful of rich soil may have millions of roundworms. They help to convert fallen leaves and dead animals into humus. Some harmful roundworms are parasites of plants and animals. It is wise to treat your pet dog or cat regularly for worm infections.

FIGURE 20–10. Roundworms are often parasites of pets.

20:5 Complex Invertebrates

The four phyla of complex invertebrates are segmented worms, mollusks, spiny-bodied animals, and arthropods. The members of each phyla all have well-developed organ systems.

Segmented Worms

Segmented worms are the third phylum of worms. These worms have complex digestive, circulatory, and nervous systems. Their bodies are long, tubelike, and arranged in sections called segments.

Earthworms are segmented worms that are important in the soil. As earthworms burrow through the soil, they digest dead organic matter. The tunnels of the worms allow air and water to enter the soil. Plant matter is pulled into the tunnels by the worms. These activities keep the soil loose and rich in nutrients.

Leeches are parasitic segmented worms. They are found in oceans, rivers, or streams where they feed on the blood of vertebrates. A leech has suckers at each end of its body to hold onto a vertebrate while it draws blood into its body through its mouth. When the digestive tract is full of blood, the leech drops off. A leech can survive for several months on a single meal.

FIGURE 20–11. Segmented worms have more complex digestive, nervous, and circulatory systems than do other worm phyla.

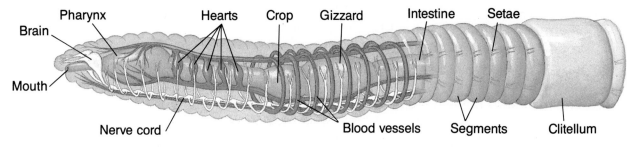

Brain

Pharynx

Hearts Crop Gizzard Intestine Setae

Mouth

Nerve cord

Blood vessels Segments Clitellum

TECHNOLOGY

Leeches — The Good, Bad, and Ugly

Until the early part of the twentieth century, doctors used leeches to remove blood from patients. The belief was that blood in sick people contained "bad" elements that caused diseases. Leeches were sometimes used because they would suck out a certain amount of blood and then drop off. The sight of the blood-sucking creature on the body probably made the patient feel even more sick.

In recent years, leeches have again been used for some very special medical purposes. For example, during an accident a person's finger may be cut off, then a surgeon must reattach the finger to the body. When they do this, they must reconnect all of the microscopic blood vessels to allow the blood to pass back into the severed finger. If the blood cannot circulate and return to the body, the blood will collect in and clog the finger. The reattached finger will then turn blue and will soon die. Surgeons have found that if they attach leeches to a re- attached body part, the blood flows freely and does not collect. When blood vessels have grown back into the body part, the leeches are removed.

ADVANCE

Blood clotting is a major cause of heart attacks and strokes in humans. Leeches produce chemicals that keep blood from clotting. A chemical from a giant leech that lives in South America could be used to dissolve blood clots before they can cause serious health problems.

422 Animals

Problem: What organ systems can you identify in an earthworm?

Materials

preserved earthworm   scissors
dissecting pan   forceps
dissecting pins   paper towels (2)
scalpel

Procedure

1. Place two folded paper towels in the dissecting pan. Lay the earthworm on the towels with its ventral side down. The ventral side feels bristly.
2. Use the diagram to identify the mouth, clitellum, setae, and anus on your specimen.
3. Pin down the first and last segments of the earthworm. Starting at the tail end, use the scalpel to cut carefully and not too deeply through the skin and body wall for about 4 cm. **CAUTION:** *Be careful when using sharp objects.* Use the dissecting pins to force the skin open and pin down the body wall. Use the scissors to cut the internal partitions between segments.
4. Continue cutting until you reach the head. Pin down the body wall as you go.
5. Use the diagram and forceps to locate the pharynx, esophagus, crop, gizzard, intestine, and anus of the digestive system.
6. Locate the five pairs of hearts around the esophagus and the upper blood vessel of the circulatory system.
7. Examine the nervous system. Locate the two-part brain above the pharynx and the two nerve cords that join to form a single nerve cord down the length of the body. Each segment contains a collection of nerve cells called ganglia. Use the scissors to remove the pharynx. Observe the ganglia.

Data and Observations

Draw your dissected earthworm. Use the diagram of the dissected earthworm to help you identify and label all the parts.

Questions and Conclusions

1. What are the five internal structures of an earthworm's digestive system?
2. What structures of the earthworm's circulatory system did you observe?
3. What structures of the earthworm's nervous system did you observe?
4. What organ systems can you identify in an earthworm?

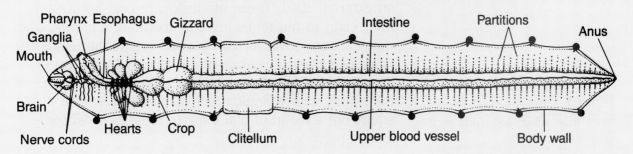

Pharynx Esophagus Gizzard   Intestine   Partitions   Anus
Ganglia
Mouth
Brain
Nerve cords   Hearts   Crop   Clitellum   Upper blood vessel   Body wall

a

b

FIGURE 20-12. A snail (a) and a squid (b) are both classified as mollusks.

Mollusks

Have you ever looked at a menu in a seafood restaurant? You may have seen such items as oysters on the half shell, clam chowder, and pasta with octopus or squid sauce. All these foods are made from mollusks. Mollusks are a favorite food for many people and also an important food for animals. All mollusks have a soft body and a head. Many have a strong muscle called a foot that is used for movement.

Many kinds of mollusks such as snails, clams, and oysters are protected by a shell. Snails have one spiral shell. Snails have a mouth with which they eat organic material. Clams and oysters have two hinged shells. These mollusks are called bivalves. Bivalves obtain their oxygen and food from the water by gills. Small organisms are trapped on the slime in the gills. Cilia move the organisms from the gills into the body.

How do bivalves obtain oxygen?

Squids and octopuses are mollusks that do not have an external shell. These mollusks are best known for their eight to ten tentacles that surround a mouth. The tentacles are covered with suction cups that help them hold their prey. They can move quickly by a form of jet propulsion. They squirt back a jet of water from their body cavity. Squids and octopuses can also squirt out a cloud of black ink to hide their escape from a predator.

F.Y.I. The giant squid may be more than 18 m long and is the largest invertebrate.

424 Animals

Spiny-bodied Animals

A starfish moves along the bottom of the ocean floor. A predator grabs one of the starfish's five arms. The arm breaks off and is eaten. The starfish escapes. Within a few months the starfish has grown a new arm by regeneration (rih jen uh RAY shun). **Regeneration** is the repair and regrowth of a missing part of the body.

Starfish, sea urchins, and sand dollars are all spiny-bodied animals. Inside the wall of the body, there is a skeleton of hard plates with spines. The spines help to protect these animals from predators. Tiny tube feet along the underside of the arms act like suction cups. The tube feet help the animal to move across the ground and can also wrap around a bivalve to force it open. The mouth of a starfish is on the underside in the center of its body. The starfish pushes out its stomach through the mouth, between the bivalve's shells, and sucks out the mollusk.

How does a starfish consume a mollusk?

FIGURE 20–13. The tube feet of a sea urchin extend out from the spiny body to capture prey.

F.Y.I. The antennas on an arthropod are sometimes called feelers.

Arthropods

Arthropods are animals with an exoskeleton. The exoskeleton protects the soft body of the arthropod. The exoskeleton cannot enlarge as the body grows. The animal must molt. When an arthropod molts, its exoskeleton is shed. A new exoskeleton hardens around the larger body. Arthropods have six or more jointed legs called appendages. Appendages are used as legs, for sense organs called antennas, or as mouthparts. Examples of arthropods include centipedes, spiders, crabs, and insects.

FIGURE 20–14. Arthropods have appendages.

a b c d

FIGURE 20–15. Like many other insects, a bumblebee goes through complete metamorphosis of egg (a), larva (b), pupa (c), and adult (d).

What are the three body parts of an insect?

F.Y.I. The case of an insect's pupa is a cocoon. The pupal stage of a butterfly is called a chrysalis.

F.Y.I. Two spiders in the United States that can cause severe discomfort with their bites are the black widow spider and the brown recluse spider.

There are more species of insects than all other animal species combined. They all have a head, thorax, and abdomen. The head has antennas and mouthparts. Mouthparts are used either for sucking, biting, chewing, or lapping. The thorax has three pairs of legs and often one or two pairs of wings. The abdomen has appendages adapted for reproduction.

Insects go through a process called metamorphosis (met uh MOR fuh sus). **Metamorphosis** is a series of changes in the appearance of an organism as it develops from an egg to an adult. Metamorphosis in insects can be complete or incomplete. A grasshopper has incomplete metamorphosis. The egg hatches into a nymph that looks like a small form of the adult. The nymph grows and molts several times until it reaches adult size. A moth has complete metamorphosis. The egg of a moth hatches into a wormlike larva called a caterpillar that eats, grows, and changes into a pupa. Inside the pupa, the insect's form changes. When the case of the pupa opens, the adult moth emerges.

Most flowering plants are pollinated by insects such as the honeybee. Some insects such as the ladybug beetle feed on other insects that are pests and keep their numbers under control. Insects can also be harmful. The crops that are grown to feed people are also food for the larvae of many insects. Some insects such as fleas are parasites on warm-blooded vertebrates.

6. How does a coral obtain its food?
7. What is one example of a parasitic worm?
8. How do bivalves obtain oxygen?
9. What are the four stages of complete metamorphosis?
10. How are segmented worms, mollusks, spiny-bodied animals, and arthropods alike?

What Is a Vertebrate?

20:6 Cold-blooded Vertebrates

Vertebrates are animals that have the most complex organ systems. Remember that vertebrates have an endoskeleton that supports and protects the soft body from inside. There are seven major classes of vertebrates. Five of the classes of vertebrates are cold blooded. These are three kinds of fish, amphibians (am FIHB ee unz), and reptiles.

Fish

Fish live in water and obtain oxygen by means of gills. The body of a fish is usually covered by scales and is coated with slime. Movements of the body and tail push the fish smoothly through the water. Most fish have fins that help to guide them. Most fish lay eggs but only a few species of fish have internal fertilization.

There are three groups of fish: jawless fish, cartilage (KART ul ihj) fish, and bony fish. Jawless fish have a long, tubelike body, no fins, and no scales. Instead of a jaw, they have a round, sucker mouth. The skeleton of a jawless fish is made of cartilage. **Cartilage** is a tough, flexible tissue in the bodies of vertebrates.

GOALS

You will study . . .
1. some characteristics of vertebrates.
2. how to distinguish the seven major vertebrate classes.

Name the three groups of fish.

FIGURE 20–16. A lamprey is a jawless fish that is often parasitic on a bony fish.

F.Y.I. Lungfish are an ancient type of fish that have both gills and lungs. When the shallow ponds they live in become low in oxygen, the lungfish can breathe air.

Cartilage fish have a skeleton of cartilage, but they also have a jaw. Cartilage fish such as sharks have fins. They feed on other fish with a mouth that is filled with many rows of sharp teeth. Cartilage fish have toothlike scales that cover their bodies. They usually have internal fertilization.

Bony fish are the fish in your local fishing stream and most of the fish in the oceans. Bony fish have a skeleton made of bone. Bony fish of oceans include tuna, haddock, and sea bass. Common bony fish of fresh water are carp, sunfish, rainbow trout, and catfish. The scales of bony fish are smooth. Most kinds of bony fish have external fertilization.

Amphibians

What does the word *amphibian* mean?

The word *amphibian* means "having a double life." This is a good description of amphibians such as frogs, toads, and salamanders. A frog begins life in the water where a female has laid her eggs. The eggs are immediately fertilized by a male. A larva that hatches from a frog's egg is called a tadpole. Tadpoles obtain their oxygen from the water by means of gills. They go through metamorphosis and develop into adult frogs that breathe air with lungs.

Salamanders are amphibians with a tail. Some salamanders do not go through all the stages of metamorphosis. When they hatch, they are like small adults with gills. All amphibians have smooth skin covered with slime that protects the skin from drying out.

F.Y.I. In the colder northern climates, bullfrog tadpoles may take more than two years to go through metamorphosis into frogs.

FIGURE 20–17. Some species of salamander do not go through metamorphosis. They take in oxygen through their gills.

Problem: What are the early stages of frog metamorphosis?

Materials

frogs' egg masses   water plants
small aquarium   aquarium net
pond or lake water   stereo microscope
plastic bucket   watch glass
washed gravel   goldfish food

Procedure

1. Place washed gravel in the bottom of the aquarium.
2. Fill the aquarium with the pond or lake water. Place the roots of several water plants under the gravel.
3. Carefully place the egg masses into the water.
4. Use a net to collect a few fertile frogs' eggs from the aquarium. Fertile eggs will be dark on top and lighter below.
5. Place the fertile eggs in a watch glass. Observe them with a stereo microscope. Record your observations in a data table like the one shown. Return the eggs to the aquarium.
6. Examine the eggs twice a week. Record your observations in the data table.
7. After the eggs hatch, add a small amount of goldfish food daily to the aquarium.
8. Observe the tadpoles twice a week until almost fully developed into frogs. Record your observations in the data table. Use the diagram to help you identify the tail fin, mouth, eyes, gill cover, nostrils, hind legs, and forelegs of a tadpole.
9. Before the forelegs are fully developed, release the tadpoles in the pond or lake from where they came.

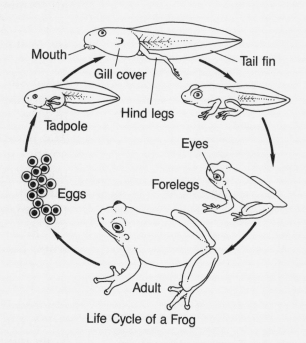
Life Cycle of a Frog

Data and Observations

Date	Observations

Questions and Conclusions

1. How do tadpoles obtain oxygen?
2. Which pair of legs appeared first?
3. What happened to the tadpole's tail?
4. What did you observe about the eyes as the tadpole grew larger?
5. What are the stages of frog metamorphosis?
6. Why were the tadpoles returned to their natural habitat before they completed metamorphosis into adult frogs?

What Is a Vertebrate?   429

Reptiles

Reptiles are often kept as pets. Maybe you have looked after a turtle or a lizard. There are other reptiles that are best left in their natural habitats. Alligators, crocodiles, turtles, lizards, and snakes are all reptiles. Reptiles are cold-blooded vertebrates with scales, internal fertilization, and shelled eggs. When the young hatch they look like the adults.

Dinosaurs are an ancient group of reptiles that died out about 70 million years ago. Alligators and crocodiles are probably the most ancient group of modern reptiles. They are adapted for life in the water. The nostrils and eyes are located on top of the head so that the rest of the body can remain hidden underwater. The long, powerful tail moves the animal through the water in search of prey. In the summer, the female alligator builds a nest of leaves and mud. She guards her eggs and then cares for the young when hatched.

Turtles are shelled reptiles. The shell is an outer growth of the endoskeleton. They do not have teeth but can tear food apart with their sharp beaks.

Lizards are common reptiles of warmer climates. They move quickly in search of insects and to escape predators. Some lizards can regenerate a new tail if it is broken off by a predator.

Snakes are reptiles without legs. They move by crawling. A snake catches its prey with its mouth or wraps coils of its body around the prey. Some snakes have fangs to inject venom (VEH num). Venom is a poisonous chemical that affects the nervous system. Lizards and snakes molt as they grow.

Name five groups of reptiles.

F.Y.I. Rattlesnakes, copperheads, and cottonmouth moccasins sense the heat of small mammals by heat-sensitive pits on their heads.

FIGURE 20–18. Reptiles hatch from shelled eggs (a) and molt as they grow (b).

a

b

20:7 Warm-blooded Vertebrates

Birds and mammals are warm-blooded vertebrates.

Birds

Birds are the only animals with a body covering of feathers. The overlapping feathers insulate the bird to keep its body warm. The skeleton of a bird is made up of hollow bones that reduce body mass. Bird flight would not be possible if the bird were heavy. Some birds such as penguins, although covered with feathers, cannot fly.

Birds have internal fertilization and lay shelled eggs. A parent bird must sit on the eggs to provide heat for them to hatch. Some young birds such as chickens and ducks are able to get up and move about as soon as they hatch. The young of other birds such as robins and eagles are helpless for several days. Their parents must care for them until they are able to leave the nest.

F.Y.I. There are three kinds of feathers: downy for warmth, contour for shape, and flight for flight.

FIGURE 20–19. The feathers of a bird help to keep the body temperature constant.

Mammals

Of all the animals, you are probably most familiar with mammals. Mammals include dogs, cats, horses, lions, and elephants. Humans are also classed as mammals. The nervous systems and brains of mammals are highly developed. The bodies of mammals are covered with hair. Mammals are named for their method of feeding their young with milk from mammary (MAM uh ree) glands. **Mammary glands** are milk-producing organs of female mammals. Mammals care for their young much longer than any other class of animals.

How do mammals feed their young?

a

b

FIGURE 20–20. A marsupial (a) and a placental (b) are two kinds of mammals.

There are three groups of mammals: monotremes (MAHN uh treemz), marsupials, (mar SEW pee ulz), and placentals (pluh SENT ulz). Each of these groups reproduces in a different way. Monotremes such as the Australian platypus produce shelled eggs. Marsupials such as the opossum give birth to very immature young that continue their development in a pouch on the female's body.

Most mammals are placentals. The young of placentals develop inside the female's body. Although the young are fully developed when born, they still need much care from the parents. There are several groups of placental mammals. The largest group is rodents which includes mice, squirrels, and chipmunks. Hoofed animals such as horses and carnivores such as cats are two other groups of placentals.

Primates are placental mammals that use their hands and sometimes their feet for grasping and holding things. Many of the primates are able to walk upright. Monkeys, orangutans, chimpanzees, and humans are examples of primates. Primates have the most highly developed brains of all animals. Humans belong to the species *Homo sapiens* and are the most highly evolved of all animals.

F.Y.I. The world's largest rodents are the capybara of South America. They may be more than 1 m long and weigh 40 kg.

REVIEW

11. How are a lamprey and a shark different?
12. Why is a frog classified as an amphibian?
13. How are crocodiles and snakes alike?
14. What two characteristics help a bird fly?
15. How are a whale, a bat, and a human similar?

432 Animals

CHAPTER 20 REVIEW

SUMMARY

1. The animal kingdom is made up of nine major phyla. Animals are either invertebrates or vertebrates. 20:1
2. Animals have many different adaptations for survival in almost any environment. They have gills or lungs for taking in oxygen; they are warm or cold blooded; they have internal or external fertilization; and they have many methods of communication. 20:2
3. Zoos can be menageries or preserves where endangered species of animals can be protected. 20:3
4. There are eight major phyla of invertebrates. Simple invertebrates include sponges, stinging-celled animals, flatworms, and roundworms. 20:4
5. Complex invertebrates include segmented worms, mollusks, spiny-bodied animals, and arthropods. Some arthropods go through complete metamorphosis. 20:5
6. There are seven classes of vertebrates. Jawless fish, cartilage fish, bony fish, reptiles, and amphibians are cold-blooded vertebrates. Amphibians go through stages of metamorphosis. 20:6
7. Birds and mammals are warm-blooded vertebrates. Monotremes, marsupials, and placentals are three groups of mammals. 20:7

VOCABULARY

a. camouflage
b. cartilage
c. endangered species
d. endoskeleton
e. exoskeleton
f. external fertilization

g. habitat
h. internal fertilization
i. invertebrate
j. larva
k. mammary glands
l. metamorphosis

m. predator
n. prey
o. regeneration
p. vertebrate
q. warning colors

Match each description with the correct vocabulary word from the list above.
1. tough flexible tissue in the bodies of vertebrates
2. a kind of animal that has a backbone
3. when an egg and a sperm join outside of the body
4. an early undeveloped and active stage of an insect's life cycle
5. the outer covering of an insect
6. changes in an insect as it develops from an egg to an adult
7. an animal that captures and feeds on other animals
8. bright patterns that protect an animal from its predators
9. joining of a sperm with an egg inside the female
10. milk-producing organs of a female mammal

MAIN IDEAS

A. Reviewing Concepts

Choose the word or phrase that correctly completes each of the following sentences.

1. The process that releases energy from foods is _____.
   - **a.** fertilization
   - **c.** respiration
   - **b.** communication
   - **d.** preservation

2. A pattern of orange and black colors on an animal is known as _____.
   - **a.** bright colors
   - **c.** camouflage
   - **b.** warning colors
   - **d.** flashes

3. A mammal that produces shelled eggs is a _____.
   - **a.** primate
   - **c.** rodent
   - **b.** monotreme
   - **d.** marsupial

4. A _____ is an example of an invertebrate.
   - **a.** shark
   - **c.** salamander
   - **b.** turtle
   - **d.** bee

5. _____ are very simple invertebrates.
   - **a.** Fish
   - **c.** Sponges
   - **b.** Arthropods
   - **d.** Snails

6. Rich soil may contain large numbers of _____.
   - **a.** roundworms
   - **c.** placentals
   - **b.** corals
   - **d.** leeches

7. An amphibian is covered with _____.
   - **a.** scales
   - **c.** spines
   - **b.** hair
   - **d.** slime

8. A(n) _____ is a bivalve mollusk.
   - **a.** oyster
   - **c.** leech
   - **b.** octopus
   - **d.** snail

9. In complete metamorphosis, the stage after the larva is the _____.
   - **a.** egg
   - **c.** tadpole
   - **b.** nymph
   - **d.** pupa

10. One characteristic of arthropods is the presence of _____.
    - **a.** shells
    - **c.** feathers
    - **b.** tentacles
    - **d.** appendages

11. A common segmented worm is the _____.
    - **a.** coral
    - **c.** tapeworm
    - **b.** earthworm
    - **d.** planarian

12. Fleas, moths, and grasshoppers are all examples of _____.
    - **a.** insects
    - **c.** vertebrates
    - **b.** mollusks
    - **d.** endoskeletons

13. The _____ is a cartilage fish.
    - **a.** lamprey
    - **c.** shark
    - **b.** trout
    - **d.** carp

14. Two classes of vertebrates that lay their eggs in water are _____.
    - **a.** fish and amphibians
    - **b.** amphibians and reptiles
    - **c.** reptiles and birds
    - **d.** birds and mammals

15. The horse is a _____ animal.
    - **a.** meat-eating
    - **c.** scale-covered
    - **b.** warm-blooded
    - **d.** slime-covered

B. Understanding Concepts

Answer the following questions using complete sentences.

16. Why do animals need to move?
17. What is the purpose of the gills of a fish?
18. What is external fertilization?
19. What are the three main groups of mammals and by which characteristic are they distinguished?
20. What was the purpose of the first zoos?
21. What are four ways one animal communicates with another?
22. How does a tapeworm obtain food?
23. What are the three main body parts of an insect?
24. Which classes of vertebrates have bodies covered with scales?
25. Which classes of vertebrates have internal fertilization?

CHAPTER 20 REVIEW

C. Applying Concepts

Answer the following questions using complete sentences.

26. What is the advantage of internal fertilization?
27. How does camouflage help an animal?
28. How is regeneration in a spiny-bodied animal and a reptile the same as the healing of a scratch on your knee?
29. What do humans, cats, horses, and mice have in common?
30. How is a segmented worm more complex than a flatworm?

Day	Temp. (°C)	No. of Mealworms
1	16	3
2	20	4
3	26	6
4	22	5
5	18	4

4. Use the data and observations from Question 3. What can you infer about the effect of temperature on your lizard's eating habits?
5. Classify the following as cartilage fish, bony fish, or jawless fish.
   lamprey   shark
   tuna   catfish

SKILL REVIEW

If you need help, refer to the Skill Handbook, pages 526 to 537.

1. A scientist found a mass of unfertilized fish eggs on a rock in a stream. What can he infer about the method of fertilization? Refer to Section 20:2 for help.
2. The zebra's stripes provide it with camouflage in the long grass of the African grassland. Lions are predators of zebras. What effect might the stripes have on the average lifespan of a zebra?
3. You observe a lizard in an aquarium. The daily temperature varies and the number of mealworms that the lizard eats also changes each day. You decide to determine if there is any connection between temperature and the eating habits of the lizard. Each day you record the temperature in the aquarium and the number of mealworms the lizard eats. Below are the data you collect. Make a line graph of the data. Be sure to correctly label the axes.

PROJECTS

1. Find out how meat is inspected for the presence of parasites. Write the U.S. Department of Agriculture for information about federal meat inspection.
2. Fill two jars with warm water. Determine the temperature of the water in each jar. Wrap one jar with a piece of fur and the other jar with a piece of cotton cloth. These will represent skin with and without fur. After 15 minutes take the temperatures of the two jars of water. Note which covering was the better insulator.

READINGS

1. Crump, Donald J. *Animal Architects.* Washington, DC: National Geographic Society, 1987.
2. Gallant, Roy A. *The Rise of Mammals.* New York, NY: Watts, 1986.
3. Sharp, David. *Animals From the Rivers and Oceans.* Topsfield, MA: Salem House Publications, 1987.

FUN WITH

| Cyanobacteria are an early form of life on Earth. | 1665 | Mitosis is observed in plant cells. | 1924 |
| 3.5 B.Y.A. | Hooke describes a structure he calls a cell. | 1675 | Disposable handkerchiefs are produced. |

Did you know that some dinosaurs had over 2000 teeth?

Why don't fish in the Antarctic freeze during the winter?

Fish that live in the cold waters of the Antarctic contain glycoprotein. This substance is like an antifreeze that keeps their blood from freezing.

QUESTION AND ANSWER

Why did dinosaurs become extinct? There are many hypotheses about the extinction of dinosaurs millions of years ago. These include: bombardment of Earth by radiation from space; a sudden long–term drought; collapse of ecosystems that in turn broke food chains; ash from volcanoes shielding Earth from the sun; and many others. One hypothesis is that a meteorite hit Earth. Many scientists believe that the impact led to severe climate changes. These changes caused the extinction of all but the most adaptable species. Why do you think the dinosaurs became extinct?

Riddle

Q. What is a toothless grizzly?
A. a gummy bear

TEASER

FUN RECIPE

VEGETABLE SOUP

Sauté 1/4 cup diced carrots, 1/2 cup diced onions, 1/2 cup diced celery, and 1/4 cup diced zucchini in 2 tablespoons margarine. Add 3 cups water, 1 cup canned tomatoes, 1/2 cup peeled, diced potatoes, 1/2 cup chopped cabbage, 1 tablespoon parsley, 1/2 teaspoon salt, and 1/8 teaspoon pepper. Cover and cook for 35 minutes. Are any of these fruits?

436

SCIENCE

Penicillin is discovered.

1928

1948

Poliomyelitis virus strains are discovered.

Watson and Crick win Nobel Prize for work with DNA.

1962

1982

Cats opens on Broadway.

QUIZ

Allison bought two plants, a cactus and a spider plant. She repotted them both in sandy soil. Later, she noticed that the spider plant wasn't doing well although she had followed care instructions. What might be the problem?

Which plants have the largest seeds? The smallest? The largest seeds come from a palm called coco de mer. A seed from this plant can be as large as a basketball! The smallest seeds known are orchid seeds. Hundreds of them can fit on the head of a pin.

Janet and Paul went snorkeling in the Bahamas. Paul pointed out many of the plants and animals to Janet. When they were back on the boat, Janet seemed puzzled about what Paul had called a sea lily. Using a microscope, how could Janet find out whether the sea lily is a plant or an animal?

JOKE

Q. What do you call a scared flower arranger?
A. a petrified florist

THE FAR SIDE

7.4 © 1986 Universal Press Syndicate Larson

"Think about it, Ed. ... The class Insecta contains 26 orders, almost 1,000 families, and over 750,000 described species — but I can't shake the feeling we're all just a bunch of bugs."

437

Recipe: Tomatoes and zucchini are fruits.
that it has no cell wall or chloroplasts.
Teaser: She could examine a cell from a sea lily and find
Quiz: A spider plant needs soil richer in humus to hold water.
Answers

UNIT 6

Your Body

This motorcycle is built in a factory that has an internal supply system called *just in time*. Needed parts are delivered to a spot on the production line within minutes of a call from a production-line worker. Does the human body have a *just in time* system? How do body systems work together? How do they receive needed materials at the right time and in the right amounts?

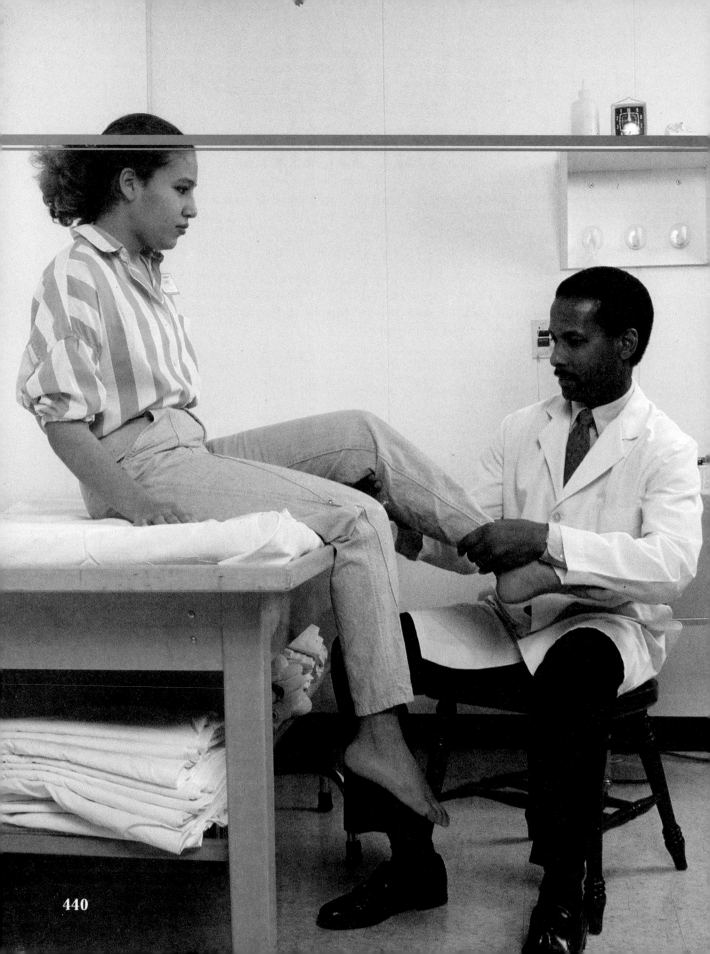

Body Support

Career: Physical Therapist

Rocio had been taking ballet for several years. She was usually careful about doing warm-up exercises, but her lower left leg had begun to hurt. Her ballet instructor knew that a hurting muscle could be a symptom of damage. He told Rocio that she should have her doctor examine the leg.

After checking Rocio's leg carefully, the doctor decided to send her to a sports-medicine clinic for therapy. The doctor wrote a prescription for her to take with her.

At the clinic, a physical therapist read the doctor's prescription and asked Rocio about her leg. He then examined Rocio's leg to determine the amount of damage to the muscles. The therapist told Rocio that she would have to keep all her weight off the leg for several days. After the muscles had had a chance to relax, the therapist would work out an exercise program that would gradually strengthen Rocio's leg. Only after the muscles were healed, would she be allowed to practice ballet. The therapist fitted Rocio with a pair of crutches. Before leaving the clinic, Rocio practiced walking with the crutches.

A physical therapist works to help a patient regain the full use of body parts after an injury. Many of these injuries involve muscles and bones. In this chapter, you will study about bones, joints, and muscles.

F.Y.I. American Physical Therapy Association, Public Relations, 111 North Fairfax Street, Alexandria, VA 22314

GOALS

You will study . . .
1. the parts of the skeletal system.
2. how bone heals.
3. how the body moves at joints.

21:1 The Skeletal System

Like most of the animals described in Chapter 20, you are made up of many cells that are organized into tissues, organs, and systems. Most of the tissues that make up your body are soft. But your body isn't a formless blob. It has a support system. Remember that arthropods have an external support system that has to be shed for these animals to grow larger. Members of the vertebrate group, such as yourself, have an internal support system. Your internal skeleton grows larger as you grow. Your skeleton consists of all the bones of your body. They are part of your skeletal system. A **skeletal system** is made up of bones, cartilage, joints, and ligaments.

Your skeletal system has five important functions. (1) The form and size of each bone gives the body its shape. Your legs and arms are long because they are made up of long bones. (2) Parts of the skeleton protect soft internal organs. For example, your ribs protect your heart and lungs, and your brain is enclosed in a hard skull. (3) Bones have places where muscles are attached. (4) Blood cells are made in the bones of the upper arm, leg, ribs, and the sternum. (5) Minerals such as calcium, phosphorus, magnesium, and sodium are stored in bone. Calcium makes bone hard. Bone is also a source of calcium for muscle contraction and blood clotting. Vitamin D is needed for bone to make use of calcium.

FIGURE 21–1. Some organisms have an exoskeleton that is shed when growth takes place (a). An internal skeleton grows with an organism (b).

a

b

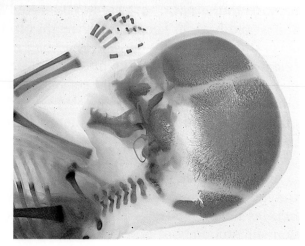

FIGURE 21–2. Cartilage covers the ends of most bones.

21:2 Structures of Bone

Pick up a bone and you will see that it is not really very smooth. There are bumps, sharp edges, round ends, and many pits and holes. Each of these marks has a purpose. Muscles attach to some of the bumps and pits. Blood vessels enter and leave the bone through the holes. Covering the ends of many bones is a material that is smoother and softer than bone. This is cartilage. Cartilage is a tough, flexible tissue. It does not contain minerals or blood vessels. It absorbs stress where bones come together. Cartilage is found in disks between the small bones of your backbone. It forms the tip of your nose and your outer ear. Your ribs are attached to your breast bone by cartilage.

What is one function of cartilage?

Many characteristics of bone are easily seen in the humerus, the bone in your upper arm. Bone is covered by the periosteum (per ee AHS tee um). The **periosteum** is a tough membrane that fits tightly over the outside of bone. Under the periosteum is a very hard layer called compact bone that contains cells and blood vessels. Most of the calcium that the body needs is stored in compact bone. Compact bone also contains special elastic fibers that are flexible. Therefore, your bones are not brittle. Blood vessels supply the periosteum and bone cells with oxygen and food. At the ends of the bone, the hard material has many open spaces. Because of its appearance, it is called spongy bone.

If your bones were completely solid, you would have a much greater mass. However, as you can see in the humerus, there is a cavity. It is filled with a yellow substance. In the spongy bone, there is a red substance. These red and yellow substances are called marrow (MER oh).

FIGURE 21–3. The humerus is a typical long bone.

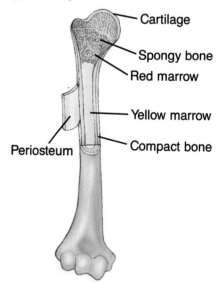

- Cartilage
- Spongy bone
- Red marrow
- Yellow marrow
- Compact bone
- Periosteum

What is a simple fracture?

What is a compound fracture?

FIGURE 21–4. Greenstick fractures are common in young children (a). A cast is worn while bones heal (b).

Marrow is a soft tissue found in the cavities of bones. Blood cells are made in red marrow. Yellow marrow is a fatty material. Blood cells also can be formed by yellow marrow when the body has lost large amounts of blood. Young children have mostly red marrow in their bones. As the body ages, more yellow marrow is formed.

Bone has two types of cells. One type of cell constantly builds up calcium in bone. The second type of cell releases calcium for use by the body. These two actions go on continuously in healthy bone. This means that your bones are always being renewed.

Because it is a living tissue, healthy bone can heal if it fractures. A **fracture** is a break in a bone. There are three kinds of fractures: greenstick, simple, and compound. When a greenstick fracture occurs, only some of the fibers of the bone break. The bone does not break all the way through. In a simple fracture, a bone breaks into two pieces but the broken ends remain near each other. The most serious kind of break is the compound fracture. In a compound fracture, the broken ends push through the muscle and skin.

When a bone fractures, the broken ends need to come in contact with each other for healing to take place. The periosteum immediately starts to make new bone-forming cells. A thick band of cartilage forms around the two broken edges of the bone much like a bridge. New bone cells eventually replace the bridge

a

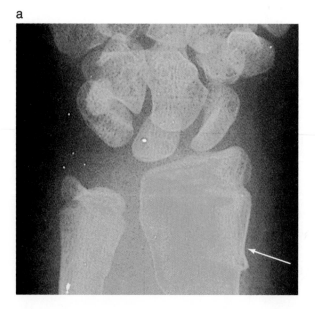

b

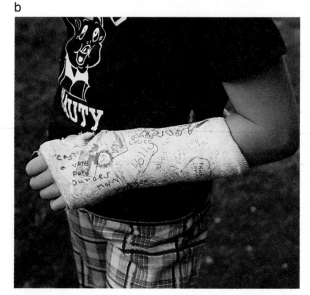

with compact bone and the fracture heals. A cast is often used to hold broken bones in place to help them heal. Flat bones such as ribs tend to break more easily than bones that are shaped like a tube, like the humerus.

21:3 The Human Skeleton

Your skeleton is made up of 206 bones. They are classified according to their shapes. Bones are long, short, flat, or irregular in shape. Long bones are those of the arms and legs. Short bones are found in your hands and feet. Flat bones make up your skull, ribs, and the shoulder blades. Irregular bones have many shapes and include the vertebrae, wrist and ankle bones, and the small bones of the face and the middle ear. The function of a bone is related to its shape. Long, tubular bones withstand stress and carry body weight better than flat bones.

There are two main groups of bones in your body: the axial (AK see ul) and the appendicular (a pen DIH cu lur) skeletons. The **axial skeleton** is made up of bones and cartilage that support and protect your head, neck, heart, and lungs. These are the skull, backbone, breastbone, and ribs. Your backbone is made up of 26 irregular bones called vertebrae (VUR tuh bray). There are twelve pair of ribs.

The **appendicular skeleton** is made up of the limbs and the bones that attach the limbs to the axial skeleton. Your shoulder blade, collarbones, arms, hands, hip bones, legs, and feet are the bones of the appendicular skeleton.

F.Y.I. Some snakes have nearly 400 vertebrae. The giraffe has only seven neck vertebrae.

What are the shapes of bones?

F.Y.I. The largest bone in the body is the tibia in the shin. The smallest bones of the body are the middle ear bones—the hammer, stapes, and anvil. The stapes is also called the stirrup.

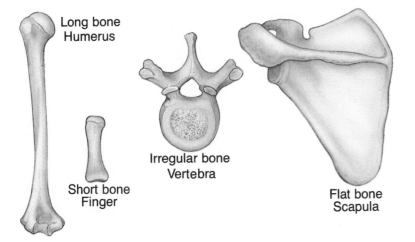

Long bone
Humerus

Short bone
Finger

Irregular bone
Vertebra

Flat bone
Scapula

FIGURE 21–5. Bones are classified according to shape.

F.Y.I. At birth, an infant has more bones than an adult. Many fuse as development occurs.

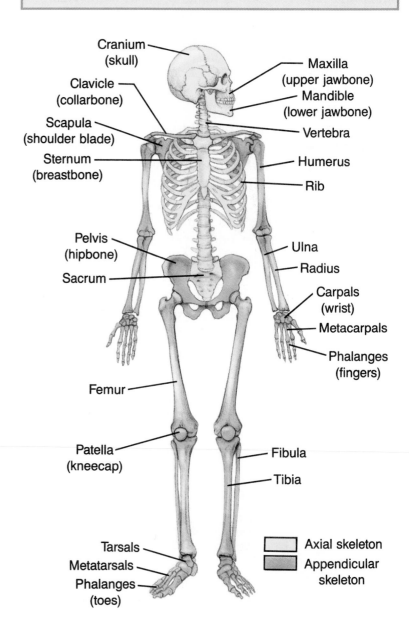

F.Y.I. Vitamin D, made in the skin in the presence of sunlight, enables calcium to be absorbed by bone.

FIGURE 21–6. Bones of the human skeletal system

Problem: What are the functions of the bones of the human skeleton?

Materials
diagram or model of human skeleton
Figure 21–6 of your textbook

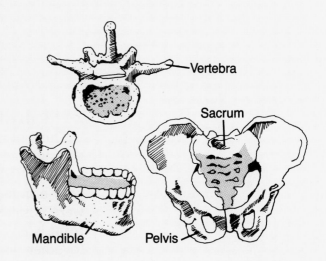

Procedure
1. Make a data table like the one shown.
2. Obtain a diagram from your teacher or use a chart or model to observe the bones in the human skeleton.
3. Find the location of each bone listed in the data table. Record its location.
4. Determine the function of each bone based on its location and shape. If the bone *protects* a body organ, write P for protection in the right-hand column. If the bone *holds up* a body part, write S for support. If the bone is *moved* when a muscle contracts, write M for movement.

Questions and Conclusions
1. Which bones protect the lungs?
2. Which bones protect the spinal cord?
3. Which bones support the head?
4. Which bones help the body stand up?
5. Which bones contain marrow?
6. What is the primary function of flat bones?
7. What is the primary function of round bones?
8. What are the functions of the bones of the human skeleton?
9. Why is it important to include calcium and vitamin D in your diet?

Data and Observations

Bone	Location	Protection/Support Movement
Cranium		
Maxilla		
Mandible		
Sternum		
Clavicle		
Scapula		
Ribs		
Humerus		
Radius		
Ulna		
Vertebrae		
Pelvis		
Femur		
Tibia		
Fibula		

FIGURE 21–7. Joints allow the body to be flexible.

F.Y.I. A sprain is an injury to a ligament.

How are joints classified?

FIGURE 21–8. Athletic activities rely on healthy muscles and joints.

21:4 Joints

Think of all the movements you made this morning getting ready for school. You opened your mouth to eat, reached for your toothbrush, and stretched out your arm as you put on your coat. All these motions were possible because your skeleton has joints. A **joint** is any place where two or more bones come together. Joints allow you to make skeletal movements. Without joints, your body would be unbendable, like a board. Someone would have to carry you and feed you. It wouldn't be a very interesting way to live.

Joints are classified as movable or immovable depending on how much movement takes place. A **movable joint** allows body parts to move. Elbows and knees are movable joints. The bones in movable joints are held together by ligaments. A **ligament** is a band of strong tissue that connects bones to each other at joints. Ligaments are attached to the periosteum of the bone. Movable joints also have fluid between the bones. The fluid helps keep the surfaces of the bones from rubbing against each other. Cartilage also covers the ends of the bones to make movement smooth. The smooth surface of the cartilage and the fluid work together to reduce friction in the joint when the bones move.

There are several types of movable joints. Hinge joints allow back and forth motion. Elbows, knees, and fingers have hinge joints. In a gliding joint, bones glide back and forth over each other. Gliding joints are found in the wrists and ankles. At a pivot joint, the round surface of one bone rotates in a ring of a second bone. The pivot joint where the radius and

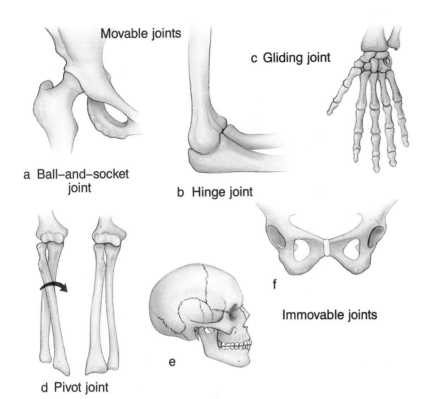

Movable joints

c Gliding joint

a Ball–and–socket joint

b Hinge joint

d Pivot joint

e

f

Immovable joints

FIGURE 21–9. The skeletal system has movable joints (a–d) and some immovable joints (e–f).

ulna meet lets you turn your palm up or down. Ball-and-socket joints allow the greatest amount of movement. The humerus in Figure 21–3 has a ball-like structure that fits into a cuplike cavity in the scapula. The joint between the femur of the leg and the pelvis is also a ball-and-socket joint.

A joint that allows no movement is an **immovable joint.** The joints in a human adult skull are all immovable. When you were born, these joints were covered by a tough, but flexible, layer of tissue. By the time you are 17 years old, these bones will have grown together so tightly that no movement will be possible. Immovable joints in the skull protect brain tissues. The joint between the two pelvic bones is also an immovable joint.

F.Y.I. The owl is able to turn its head 270° because of the pivot joint in its neck.

What type of joint is in the skull?

REVIEW

1. What are five functions of the skeletal system?
2. What gives bone its strength?
3. How does the periosteum help in bone repair?
4. What are four types of movable joints? Give an example of each.
5. What is the function of a ligament?

Replacement Parts

Many athletes undergo knee or shoulder operations to correct problems that result from injuries in sports. Other joint problems come from diseases such as arthritis. Arthritis causes joints to become inflamed and swollen. Bone is damaged and movement is painful.

In some cases, metal, plastic, or ceramic copies have been used to replace damaged joints. Replacement of a joint with an artificial device is called a joint implant.

Computers are being used to design joint implants that will fit a specific individual. A computer program is written to design an implant for a person. Computer programs also direct machines that construct and place the implant.

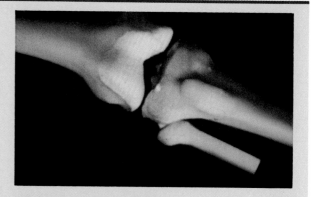

ADVANCE

One problem in joint replacement is finding a material to cement or glue the joint implant to any bone part that is still there. Materials are being tested that will enable the bone to grow into the implant.

What Are Muscles?

GOALS

You will study . . .
1. the structure and function of muscles.
2. how muscle and bone work together in movement.

How is muscle action classified?

21:5 The Muscular System

Nearly half the weight of your body is in the form of muscles. **Muscle** is a tissue that contracts or shortens, resulting in the movement of body parts. What comes to mind when you think of muscle? Ads for gym equipment show people with flexed, bulging muscles under shining skin. But muscles also mix food in your stomach and move blood throughout your body. There is a small muscle at the base of every hair on your body. When these muscles contract, you get "goose bumps."

Muscle action is classified as either voluntary or involuntary. A **voluntary muscle action** is a movement that you control. Running, chewing, reaching, and walking are voluntary actions. You consciously start or stop these actions. An **involuntary muscle action** is a movement you cannot control. The beating of your heart, goose bumps, shivering, and the movement of food through your stomach are involuntary actions. You don't consciously start or stop these activities.

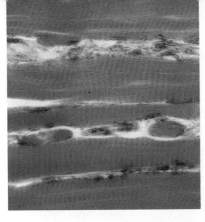

a

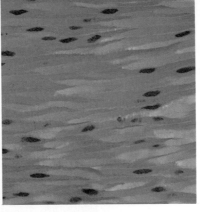

b

c

The human body has three types of muscle cells: skeletal, smooth, and cardiac. **Skeletal muscle** is muscle that moves the bones of the body. These muscles are attached to bones by one or more tendons. A **tendon** is a tough band of tissue that connects muscles to bones. You can see tendons over your knuckles when you make a fist. Skeletal muscles are voluntary in action. Under a microscope, skeletal muscle looks like a long fiber with dark bands or striations (stri AY shunz). A single skeletal muscle cell may be 40 mm long.

Smooth muscle is muscle that makes up the walls of the stomach, intestines, and blood vessels. Smooth muscle cells are called smooth because they don't have striations. Smooth muscle is involuntary in action. You can't stop food or blood from moving throughout your body.

Cardiac muscle is found only in the walls of the heart. The cells of cardiac muscle have heavier bands than skeletal muscle cells. Cardiac muscle is involuntary in action. The rhythmic beating of your heart is not under your control. It beats day and night for as long as you live.

FIGURE 21–10. skeletal muscle (a), smooth muscle (b), cardiac muscle (c)

What do tendons connect?

F.Y.I. In humans, cardiac muscle begins to contract when an embryo is about 45 days old.

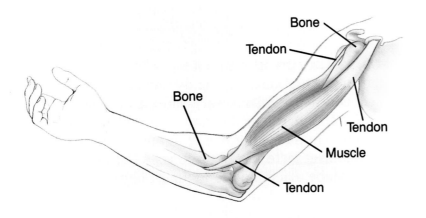

Bone

Tendon

Bone

Tendon

Muscle

Tendon

Tendon

FIGURE 21–11. Muscles are attached to bones by tendons.

What Are Muscles? 451

F.Y.I. The chest or pectoral muscles of birds may be one quarter of their total mass. In humans these muscles are only about one percent of total mass.

FIGURE 21–12. Human body muscles

Groups of each of these different types of cells form skeletal muscle tissue, smooth muscle tissue, and cardiac muscle tissue. The bulk of your body muscles are skeletal muscles. Figure 21–12 shows some of the major skeletal muscles of the body. These muscles are named for their shape, location in the body, or the bone or body part to which they are attached.

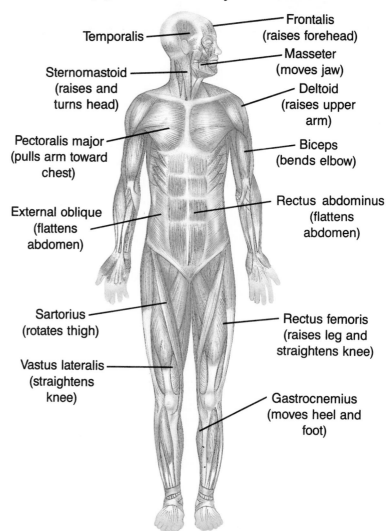

Temporalis

Frontalis (raises forehead)

Masseter (moves jaw)

Sternomastoid (raises and turns head)

Deltoid (raises upper arm)

Pectoralis major (pulls arm toward chest)

Biceps (bends elbow)

Rectus abdominus (flattens abdomen)

External oblique (flattens abdomen)

Sartorius (rotates thigh)

Rectus femoris (raises leg and straightens knee)

Vastus lateralis (straightens knee)

Gastrocnemius (moves heel and foot)

21:6 Muscles at Work

Remember that muscle acts by contracting. When a muscle contracts, units in each muscle cell slide together. The muscle cell becomes shorter in length and thicker in the center. When a muscle relaxes, these units separate. The muscle goes back to its original shape. Each muscle in your body acts this way.

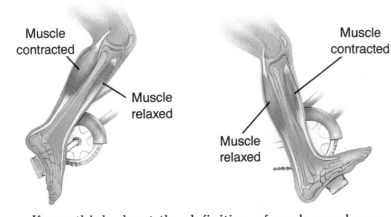

Muscle contracted

Muscle relaxed

Muscle contracted

Muscle relaxed

FIGURE 21-13. When muscles contract, work is done.

F.Y.I. There are six different muscles that control the movement of the eyeball.

What is muscle tone?

If you think about the definition of work, you know that when a muscle contracts work is done. Muscles do work because movement takes place. There are always muscles contracting or relaxing in your body. The muscles in your body rarely relax completely. Even if you are not consciously moving, your muscles are in a state of partial contraction. **Muscle tone** is a continuous state of partial contraction. This means that your muscles are always ready to do work. If muscle tissue does not work, it begins to break down. Muscles confined to a cast because of a broken bone frequently show some damage from lack of use. Muscle tissue is lost. Regular use of muscle generally prevents this from happening.

PROBLEM SOLVING

The Broken Leg

Robert arrived at school Monday morning using crutches and wearing a cast on his leg. His classmates were interested in knowing what had happened. He explained how he had broken his leg playing football on Saturday.

For the first week, Robert enjoyed the attention he received. His classmates signed the cast that had been put on to keep his leg from moving. But after a while, Robert couldn't wait for the cast to be removed. He wanted to be able to walk, and his leg was always itching.

Finally after six weeks, the cast was cut off. Robert was surprised to see that

his healed leg looked a lot thinner than the other leg. How can you explain the appearance of Robert's leg? What should Robert do?

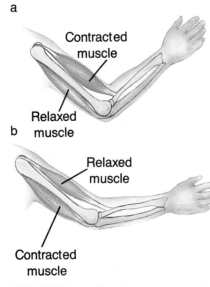

a

Contracted
muscle

Relaxed
b muscle

Relaxed
muscle

Contracted
muscle

FIGURE 21–14. Muscles work in pairs.

Your skeleton moves when a muscle connecting two bones contracts. Muscles never push. Muscles move body parts by pulling on the bones. Skeletal muscles act in pairs. For example, when the biceps muscle contracts, the triceps muscle relaxes. This causes the arm to bend at the joint in the elbow. The lower arm is moved toward the upper arm. When the triceps muscle contracts and the biceps relaxes, the arm is straightened. The lower arm is moved away from the upper arm. The contraction of the triceps muscle pulls the lower arm straight.

Muscles need energy to do work. **Glycogen** (GLI kuh jun) is a high-energy chemical stored in skeletal muscles. When a muscle contracts, glycogen is used as the source of energy. If there is only a little activity, chemical waste products from the contraction are carried away easily by the blood stream. If the muscle has to work hard, more energy is used, and the waste products may not be removed quickly enough. When chemical wastes build up in the muscle, it is not able to contract as strongly to do work. This is known as muscle fatigue. To overcome fatigue, the muscle has to rest. During rest, chemical waste products are removed and more glycogen is delivered to the muscle.

Muscles produce thermal energy when they contract. This is the main source of thermal energy for keeping body temperature constant. When your body is cold, you shiver. The muscle activity involved in shivering produces thermal energy for warming the body.

What happens to glycogen when a muscle contracts?

FIGURE 21–15. Muscle contraction generates thermal energy.

Problem: How is a chicken able to bend and straighten its leg?

Materials 🖐️ 💪 🚯

human muscle and   forceps
   bone chart   paper towels
boiled chicken leg   apron
dissecting pan   scissors
scalpel

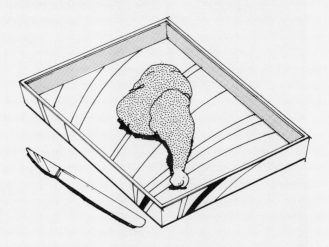

Procedure

1. Place a paper towel in a dissecting pan. Lay the chicken leg on the towel.
2. Use forceps to remove the skin from the chicken leg. Set the skin aside on a paper towel.
3. Locate and observe the muscles and tendons in the leg and the thigh.
4. On a piece of paper draw and label the leg and thigh. Label the muscles and tendons of these parts.
5. Hold the chicken leg with both hands. Carefully bend and straighten the leg and thigh at the joint. Observe what happens to the muscles.
6. Use the scalpel and scissors carefully to remove just the muscle tissues and tendons from the bones. **CAUTION:** *Be careful with the scalpel and scissors. Always cut away from yourself.* Locate and observe bones, joints, ligaments, and cartilage.
7. On a piece of paper draw and label the leg and thigh bones, joint, ligaments, and cartilage.
8. Record the parts of the skeletal and muscular systems that you located in the data table.
9. **CAUTION:** *Give all dissected materials to your teacher for proper disposal.*

Data and Observations

Body systems	Name and location of leg parts
Muscular	
Skeletal	

Questions and Conclusions

1. What type of muscle did you observe and what is its muscle action?
2. What is the purpose of a tendon?
3. Describe the appearance of tendons in the chicken leg and thigh.
4. What kind of joint is between the leg bone and thigh bone?
5. What is the purpose of a ligament?
6. Describe the location and appearance of any cartilage.
7. How is a chicken able to bend and straighten its leg?
8. How is the chicken leg similar to a human leg?

What Are Muscles? 455

FIGURE 21–16. Use of steroids by bodybuilders may result in serious health problems.

SCIENCE AND SOCIETY

21:7 Developing Pecs and Quads

Superman flies to the rescue! With one arm he lifts up the get-away car, gives it a shake, and the bank robbers fall out into the hands of the police. What power! What strength in those bulging muscles! Some people admire the bulging pecs, or pectoral muscles, and quads, the upper leg muscles of weight-lifters and athletes. The development of bulging muscles requires dedication to exercise. Exercise causes muscle cells to increase in size. Muscle tissue becomes larger and produces the bulging effect. No new muscle cells are produced through exercise.

Is bodybuilding really good for you? A program of regular exercise, under the supervision of a qualified trainer, can produce positive effects. Exercise may result in an improved appearance, change in mass, greater strength, and endurance.

What are the problems related to bodybuilding? Once these activities are started, they need to be continued. Muscles that are not exercised gradually decrease in size. Sometimes chemicals called anabolic steroids (STIHR oydz) have been used to increase muscle size and strength. Steroids have been shown to build muscle tissue more quickly and give added strength. However, the use of steroids is illegal. They have been shown to stop bone growth and cause drastic mood changes. There is also evidence that steroid use may cause liver cancer, changes in the face, and damage to the reproductive system. The long-term effects have yet to be studied, but enough is known so that athletes are warned not to use steroids. Should athletes risk permanent damage to break a record that is later disqualified? Should health be risked for a world record?

REVIEW

6. Name the three types of muscles.
7. How does cardiac muscle differ from skeletal and smooth muscle?
8. What is a tendon?
9. How do muscles perform work?
10. What are some disadvantages of body building?

CHAPTER 21 REVIEW

SUMMARY

1. The skeleton shapes the body, protects internal organs, provides muscle attachments, makes blood cells, and stores minerals. 21:1
2. Bone is a tissue made up of minerals and flexible fibers. 21:2
3. The two main groups of bones of the skeleton are the axial skeleton and the appendicular skeleton. 21:3
4. A joint is the place where two or more bones come together. Joints are movable or immovable. 21:4
5. Muscles are either voluntary or involuntary in function, and skeletal, smooth, or cardiac in type. 21:5
6. Movement takes place and work is done when muscles contract. 21:6
7. Muscle building exercises can produce positive benefits, but steroids are harmful to body systems. 21:7

VOCABULARY

a. appendicular skeleton
b. axial skeleton
c. cardiac muscle
d. fracture
e. glycogen
f. immovable joint
g. involuntary muscle action
h. joint
i. ligament
j. marrow
k. movable joint
l. muscle
m. muscle tone
n. periosteum
o. skeletal muscle
p. skeletal system
q. smooth muscle
r. tendon
s. voluntary muscle action

Match each description with the correct vocabulary word from the list above.

1. a break in a bone
2. muscle action that can be controlled
3. banded muscle attached to bones
4. tissue that contracts and moves body parts
5. place where two or more bones come together
6. bones of the skull and vertebral column
7. tissue that connects muscles to bone
8. condition of partial contraction
9. membrane that covers bone
10. soft fatty tissue inside cavity of long bone

MAIN IDEAS

A. Reviewing Concepts

Choose the word or phrase that correctly completes each of the following sentences.

1. A _____ fracture occurs when the broken ends of a bone push through the skin.
   - **a.** sprain
   - **b.** greenstick
   - **c.** compound
   - **d.** simple

2. There are _____ bones in the adult human body.
   - **a.** 602
   - **b.** 226
   - **c.** 260
   - **d.** 206

3. Disks between vertebrae are made of _____.
   - **a.** cartilage
   - **b.** bone
   - **c.** muscle
   - **d.** tendons

4. Blood cells are made in _____.
   - **a.** bone marrow
   - **b.** compact bone
   - **c.** ligaments
   - **d.** periosteum

5. The _____ is a large bone of the appendicular skeleton.
   - **a.** skull
   - **b.** pelvis
   - **c.** breastbone
   - **d.** vertebra

6. _____ is the most important mineral found in bone.
   - **a.** Sodium
   - **b.** Copper
   - **c.** Calcium
   - **d.** Potassium

7. An example of a pivot joint is the _____.
   - **a.** ankle
   - **b.** ulna and radius
   - **c.** shoulder and arm
   - **d.** jaw

8. _____ in movable joints helps to reduce friction.
   - **a.** Blood
   - **b.** Cartilage
   - **c.** Mineral
   - **d.** Marrow

9. Smooth muscle is found in the _____.
   - **a.** stomach
   - **b.** heart
   - **c.** arm
   - **d.** foot

10. The _____ are examples of flat bones.
    - **a.** wrists
    - **b.** toes
    - **c.** fingers
    - **d.** ribs

11. _____ is the source of energy that allows muscles to contract.
    - **a.** Calcium
    - **b.** Cytoplasm
    - **c.** Marrow
    - **d.** Glycogen

12. The wrist is a _____ joint.
    - **a.** hinge
    - **b.** gliding
    - **c.** ball and socket
    - **d.** pivot

13. Exercise causes muscle cells to increase in _____.
    - **a.** kinds
    - **b.** number
    - **c.** size
    - **d.** calcium

14. Joints in the _____ are immovable.
    - **a.** skull
    - **b.** knees
    - **c.** fingers
    - **d.** wrist

15. Bone with open spaces filled with red marrow is called _____.
    - **a.** periosteum
    - **b.** compact bone
    - **c.** spongy bone
    - **d.** compound bone

B. Understanding Concepts

Answer the following questions using complete sentences.

16. What are the skeletal system functions?
17. What is the role of the periosteum in healing a fracture?
18. How do bone and cartilage differ?
19. Where are compact bone and spongy bone found in a long bone?
20. How do skeletal muscles work in pairs?
21. The backbone and skull bones are part of which main group of bones?
22. What are the differences between skeletal and smooth muscle?
23. How does a muscle cause movement?
24. Why can it be said that muscles do work?
25. What causes muscle fatigue?

C. Applying Concepts

Answer the following questions using complete sentences.

26. What features of a movable joint reduce friction in movement?
27. Compare simple and compound fractures.
28. What kinds of joints in the arm are involved in pitching a ball?
29. How can a muscle recover from muscle fatigue?
30. What are the advantages and disadvantages of bodybuilding?

SKILL REVIEW

If you need help, refer to the Skill Handbook, pages 526 to 537.

1. A father kept a record of his daughter's growth from the time she was born until she was 8 years old. Construct a graph from his data.

Year	Height
Birth	42 cm
1	50
2	86
3	92
4	104
5	112
6	118
7	124
8	128

2. Using the graph, determine between which two years the girl's skeleton grew the most.
3. What is the cause of muscle fatigue? What is the effect of muscle fatigue?
4. Measure and record in a data table the length of each of your fingers and thumb on your left hand. Do the same for your right hand. How many columns will your data table have? How many rows?
5. Classify the following as either cartilage or bone: outer ear, ribs, sternum, vertebrae, tip of nose.

PROJECTS

1. Find out which muscles and bones are best used when lifting heavy objects to avoid injuring the muscles and bones of the back.
2. Obtain the sternum of a chicken. Notice the ridge or keel on the breastbone. This is for the attachment of the powerful pectoral muscles needed for wing movements. The pectoral muscles are the breast meat of chickens and turkeys. Compare the sternum of the chicken with the sternum found on a human skeleton. Describe any differences between them. Discuss the differences in the two and relate them to arm and wing movements, and the amount of pectoral muscle in each organism.

READINGS

1. Killgore, J. "Weightlifting Cats Reveal Secrets of Human Muscles." *Science World.* November 15, 1985, pp. 10–12.
2. Reader's Digest Association. *ABC's of the Human Body.* New York: Reader's Digest Association, 1987.
3. Tiger, Steven. *Arthritis.* New York: Messner, 1986.

Body Control

CHAPTER 22

Career: Pharmacist

Diego had a terrible cold. He had coughed all night. During the day he blew his nose until it was red and sore. Finally, he asked his mother for advice. He knew that he had to feel better in time for the basketball game on Friday evening.

As they stood in the aisle of the drugstore, Diego and his mother saw a confusing number of different cold medicines. The pharmacist was busy filling prescriptions, but asked if they needed help. Diego described his symptoms. His mother said she didn't think he needed to see a doctor. The pharmacist asked Diego his age and weight and whether he had any allergies to medicine. She then suggested several over-the-counter cold medicines. Diego's mother selected one. The pharmacist explained when to take the medicine and pointed out the warnings on the label. She also told Diego to see a doctor if his symptoms did not go away in a few days.

Diego looked at the pharmacist's license on the wall. He asked what a person had to do to become a pharmacist. The pharmacist explained that she had gone to college, and she had learned about the human body and how chemicals affect body systems.

In this chapter, you will study about the nervous and endocrine systems of the body. Many drugs interact with these body systems and change the way they function. You will study how some drugs affect the body.

F.Y.I. American Association of Colleges of Pharmacy, 1426 Prince Street, Alexandria, VA 22314

What's in Control?

GOALS
You will study . . .
1. the parts and functions of the nervous system.
2. the senses and how they work.
3. the endocrine system.

22:1 Your Nervous System

The systems of your body operate in a balanced way. Your body temperature generally is kept at 37°C, and the amount of oxygen in your blood is about the same from day to day. How does the body maintain this balance? Feedback mechanisms are signals that the body uses to increase, decrease, or continue body activities to maintain homeostasis (hoh mee oh STAY sus). **Homeostasis** is the series of responses an organism constantly uses to keep itself in a balanced state. Two body systems that help maintain homeostasis are the nervous system and the endocrine (EN duh krun) system.

Your nervous system receives and then responds to stimuli inside and outside your body. Your nervous system has two main parts, the central nervous system and the peripheral (puh RIHF rul) nervous system. The **central nervous system** is made up of the brain and spinal cord. The **peripheral nervous system** consists of all the nerves of the body other than those nerves in the brain and spinal cord.

What are the two main parts of the nervous system?

F.Y.I. The brain of a 15-m long whale weighs nearly 8 kg.

22:2 The Central Nervous System

The **brain** is the major control center of all body activity. It is made up of about 14 billion cells. Your brain uses large amounts of energy and oxygen each day. The three main parts of the brain are the cerebrum (suh REE brum), cerebellum (ser uh BEL um), and medulla (muh DUL uh).

FIGURE 22–1. Nerve tissue is made up of masses of nerve cells (a). The human brain is the control center for body activity (b).

a

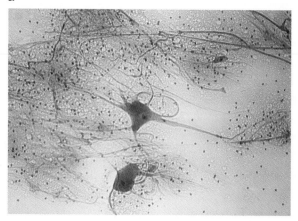

b

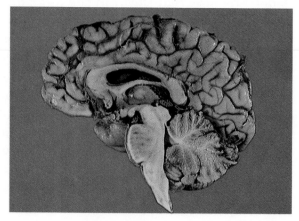

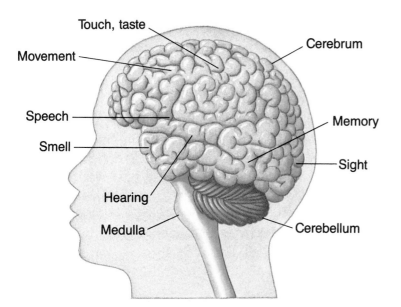

Touch, taste
Movement
Cerebrum
Speech
Memory
Smell
Sight
Hearing
Medulla
Cerebellum

FIGURE 22–2. Different areas of the brain control different body functions.

The cerebrum is the largest part of the brain and is divided into two sides called hemispheres. The surface of the cerebrum is gray and wrinkled. The cerebrum responds to stimuli from your sense organs. It also helps you to move your muscles and to remember. Because of the cerebrum, you automatically think "stop" when you see a red light or picture a glass of white liquid when you hear the word "milk." These activities are called association functions. The cerebellum is the second largest part of the brain. Like the cerebrum, it also has two hemispheres. The cerebellum is the part of the brain that coordinates muscle movements and helps you stand up straight. If the cerebellum is injured, muscle movements become jerky or uncontrolled. The medulla is the part of the brain located under the cerebellum. It is at the beginning of the spinal cord. The medulla controls breathing, blood pressure, and heartbeat rate. It is also the center for reflexes such as coughing and sneezing.

The **spinal cord** is a narrow bundle of nerve fibers that extends down through the bony vertebral column. Your spinal cord is about 45 cm long. It is about as big around as an adult thumb and tapers at the end. Toward the end of the spinal cord, many small nerves branch from it in a bushy arrangement. Both the brain and the spinal cord are protected by three thin, but sturdy membranes and a clear fluid called cerebrospinal (suh ree bro SPINE ul) fluid.

What is the largest part of the brain?

F.Y.I. About 100 mL of cerebrospinal fluid circulates around the brain and spinal cord in humans.

FIGURE 22–3. The spinal cord is protected by vertebrae and disks.

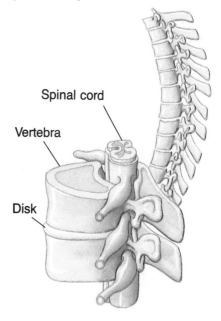

Spinal cord
Vertebra
Disk

What's in Control?   463

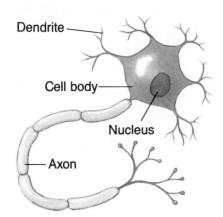

FIGURE 22–4. The parts of a neuron

F.Y.I. The gap of a synapse may be only 20 millimicrons (.000020 mm).

How fast do impulses travel through your nervous system?

22:3 The Peripheral Nervous System

Information about the body and its environment travels to and from the brain and spinal cord by way of the nerves of the peripheral nervous system. The peripheral nervous system is made up of all the nerves of the body except those of the brain and spinal cord.

What is a nerve? The term nerve or nerve fiber refers to bundles of individual cells called neurons. A **neuron** is a single nerve cell and the basic unit of the nervous system. A typical neuron is made up of a cell body, an axon (AK sahn), and dendrites (DEN drites).

Neurons carry messages or impulses. An impulse is picked up by dendrites. It travels through the cell body and then along the axon. When an impulse reaches the end of an axon, there are one or more other neurons. The impulse has to be sent on to these other neurons. But neurons do not touch. They are separated by a small space. A **synapse** (SIHN aps) is the small space between neurons. How does the impulse get across the synapse? At the ends of the axon, the impulse causes a chemical to be released from the axon into the synapse. The chemical pours out over the dendrites of the next neuron. This causes an impulse to start up in that neuron. Impulses travel through your nervous system by this method at about 120 m/s.

There are three types of neurons. They are classified according to how they work as sensory neurons, motor neurons, and interneurons. A sensory neuron carries messages from sense organs *to* the central

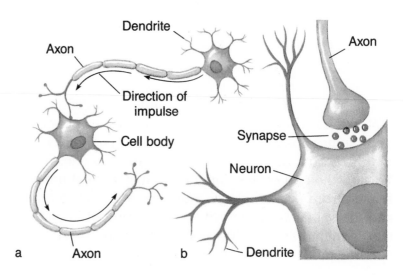

FIGURE 22–5. Nerve impulses move across a synapse from one neuron to another (a). A chemical released by one neuron stimulates an impulse in the next neuron (b).

TECHNOLOGY

Computer Nerve Models

Scientists have known for some time that when an impulse is transmitted, many nerve cells are involved in getting the information to the right part of the brain. When an impulse reaches a synapse, it stimulates new impulses in many neurons that are near it. Therefore, impulses from the ear or eye reach the brain through a network of nerves. In an effort to learn more about how the brain reacts to information from the senses, computer models of nerve networks and computer chips similar to the eye and the ear are being developed. The work is an attempt to learn more about how the brain works.

ADVANCE

A computer nerve-net model, called NETtalk, has been programmed to read letters aloud in groups of three. It also corrects its own pronunciation with information supplied to it by its researchers.

---

nervous system. Sense organs of the body are the eyes, ears, nose, mouth, and skin. Each of these organs contains groups of cells called receptors that react to changes in the environment. You feel a change in temperature because receptors in your skin send impulses to your spinal cord and brain. In the brain, impulses from sensory neurons stimulate motor neurons. A motor neuron is a nerve cell that carries impulses *from* the central nervous system to effectors. Muscles are effectors that contract in response to the impulse from a motor neuron. Impulses move from sensory neurons to motor neurons in the brain and spinal cord with the help of small neurons called interneurons.

What are the sense organs of the body?

22:4 Reflex Actions

One of the features of living things that you learned about in Chapter 17 is their ability to respond to a stimulus. You know how fast your hand and arm move when you touch something hot. This is an example of a reflex action. A **reflex action** is an involuntary action in response to a stimulus. You don't have to think about how to react. Your nervous system responds automatically and instantly.

F.Y.I. There are no pain receptors in the brain.

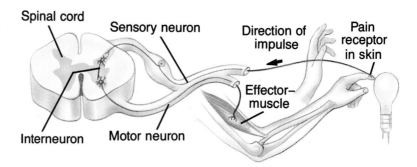

FIGURE 22–6. Reflex actions are processed in the spinal cord, not the brain.

Spinal cord
Sensory neuron
Direction of impulse
Pain receptor in skin
Effector-muscle
Interneuron
Motor neuron

Receptors in your hand receive a stimulus from a hot light bulb. Impulses are carried along sensory neurons from your hand to interneurons in the spinal cord. There they are sent immediately to motor neurons that stimulate a muscle in your arm to contract, pulling your hand away with lightning speed. The impulse in a reflex action goes to and from the spinal cord, not the brain. What else happens as a result of a reflex? Another impulse is sent to the brain where the message is interpreted. Your brain makes you realize what has happened. You yell, "Ouch!" You begin blowing on your finger to try to relieve the pain. The knee jerk, coughing, and sneezing are also reflex actions.

Name three reflex actions.

F.Y.I. Cones enable the brain to recognize color. Rods react to black and white and dim conditions.

FIGURE 22–7. The retina is the sensory receptor in the eye.

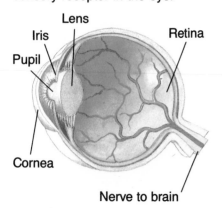

Lens
Iris
Retina
Pupil
Cornea
Nerve to brain

22:5 The Senses

Under everyday conditions, you receive a continuous flow of information about the world around you with the help of your **sense organs**—the eyes, ears, nose, mouth, and skin. Nerve impulses from different sense organs travel to the brain where they are interpreted. As a result you see color and light, hear sounds, taste food, and smell odors. You also notice whether objects are heavy, rough, sharp, or hot. Your reaction depends on which sense organ is stimulated and which part of the brain receives the message.

The eye is the sense organ that reacts to light energy. Light passes through a lens and hits a receptor called the retina. The retina contains cells called rods and cones. Nerves attached to the rods and cones send impulses to the brain. The brain interprets these impulses, and you see an object.

The ear contains receptors that react to energy in the form of sound waves and to changes in position.

466 Body Control

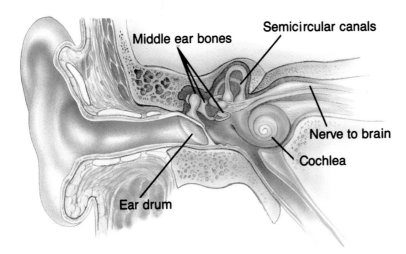

Middle ear bones
Semicircular canals
Nerve to brain
Cochlea
Ear drum

FIGURE 22–8. Hearing and balance are sensory functions of the ear.

F.Y.I. The Eustachian tube connects the inner ear with the throat and allows equal air pressure on each side of the eardrum.

Figure 22–8 shows the three parts of the human ear: the outer ear, the middle ear, and the inner ear. Sound waves are collected by the outer ear and carried to the eardrum, causing it to vibrate. The vibration is passed to the three tiny bones of the middle ear called the hammer, the anvil, and the stirrup. The stirrup vibrates against an inner ear structure called the cochlea (KAHK lee uh). Inside the cochlea, vibrations pass through a fluid and move tiny hairs connected to neurons. Impulses from the vibrating hairs are carried to the brain, and sound is heard.

The inner ear also has structures called semicircular canals that send information to the brain whenever you change the position of your head. Fluid in the canals moves to adjust to changes in your position.

The odors of baked bread, flowers, or the gym after a basketball game cause receptors in the nose to respond to chemical stimuli. Odors that you detect are made up of molecules given off into the air by different substances. Molecules enter the nose and brush past neurons high up in the nasal cavity. This contact starts an impulse that is carried to the brain, and you detect an odor.

Your tongue contains receptors called taste buds for detecting chemicals in solution. Food in your mouth gets mixed with a watery substance called saliva (suh LI vuh). This mixture washes over the taste buds. Neurons at the bottom of each taste bud send impulses to the brain, and you are able to recognize a particular flavor.

Your skin is the largest organ of your body. It is made up of the epidermis and the dermis.

Name the three bones of the middle ear.

F.Y.I. There are over 10 000 taste buds on the tongue. Each is replaced about every ten days.

FIGURE 22–9. The tongue is equipped with receptors called taste buds.

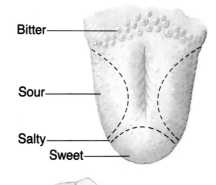

Bitter
Sour
Salty
Sweet

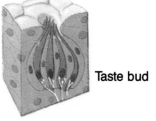

Taste bud

FIGURE 22-10. Skin contains many different receptors.

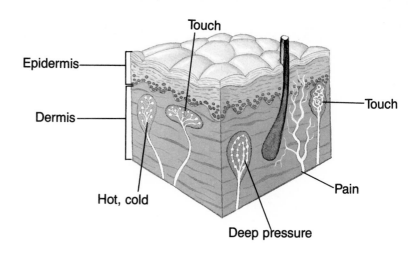

How are hormones sent to target tissues?

BIOGRAPHY

Alonzo Atencio
1929–

At the University of New Mexico, School of Medicine, Alonzo Atencio studies fibrinogen, a blood-clotting protein found to be controlled by the endocrine system. Dr. Atencio also encourages minority students to become physicians.

SKILL BUILDER

Sequencing

List the order of events from the time sound waves enter your ear until sound is heard. If you need help, refer to Sequencing on page 537.

Questions

1. What is the sequence of vibrations through the following parts: bone, fluid, air, neurons?
2. What is the order of bones in the middle ear?

The dermis contains receptors that react to changes in temperature, pain, touch, and pressure. You respond to each stimulus by making adjustments. You may pull on a sweater to warm up or put down a grocery bag that is too heavy. Skin is so well equipped with receptors that it is a major factor in homeostasis.

22:6 The Endocrine System

The endocrine system is made up of tissues called ductless glands that produce hormones. A **hormone** is a chemical made by an endocrine gland in one part of the body that brings about an effect in another part of the body. Hormones are needed in very small quantities and are sent directly into the blood stream. The tissue affected by a specific hormone is its **target tissue.** A target tissue may be located far from the gland that makes the hormone. The thyroid (THI royd) gland is found in the neck and produces a hormone that affects your kidneys.

Problem: How can you test skin sensitivity?

Materials

large paper clip   notebook paper
metric ruler

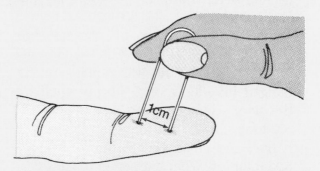

Procedure

1. Copy the data table.
2. On a separate sheet of paper, hypothesize the sensitivity of each location listed in the data table.
3. Open a large paper clip and bend it into a U-shape. Push the two ends of the clip together until they are 1 cm apart.
4. Have your partner look away while you touch the points of the paper clip lightly on his or her fingertip. Have your partner respond as to whether one or two points is felt. Record the response in the data table.
5. Repeat step 4 with each part of the arm listed in the data table. Change to touching only one point on each area so that your partner is not always expecting two points. If your partner feels two points, try another location on that part of the arm to confirm the response. Do not record two points unless your partner responds feeling two points.
6. Repeat steps 4 and 5 for all locations. Open the paper clip to 3, 5, and 7 cm. Record your partner's responses.
7. Have your partner test the sensitivity of your skin.

Questions and Conclusions

1. Which was the most sensitive area tested? The least sensitive?
2. How sensitive are different parts of the hand and arm?
3. What happens to the sensitivity of the arm as you move from the fingertips to the shoulder?
4. Were your hypotheses supported by the test? Explain.
5. How can you test skin sensitivity?
6. How can you explain why the fingertips were the most sensitive place tested?
7. In which test location would a cut be most painful? Explain.

Data and Observations

Location	Number of points felt at different distances			
	1 cm	3 cm	5 cm	7 cm
Finger				
Palm of hand				
Back of hand				
Forearm				
Forearm back				
Upper arm				

PROBLEM SOLVING

What's So Funny?

George was the last student to check out of the library. The librarian told him he had better hurry or he would be late for class.

George picked up his books and rushed to the door. He wasn't paying attention to where he was going, and he banged his elbow on a library shelf by the door. George yelled out, "Ow, I hit my funny bone!" But he wasn't laughing. It hurt and continued to hurt for about five minutes. What happened to George's elbow? How can you explain the pain George felt when he hit his elbow?

Why is the pituitary gland called the master gland?

The pituitary (puh TEW uh ter ee) gland is a small gland located at the base of the brain. Because it produces many different hormones, the pituitary gland is called the "master" gland. Hormones produced by the pituitary gland cause many other endocrine glands to produce their particular hormones.

The thyroid gland has two large lobes and is located around the upper part of the windpipe. This gland makes the hormone thyroxine (thi RAHK sun), which regulates cell metabolism and stimulates growth. A second hormone controls the amount of calcium in the blood. Your body needs the element iodine to make thyroxine. Iodine is supplied in your diet by iodized salt and seafood. When not enough iodine is present, the thyroid gland enlarges and becomes a goiter (GOY tur).

Four parathyroid glands are embedded in the back of the thyroid gland. The hormone made by these glands controls the amount of calcium and phosphorous in blood and bones. It also activates Vitamin D, helping the body to absorb calcium from food.

An adrenal gland is found on top of each kidney. The outer cortex makes hormones that regulate minerals in the blood and control the body's use of sugar, starch, proteins, and fats. The adrenal medulla makes adrenaline, which prepares your body for quick

F.Y.I. A man with a pituitary disorder grew to a height of more than 2.7 m.

reactions. When released, these hormones cause an increased heartbeat rate, breathing rate, and blood sugar level. Blood is sent to organs such as your muscles, which help the most in stressful situations, and away from skin and digestive organs.

Insulin is a hormone produced by the pancreas. Insulin enables cells to take in sugar. Cells use sugar as a source of energy. A diabetic (di uh BET ihk) is a person whose pancreas does not make enough insulin. Therefore, body cells in a diabetic cannot take up the sugar they need. Diabetics test their blood sugar level every day to determine what amount of insulin they need to take that day.

You have learned that the nervous system controls the body with impulses carried by neurons. These result in a quick response by the body. In contrast, the endocrine system controls body activities by sending hormones into the blood. The effects of a hormone often take longer to begin and last longer than those of a nerve impulse. Table 22–1 compares these two systems.

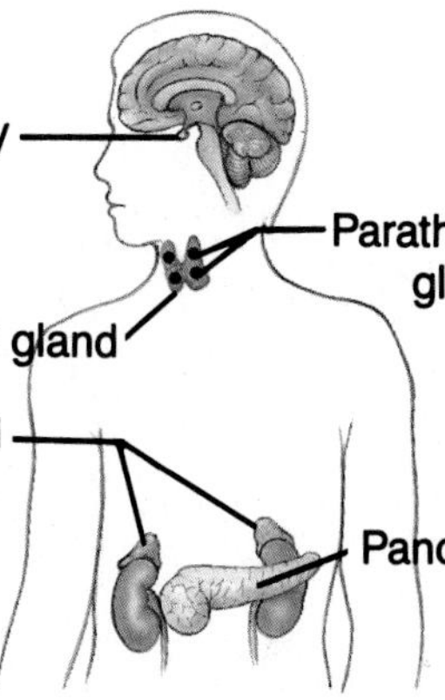

FIGURE 22–11. Hormones are produced in endocrine glands throughout the body.

How do the effects of a hormone compare with those of a nerve impulse?

Table 22–1

Body Control Systems	
Endocrine System	**Nervous System**
Produces hormones carried in body fluids	Produces impulses carried by neurons
Affects target tissues far from gland	Affects muscles and glands
Effects may be fast or slow	Effects are rapid
Effects may last hours, days, years	Effects pass quickly

REVIEW

1. What are the two major divisions of the nervous system?
2. What is a synapse?
3. To what do the receptors in the five senses of the body respond?
4. What is the pathway of an impulse in a reflex action?
5. What is a target tissue?

GOALS

You will study . . .
1. over-the-counter drugs and prescription drugs.
2. the effects of drugs on the body.

How can a prescription drug be obtained?

F.Y.I. About 11.5 million kg of aspirin are sold in the U.S. every year.

FIGURE 22–12. Over-the-counter drugs treat symptoms of illness.

22:7 Drugs and How They Work

Pharmacy shelves are filled with products that claim to make you feel better or more healthy. Many of these are classified as drugs. A **drug** is any chemical that, when taken into the body, changes the way the body works. Drugs are made into powders, pills, liquids, inhalants, or creams rubbed onto the skin.

Two types of drugs used by people are over-the-counter drugs and prescription drugs. An over-the-counter drug or OTC can be obtained without written permission of a doctor. OTCs usually only treat symptoms. They do not cure disease.

A prescription drug is a drug that can be obtained only with a written instruction from a doctor. These drugs are ordered by a doctor to help a specific patient overcome a specific illness. Examples of prescription drugs are antibiotics that destroy bacteria and insulin for the control of blood sugar levels.

If you have to take a drug, you want the drug to work the way it is supposed to work. Sometimes, however, a drug causes a side effect. A **side effect** is an unexpected and unwanted reaction to a drug. Side effects may make you feel sick to your stomach, keep you awake, or make you feel drowsy. If side effects occur, you should stop using the drug immediately and tell your doctor. Possible side effects are listed on drug labels. If two drugs are taken at the same time, one drug may affect the action of the other. This is a drug interaction. Some foods interact with drugs.

How are drugs related to the nervous system? Two groups of drugs, stimulants and depressants, affect impulses at synapses. A **stimulant** is a drug that speeds up the activity of the central nervous system and causes prolonged and increased activity at a synapse. Caffeine and nicotine are stimulants. A **depressant** is a drug that slows or blocks impulses at the synapse. Alcohol, in any quantity, is a depressant.

Caffeine is a stimulant found in many soft drink beverages, coffee, tea, diet pills, some cold medicines, candy , and pain relievers. Caffeine has been shown to cause loss of sleep, nervousness, and high blood pressure. Because of these effects, many products are also now found in "caffeine-free" form.

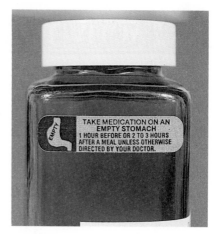

FIGURE 22–13. Read all warning labels on drugs carefully.

FIGURE 22–14. Certain drugs are widely available, but still can be harmful.

The stimulant drug in cigarettes, cigars, pipe tobacco, and smokeless tobacco products is nicotine. Except for smokeless tobacco products, this drug is inhaled. It enters the blood stream quickly through the nasal passages and lungs. Nearly 3000 harmful chemicals have been found in cigarette smoke. People who smoke cigarettes regularly risk death from heart attack, cancer, and lung diseases. They also endanger the health of others. A nonsmoker near someone who smokes in the workplace may develop nicotine-related health problems. The nonsmoker inhales the harmful chemicals that the smoker is exhaling as well as smoke from the burning cigarette.

How many harmful chemicals have been found in cigarette smoke?

Smokeless tobacco products include chewing tobacco and snuff. Use of smokeless tobacco can result in cancer of the mouth, loss of taste and smell, and permanent loss of gum and tooth tissue.

Problem: How does caffeine affect a guppy?

Materials

guppy
600-mL beakers (2)
water (aged 3 days)
masking tape
scissors
aquarium net

marking pen
brewed coffee
dropper
watch or clock
   with second hand

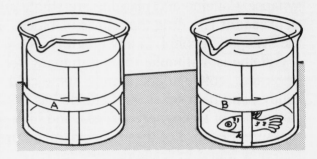

Procedure

1. Cut an 8-cm strip of masking tape in half lengthwise. Use one strip to make a horizontal line on a 600-mL beaker at the 200-mL mark. Use the other strip to make a vertical line that divides the horizontal line in half. Repeat this on a second beaker.
2. Mark one beaker A and the second beaker B. Pour 400 mL of aged water into each beaker.
3. Place a guppy carefully into beaker A. Copy the data table while it adjusts to its new environment.
4. Observe the activity of the guppy in beaker A. Count each time the guppy moves across the tape from one section of the beaker to another for one minute. Record the number of crossings.
5. Repeat step 4 two more times. Record your results.
6. Add 30 drops of coffee to beaker A.
7. Hypothesize the effect of caffeine on the guppy.
8. Wait five minutes. Count each movement of the guppy across the tape in beaker A for three, one-minute intervals. Record the number of movements for each minute.

9. Move the guppy from beaker A to beaker B. Allow the guppy to adjust and repeat step 8.
10. Average the number of movements for the tests in each beaker.

Data and Observations

Test	Number of Movements		
	Beaker A	Beaker A + caffeine	Beaker B
1			
2			
3			
Average			

Questions and Conclusions

1. Under which conditions did the guppy make the highest average number of movements? The least?
2. How does caffeine affect a guppy?
3. Why were three tests averaged?
4. Why were movements counted before caffeine was added?
5. Why was the guppy moved to the water in beaker B?
6. How does your hypothesis compare with the results of the activity?

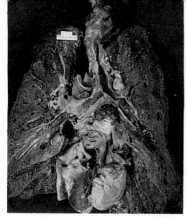

a b

FIGURE 22–15. Drugs damage body organs such as the lungs (a) and the liver (b).

Alcohol is a depressant drug found in beer, wine, distilled beverages, and some foods and medicines. The drug enters the blood stream through the stomach and small intestine and is carried quickly to the brain and other body organs. An immediate effect of low levels of alcohol is to give a false sense of self confidence. In addition, vision and judgment are affected. Taste, smell, and the ability to feel pain are reduced. At higher levels, reaction time is slowed, and the eyes have a difficult time adjusting to light and are less sensitive to the color red. Large amounts of alcohol have been shown to damage the nervous system, liver, digestive system, and kidneys.

An individual who consumes large quantities of alcohol and who is addicted to the drug is classified as an alcoholic. Alcoholism is a disease characterized by uncontrolled drinking of alcohol. An alcoholic may have a difficult time admitting that he or she has a problem controlling the use of alcohol. Alcohol does more than harm the individual with the disease. Frequently, jobs are neglected, and families are harmed. It is also possible that children of alcoholics have an inherited tendency toward the disease.

What type of drug is alcohol?

F.Y.I. In 1960, the American Medical Association declared alcoholism to be a disease.

FIGURE 22–16. Many groups are actively involved in stopping the use of alcohol.

22:8 Drug Abuse

Some people use certain drugs to feel better, more confident, or accepted by friends. **Drug abuse** occurs when a drug is purposely used for reasons other than its intended use. Almost any drug can be abused. Drugs that are most often abused are alcohol, marijuana, cocaine, and "crack." Abuse of these drugs can lead to addiction (uh DIHK shun). An **addict** is a person who can no longer control the use of a drug and may even be unaware that he or she is dependent on the use of the drug. Tolerance develops when an addict feels the need to take larger and larger quantities of a drug to reach the desired effect of the drug. If an addict tries to stop using a drug, withdrawal symptoms begin. **Withdrawal** is the reaction the body undergoes when use of a drug is stopped. Withdrawal frequently includes severe muscle cramping, vomiting, and diarrhea. Overdosing drugs may lead to death. An **overdose** means that more drug has been taken than the body can metabolize.

What drugs are most often abused?

SCIENCE AND SOCIETY

22:9 Polydrug Use

People who abuse drugs frequently use two or more drugs at the same time. **Polydrug use** is the use of more than one drug at a time. Sometimes a second drug is used to extend the effect of the first drug. Alcohol is the most frequently used second drug. It makes the depressant effects of sedatives and tranquilizers last longer. Polydrug use may also be practiced in an effort to stop the undesirable effects of a drug. Some diet pills can cause an individual to feel jittery. People drink alcohol with these pills thinking that it will calm the jittery feeling.

Because many drugs such as alcohol, nicotine products, and diet pills are so easily available, people tend to think they aren't very harmful. But abuse of these drugs or combinations of them has resulted in permanent damage and death.

It is difficult to treat someone who is addicted to two drugs. If use of all drugs is stopped, an addict will show withdrawal symptoms for each drug abused. Why should individuals help stop the abuse of harmful substances?

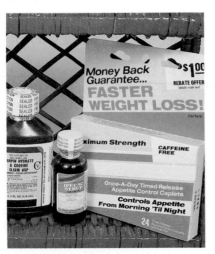

FIGURE 22–17. Polydrug use is the use of two or more drugs at one time.

22:10 Illegal Drugs

The use of many drugs is controlled by law. Morphine, codeine, heroin, cocaine, amphetamines, and marijuana are examples of controlled drugs. People who use these drugs without medical supervision do so illegally. Illegal use of these drugs is widespread.

Morphine (MOR feen) and codeine (KOH deen) are opiates (OH pee uts), addictive drugs made from the opium poppy. They are also called narcotics. A narcotic is any drug that causes sleepiness or relieves pain. Codeine has beneficial effects in some cough medicines. Morphine is used to relieve pain in terminal cancer patients. In spite of these beneficial uses, these drugs are addictive. Heroin (HER oh un) is an addictive depressant that is made from morphine. Withdrawal from heroin takes a long time and generally is violent and painful. Infants born to mothers who abuse heroin may show signs of addiction and have to undergo treatment for withdrawal.

Cocaine is a fast-acting, addictive, stimulant drug made from the coca plant. Cocaine is one of the most widely used illegal stimulants. In its different forms, it is inhaled, smoked, or injected. In one form, it is a fine, white, odorless, bitter-tasting powder that is inhaled through the nose. This form is also known as coke or snow. Permanent destruction of nasal membranes and nasal cartilage has occurred in cocaine abusers. Abusers of this drug first have a feeling of great power and confidence, followed by feelings of depression and worthlessness. Cocaine affects blood circulation and has been associated with fatal heart attacks.

FIGURE 22–18. Many infants of drug-dependent mothers must be treated for drug-withdrawal symptoms.

What are some examples of controlled drugs?

a

b

FIGURE 22–19. Inhaled cocaine is addictive and destroys parts of the nose (a). Crack is addictive, inexpensive, and deadly (b).

What Is a Drug? 477

FIGURE 22–20. Cocaine is extracted from coca leaves with sulfuric acid (a). Marijuana leaves are smoked for the effects of the drug THC (b).

a　　　　　　　　　　　　b

Another form of cocaine is "crack." **Crack** is cocaine in the form of small white or brown chunks. It is smoked with cigarette tobacco or marijuana. Crack is stronger than the powdered form of cocaine. Use of crack has been shown to produce lung damage, stroke, heart attack, and death. Because it is inexpensive, it has become a source of drug addiction in young people.

How is marijuana classified?

The drug marijuana is from the cannabis plant. It is classified as both a stimulant and an hallucinogen. An **hallucinogen** is a substance that distorts the senses and causes the user to see and hear things that do not exist. The leaves of the plant are smoked in cigarette form. When smoked, the leaves release THC, the active drug ingredient. Other forms of marijuana that are used are hashish, a gum-like material extracted from the leaves, and hashish oil. Both forms have a more concentrated amount of the drug than marijuana leaves. Physically, smoking marijuana results in faster heartbeat and pulse rates, red, irritated eyes, dry mouth, lung problems, and possible damage to the body's ability to combat disease.

REVIEW

6. What is the difference between a prescription drug and an over-the-counter drug?
7. What is the difference between a side effect and a drug interaction?
8. Distinguish between a stimulant and a depressant.
9. What is drug abuse?
10. Why are certain drugs illegal?

CHAPTER 22 REVIEW

SUMMARY

1. The nervous system is a control system that receives and responds to stimuli from internal and external environments. 22:1
2. The central nervous system of the human body is made up of the brain and the spinal cord. 22:2
3. The peripheral nervous system has sensory, motor, and interneurons. 22:3
4. A reflex action is an involuntary action. 22:4
5. Sense organs contain receptors that relay messages to the brain. 22:5
6. The endocrine system produces hormones that affect specific target tissues. 22:6
7. The two main types of drugs are over-the-counter drugs and prescription drugs. Drugs stimulate or depress the nervous system. Caffeine, nicotine, and alcohol are easily available drugs. 22:7
8. Drug abuse occurs when a drug is used for a reason other than its intended purpose. 22:8
9. Polydrug use is the use of more than one drug at a time. 22:9
10. Illegal drugs are controlled by law and many are addictive. 22:10

VOCABULARY

a. addict
b. brain
c. central nervous system
d. cocaine
e. crack
f. depressant
g. drug
h. drug abuse
i. hallucinogen
j. homeostasis
k. hormone
l. neuron
m. overdose
n. peripheral nervous system
o. polydrug use
p. reflex action
q. sense organs
r. side effect
s. spinal cord
t. stimulant
u. synapse
v. target tissue
w. withdrawal

Match each description with the correct vocabulary word from the list above.
1. an involuntary action in response to a stimulus
2. a chemical that affects a target tissue
3. the major control center of the body
4. a nerve cell
5. any chemical that changes the way the body functions
6. the brain and the spinal cord
7. the space between two nerve cells
8. a highly dangerous form of cocaine
9. all the nerves of the body outside the spinal cord
10. drug that speeds up the activity of the central nervous system

A. Reviewing Concepts

Choose the word or phrase that correctly completes each of the following sentences.

1. Motor nerves carry messages to _____.
   a. muscles
   b. pain receptors
   c. rods and cones
   d. sensory neurons
2. The nervous system is divided into the _____ and peripheral systems.
   a. cerebrum
   b. central
   c. medulla
   d. neuron
3. The speed of a nerve impulse is about _____ m/s.
   a. 20
   b. 120
   c. 200
   d. 210
4. The space between two nerves is a(n) _____.
   a. neuron
   b. dendrite
   c. synapse
   d. axon
5. The _____ of the brain coordinates muscle movements.
   a. cerebellum
   b. medulla
   c. skull
   d. cerebrum
6. The _____ is protected by vertebrae.
   a. brain
   b. pituitary
   c. spinal cord
   d. pancreas
7. The _____ is the receptor in the eye.
   a. sclera
   b. iris
   c. retina
   d. pupil
8. The bones of the ear are located in the _____ ear.
   a. outer
   b. middle
   c. inner
   d. exterior
9. Flavors in the mouth stimulate neurons in the _____.
   a. saliva
   b. retina
   c. cochlea
   d. taste buds
10. Medicines ordered in writing by a doctor are called _____ drugs.
   a. over-the-counter
   b. prescription
   c. illegal
   d. social
11. In any quantity, alcohol is a(n) _____ drug.
   a. depressant
   b. stimulant
   c. opiate
   d. hormonal
12. A highly dangerous form of cocaine in solid chunk form is known as _____.
   a. crack
   b. marijuana
   c. nicotine
   d. heroin
13. The _____ is referred to as the master gland of the body.
   a. adrenal
   b. pancreas
   c. thyroid
   d. pituitary
14. A person who can no longer control the use of a drug is a(n) _____.
   a. addict
   b. depressant
   c. pharmacist
   d. narcotic
15. _____ is produced by endocrine cells in the pancreas.
   a. Adrenalin
   b. Insulin
   c. Thyroxine
   d. Estrogen

B. Understanding Concepts

Answer the following questions using complete sentences.

16. What are some functions of the medulla portion of the brain?
17. Describe how a reflex action works.
18. What stimulates the nerve endings in the nose?
19. What happens to a nerve impulse at a synapse?
20. Explain why over-the-counter drugs can be dangerous.
21. How do sensory neurons and motor neurons differ from each other?
22. Why is the pituitary gland called the master gland?
23. Why is polydrug use difficult to treat?
24. What is the relationship between an endocrine gland and its target tissue?

25. What sources of energy stimulate the ear and eye? What are the sensory receptors in the ear and eye?

C. Applying Concepts

Answer the following questions using complete sentences.

26. How are the nervous and endocrine systems alike?

27. What happens in the spinal cord in a reflex action?

28. How do the senses help the body maintain homeostasis?

29. Why should a person not take someone else's prescription drug?

30. Give reasons why alcohol is easily abused.

SKILL REVIEW

If you need help, refer to the Skill Handbook, pages 526 to 537.

1. You touch a hot pan and pull your hand away immediately. This is a reflex action. List the sequence of events that occurs in your nervous system and causes you to pull away. Refer to Section 22:4 if you need help.

2. Light hits your retina and stimulates the rods and cones. Then, impulses are sent to your brain. What is the effect of this? Refer to Section 22:5 if you need help.

3. List the three main areas of the brain. Name two bodily functions controlled by each area. Organize your answer in table form.

4. You read in a newspaper that a man riding a bicycle was hit by a car. He was not wearing a helmet. He received a brain injury. Now he has difficulty remembering. He has forgotten the names of many objects and people. Which area of his brain can you infer was injured? Refer to Section 22:2 for help.

5. Outline Section 22:3 of this chapter.

PROJECTS

1. Collect ads from newspapers and magazines for alcohol, tobacco, or over-the-counter medicines. Report to the class on the techniques being used to sell the products. Techniques may include being part of the crowd, good times, and so on.

2. Make a model of a human brain. Use different colored clay to represent the cerebrum, cerebellum, and medulla. Label each area of the brain and include information on the functions of each area.

3. Write a report on injuries to the brain or nervous system. Include a short biography of a famous person who has survived a brain or nervous system injury. Explain how everyday life changes for someone who has such an injury.

READINGS

1. Asimov, Isaac. *How Did We Find Out About the Brain?* New York: Walker and Co., 1987.

2. Brown, David. *Crack and Cocaine.* New York: Watts, 1987.

3. Ward, Brian R. *Drugs and Drug Abuse.* New York: Watts, 1988.

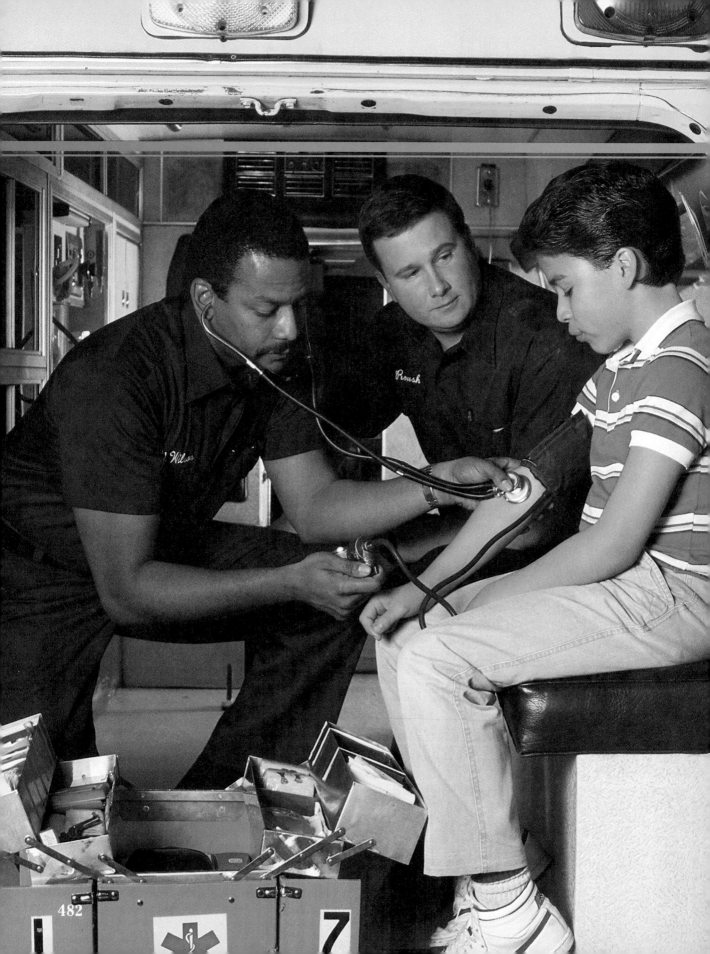

Body Circulation

CHAPTER 23

Career: Paramedic

One day in late May, Juan and his friends hurried through lunch to be able to spend time on the playground. They checked out a soccer ball from the box outside the gym office and headed outside. The day was sunny and warm, and some bees were buzzing around the edge of the soccer field. As they divided into teams, Juan felt a sting on his arm. He slumped to the ground, immediately unconscious. Mr. Davis, the playground monitor, ran to help. It was clear that Juan was having trouble breathing. Mr. Davis turned and told Miss Edwards to· call the emergency squad and Juan's parents.

Two paramedics arrived with cases full of equipment. Juan was now conscious. One of the paramedics had a transmitter and was put through to a doctor at the local hospital emergency room. The other paramedic took Juan's blood pressure and pulse rate. The paramedic saw what looked like a sting mark on Juan's arm. Juan's father arrived and told them that Juan was allergic to bee venom. The doctor listened to the paramedic's observations of Juan's symptoms. She told the paramedic to administer a drug to regulate Juan's breathing. The paramedics continued to check his blood pressure and pulse rate for a half hour.

The circulatory system is important in transporting many substances that change or regulate body processes, including the process of breathing. In this chapter, you will study circulation, respiration, and excretion.

F.Y.I. National Association of Emergency Medical Technicians, 9140 Ward Parkway, Kansas City, MO 64114

What Is Circulation?

GOALS

You will study . . .

1. parts and functions of the circulatory system.
2. the role of blood in the body.
3. how the body develops immunity.

What is the circulatory system?

Name the two main parts of the circulatory system.

23:1 The Circulatory System

The boy in the story on the previous page had a severe reaction to a bee sting. The venom acted on his nervous system, causing breathing difficulties. The venom had been rapidly moved to his brain by a huge network called the circulatory system. The **circulatory system** is a transport system made up of the heart, blood and lymph, and vessels that link all the systems of your body. Many kilometers of vessels transport fluids that contain oxygen, carbon dioxide, nutrients, blood cells, waste products, disease-causing substances, and hormones throughout your body. In this way, each cell of your body is serviced. Body cells receive needed materials from the circulatory system to keep them alive and working. Cells use up these materials and produce waste products. Wastes are also carried away by the circulatory system.

The circulatory system is also made up of two main parts: the cardiovascular system and the lymph (LIHMF) system. The heart, blood, and blood vessels make up the cardiovascular system. The lymph system is made up of vessels, masses of tissues called lymph nodes, a clear fluid called lymph, cells called lymphocytes (LIM fuh sitz), and a large organ called the spleen. The

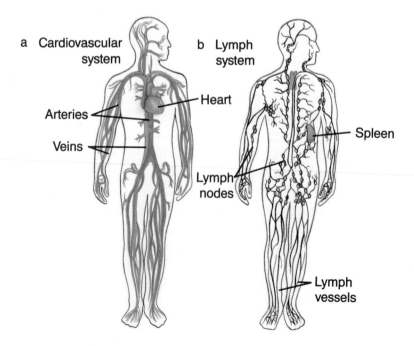

FIGURE 23–1. The circulatory system is made up of the cardiovascular (a) and lymph systems (b).

lymph system helps maintain the fluid balance in the body by collecting fluids from around tissues. Lymphocytes are large cells that are found in the lymph system, blood vessels, and tissues. Their main function is to destroy disease-causing microbes throughout the body. The spleen is a large lymph organ near the stomach. It contains many lymphocytes for the removal of disease organisms.

23:2 The Heart and Blood Vessels

Your heart is a muscular organ about the same size as a closed fist. It is made of cardiac muscle and has four chambers. The two upper chambers are the left atrium (AY tree um) and right atrium. The two lower chambers are the left and right ventricles (VEN trih kulz).

There are several large blood vessels connected to the heart. One type of vessel is an artery (ART uh ree). An **artery** is a blood vessel that carries blood away from the heart. There are many large and small arteries in your body. The largest artery in your body is the aorta (ay ORT uh). The aorta carries blood from the heart to all the other arteries of the body. A second type of blood vessel is a vein. A **vein** (VAYN) is a blood vessel that carries blood toward the heart. Veins have valves to keep blood flowing toward the heart. The vena cava (VEE nuh • CAY vuh) is the largest vein in the body.

F.Y.I. The body is equipped with about a trillion lymphocytes.

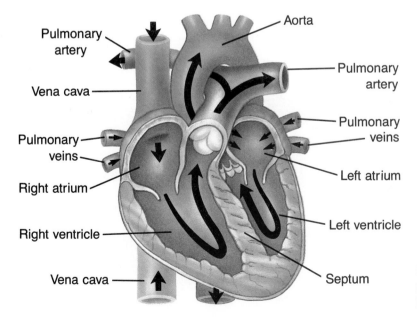

FIGURE 23–2. The heart is a pump that moves blood through body organs.

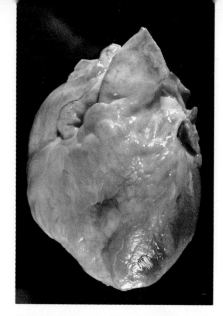

FIGURE 23-3. The heart muscle is supplied with many blood vessels.

Where does blood travel when it leaves the right ventricle?

F.Y.I. The term pulmonary refers to the lungs.

F.Y.I. Of the four heart chambers, the left ventricle has the thickest walls.

How does blood get from an artery to a vein? As an artery enters an organ, it divides into many smaller vessels. The smallest blood vessels in the body are the **capillaries.** The walls of capillaries are extremely thin, only one cell thick. Materials diffuse easily into and out of capillaries. Capillaries within organs empty into slightly larger vessels and then into veins where blood is moved back toward the heart. There are more capillaries in your body than any other type of blood vessel. The blood from most cuts you experience is usually from damaged capillaries, not from a major blood vessel.

What is the pathway of blood through the chambers of your heart? Blood that is returning from your body contains carbon dioxide that your cells have produced as a waste product. It flows into the right atrium. When the atrium is full, it contracts, and blood is pushed down into the right ventricle. The right ventricle then contracts and pushes blood out of the heart to the lungs through the pulmonary (PUL muh ner ee) arteries. In the lungs, carbon dioxide diffuses out of the blood, and oxygen enters the blood. The now oxygen-rich blood goes through the pulmonary veins back to the left atrium of the heart. The atrium contracts and this blood is pushed down into the left ventricle. Then with great force, the left ventricle contracts and blood is pushed out through the aorta to the body.

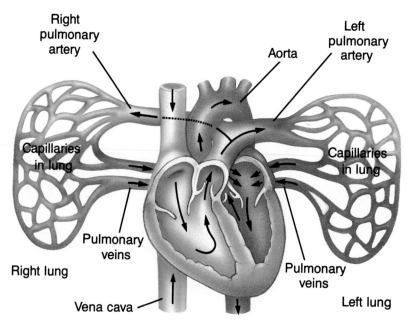

FIGURE 23-4. The flow of blood between the heart and lungs is called pulmonary circulation.

Each time the left ventricle contracts, it exerts great pressure on the blood in the aorta. When it relaxes, the pressure in the aorta becomes less. These forces can be measured. They are referred to as your blood pressure.

A healthy heart beats or contracts about 70 times per minute. The number of beats increases when you exercise. Heartbeat can be felt in several arteries in your body in the form of a pulse. Your pulse rate is really a measure of your heartbeat rate. A person with a heartbeat rate of 70 beats per minute has a pulse rate of 70.

The heart is a noisy organ when you listen to it. Blood rushes, muscle tissue moves, and valves snap open and shut. Figure 23–5 shows an artificial valve. Valves keep the blood from sloshing back into a chamber. Healthy heart valves close tightly. Each valve makes a specific sound as it closes. These sounds are part of what is heard when the doctor uses a stethoscope to listen to the heart. The typical heart makes a "lub-dup" sound. A different sound such as a hiss is called a heart murmur. A murmur occurs when a valve does not close properly and a small amount of blood flows backward. Some people are born with heart murmurs. Others may be the result of disease.

The pathway that blood takes going from the heart to the lungs and back to the heart is called pulmonary circulation. The pathway blood takes from the aorta to the body organs and back to the heart is called systemic (sihs TEM ihk) circulation. The pathway that blood takes to service the heart muscle itself is called coronary (KOR uh ner ee) circulation.

FIGURE 23–5. Artificial valves are used to replace damaged valves in the heart.

FIGURE 23–6. Systemic circulation (a) and coronary circulation (b)

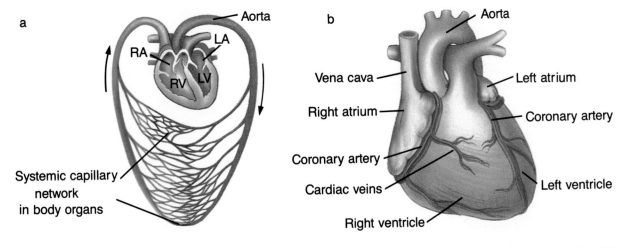

What Is Circulation? 487

ACTIVITY 23–1   Pulse and Breath Rates

Problem: What is the effect of exercise on the body supply systems?

Materials
watch or clock with second hand

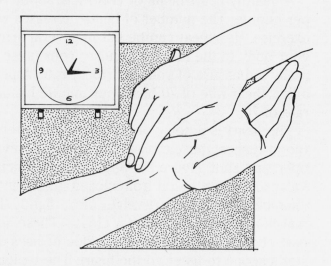

Procedure
1. Copy the data table.
2. Place the tips of your two middle fingers on the inside of the wrist of your partner. Find the pulse. Using a watch or clock, take your partner's pulse at rest for one minute. Record the number of beats in the data table.
3. Count and record the number of breaths your partner takes at rest for one minute. Breathing in and out counts as one breath. Hypothesize the effect of running in place on pulse and breath rates.
4. Have your partner run in place for three minutes. Immediately count your partner's pulse rate. Have your partner count the breath rate. Record the two rates.
5. Wait five minutes and count your partner's pulse rate. Have your partner count the breath rate. Record these rates in your data table.
6. Reverse roles and let your partner count and record pulse and breath rates for you, as in steps 3, 4, and 5. Record this information in the data table.

Questions and Conclusions
1. What is your at-rest pulse rate? After exercise?
2. What is the effect of exercise on your pulse rate?
3. What is your at-rest breath rate? After exercise?
4. What is the effect of exercise on your breath rate?
5. What is the effect of exercise on the body supply systems?
6. How does your hypothesis compare with the results of this activity?
7. Why did your pulse and breath rates decrease after five minutes?

Data and Observations

Supply System	At rest	Immediately after exercise	Five minutes after exercise
Pulse Rate (one minute)			
Breath Rate (one minute)			

488   Body Circulation

23:3 Blood

Blood is a tissue made up of liquid and solid parts. It is moved through your body by the pumping action of the heart. Blood is made up of red blood cells, white blood cells, cell fragments called platelets, and a liquid portion called plasma. Plasma is pale yellow. Blood appears red in color because of hemoglobin (HEE muh gloh bun). **Hemoglobin** is the oxygen-carrying molecule in the red blood cells. A red blood cell is about one-third hemoglobin. Table 23–1 shows approximately how many of each cell type and platelet are found in blood.

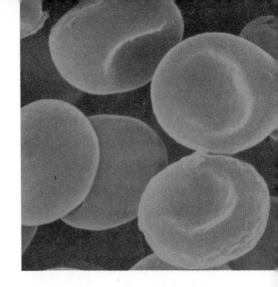

FIGURE 23–7. Red blood cells contain hemoglobin.

F.Y.I. In high altitudes people have more red blood cells to supply oxygen to cells.

What is the function of white blood cells?

Table 23–1

Components of Blood		
Part	**How Many**	**Function**
Red blood cells	males: 4 to 5.5 million per mm^3; females: 3.5 to 5 million per mm^3	transport O_2 to cells
White blood cells	5000 to 10 000 per mm^3	engulf microbes
Platelets	150 000 to 400 000 per mm^3	to help clot blood

Red blood cells make up most of the cell portion of blood. They are disc-shaped cells that do not have any nuclei. Red blood cells are formed in red bone marrow and lose their nuclei before entering the blood stream. Each red blood cell lives only about 120 days, so new ones need to be made all the time. Old ones are destroyed in the spleen.

White blood cells are a dynamic part of the circulatory system. White blood cells are different from red blood cells in appearance and function. They are much larger and can change shape. There are fewer of them, and each has a large nucleus. White blood cells protect the body from disease. To do this, they squeeze between the cells of capillary walls and move out into the tissues around the blood vessels. Microbes such as bacteria are engulfed by white blood cells the way an ameoba engulfs its food. It is as if the body were constantly being taken care of by thousands of vacuum cleaners.

FIGURE 23–8. White blood cells are large, irregular in shape, and contain nuclei.

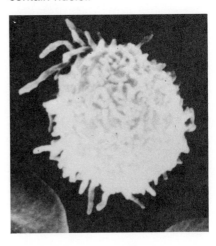

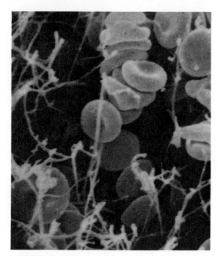

FIGURE 23–9. Blood clots when red blood cells are caught in a sticky fibrin network.

What is plasma?

F.Y.I. In a serious injury, blood begins to clot within 20 seconds.

What do you do when you get a cut on your hand? You may wash it with soap and water, put a bandage on it, and forget about it. Your body responds in a more complex way. First, white blood cells go to work to destroy bacteria that rush into the broken skin. Sometimes this is indicated by the presence of pus. Pus is a collection of white blood cells and dead bacteria. Platelets in the damaged area immediately begin to stick to the ends of broken vessels. **Platelets** are cell fragments in blood that help blood to clot. Platelets cause a chemical called fibrin to form. Fibrin forms a sticky web over the wound. Blood cells are trapped and kept from escaping through the cut. The web of fibers and trapped cells is a blood clot. The clot blocks the opening and prevents more blood from escaping. As a clot dries, it becomes a scab. In time, new cells grow under the scab and loosen it, and the scab falls off.

Plasma is the liquid portion of blood in which cells and platelets move. It is mostly water but also contains proteins and salts. Plasma transports nutrients and hormones to cells. Waste products from cell metabolism, such as carbon dioxide, are also dissolved in plasma and carried away from the cells.

23:4 Blood Types

Sometimes it is necessary to replace blood lost as a result of an injury. A **transfusion** is the transfer of blood belonging to one person into the blood stream of another person.

American Red Cross | Blood Services
Central Ohio Region
995 E. Broad Street
Columbus, Ohio 43205
1-614-253-7981

301 32 4706 16
BUCHHOLZ   BARBARA A
F
012138
0   POS

FIGURE 23–10. Blood is typed for ABO groups and the Rh factor.

For a transfusion to be successful, factors in the blood must be compatible. This means that chemicals in the donated blood must be exactly like those in the blood of the person who will receive the blood. If transfused blood is not like the receiver's type, clots form in blood vessels, and death can occur. Sometimes only the plasma portion of blood is given. Plasma is given when a supply of blood clotting factors are needed.

Blood is classified into four groups: type A, type B, type AB, and type O. Blood type names are based on the presence or absence of a certain protein in the membranes of red blood cells. If only protein A is present, it is type A blood. If only protein B is present, the blood is type B. Blood with both A and B proteins is type AB. If neither A nor B proteins are present, the blood is type O. Table 23–2 indicates the blood type combinations that are safe for transfusions.

What can happen if the wrong blood type is transfused?

F.Y.I. A person with a mass of 70 kg will have about 5 L of blood.

Table 23–2

Compatible Blood Types				
Donor Blood Type	**Receiver Blood Type**			
	A	**B**	**AB**	**O**
A	yes	no	yes	no
B	no	yes	yes	no
AB	no	no	yes	no
O	yes	yes	yes	yes

Another substance that must be considered before a transfusion is given is the Rhesus or Rh factor. Persons who have this substance are said to be Rh positive (Rh+). Persons without the substance are Rh negative (Rh−).

A person may have blood type A and be Rh positive. This person is said to be A+ and can only receive blood from donors who have blood type A or O and also are Rh+. Persons with type O blood and who are Rh negative are O−, and can only receive blood from a person with type O, Rh negative blood. How do you get your blood type? Your blood type depends on the blood types of your parents. You cannot change your blood type. Your bone marrow will always produce only the blood type you inherited.

FIGURE 23–11. Donated blood is collected in quantities called units.

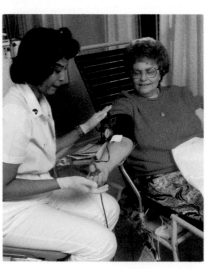

Substitutes for Blood

For nearly one hundred years, research has been done to develop a substitute for blood. It could be pulled from a shelf and given as a transfusion in emergencies. There would be no need to test it for blood type or disease organisms. The substance would have to work as real blood does by carrying oxygen to cells and carrying carbon dioxide away from cells. Research has been done with oils that can hold large amounts of oxygen and with free hemoglobin in small capsules called microcapsules.

ADVANCE

An artificial blood called Fluosol has been developed for keeping donated organs healthy before being transplanted. Fluosol can carry oxygen and carbon dioxide. It does not react with blood group proteins and has no disease microbes.

SCIENCE AND SOCIETY

23:5 Blood Donation

People receive blood transfusions after major surgery or a severe injury. Is blood donation safe? During blood donation, only sterile, disposable equipment is used. Donated blood is collected in a plastic sack that holds 450 mL. This amount of blood is called a unit. Over 10 million units of blood are collected in the United States each year.

How many mL are in a unit of blood?

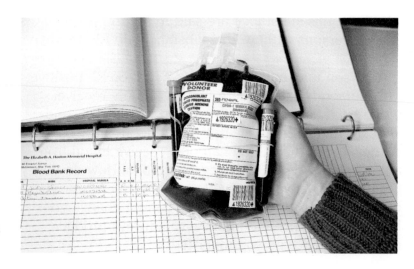

FIGURE 23–12. Donated blood is typed and stored.

Donated blood is carefully screened to protect the person who will receive it. It is checked for blood type, Rh factor, types of proteins in the plasma, and disease. Potential donors are always asked if they have had diseases such as hepatitis or malaria. All donated blood also is tested for the presence of the AIDS virus.

Some people donate their own blood before an operation. This is called autologous (aw TAHL uh gus) transfusion. Several weeks before an operation, blood is collected and stored. Then at the time of the operation, the person receives his or her own blood.

Concern over disease has resulted in fewer people donating blood. There is, however, always a need for different blood types. What can be done to ensure that all blood types are available? What methods might be used to make sure donated blood is safe? Why is it important to maintain a good supply of blood?

23:6 Staying Healthy

In Unit 5, you learned that diseases are caused by viruses, bacteria, protozoans, and fungi. How does your body fight these microbes? Long before you think about seeing the doctor for a cold medicine, your body's own defenses are at work. The skin is an organ that provides a habitat for many helpful bacteria. So long as your skin isn't broken, helpful bacteria destroy many harmful ones that you encounter. Harmful bacteria enter the body through the mouth, nose, and cuts in the skin. They pass into the body tissues and the circulatory system. Most microbes that invade the body are destroyed by white blood cells.

BLOOD SUPPLY

RED CROSS
December 21
Hospital requests...........................581 pints
Requests filled..............................564 pints
Shortage.......................................17 pints
  Red Cross blood donors must give an average of 550 pints daily, Monday through Friday, to meet all the needs of central Ohio hospitals. All blood types are needed. In short supply are B positive, and B negative. Donors can make appointments by telephoning 253-7981.

FIGURE 23–13. Newspapers report the continuous need for units of different blood types.

How do bacteria enter the body?

What destroys invading microbes?

FIGURE 23–14. White blood cells work to keep the body free of microbes.

Another body defense is immunity. **Immunity** (ihm YEW nut ee) is the body's ability to resist microbes that invade the body. A lymphocyte is a type of white blood cell that produces antibodies. **Antibodies** are proteins that are produced on lymphocytes. They react to substances on microbes that have invaded the body. These invading substances are called antigens. Antigens are engulfed by a large white blood cell called a macrophage and taken to the lymphocyte. Specific antibodies are made by the body for specific antigens. An antibody combines with its antigen. The antigen is made harmless. The lymphocyte produces more antibodies and releases them into the blood. If a specific antigen should invade the body again, the bloodstream is already equipped with antibodies to combat it. The body is said to be immune to that disease-carrying substance.

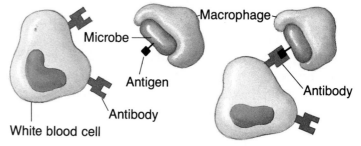

FIGURE 23–15. Specific antibodies are made for specific antigens.

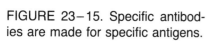

Have you had chicken pox? If so, you probably now have immunity to that disease. Having chicken pox resulted in your body producing antibodies against the chicken pox virus, which is an antigen.

Another way to obtain immunity against a disease is from a vaccine. Recall from Chapter 17 that a vaccine is a substance purposely introduced into the body to cause the production of antibodies. Whenever disease organisms enter the body, antibodies are already present to destroy them.

REVIEW

1. What is the difference between an artery and a vein?
2. Trace the path of blood through the heart from the right atrium to the aorta.
3. What is the function of hemoglobin?
4. What are two ways to make sure donated blood is safe?
5. What is immunity?

How Are Cell Wastes Removed?

23:7 The Respiratory System

A person cannot live without oxygen for more than a few minutes. Brain cells begin to die within four to five minutes if the supply of oxygen is cut off. In Chapter 17, you learned that cells use oxygen to release energy from food. In doing so, they produce carbon dioxide. This process is cellular respiration. Oxygen needed for this process is supplied by the respiratory system. The **respiratory system** is the system that brings oxygen into the body and expels carbon dioxide from the body. In addition, parts of the respiratory system make vocal sounds and filter and warm the air moving in and out of your lungs. The respiratory system is made up of a series of air passages, the lungs, and the diaphragm. The air passages are the nose, the larynx, the trachea, and bronchioles. The bronchioles lead to the lungs, which are large spongy masses of tiny sacs called **alveoli.**

The process of respiration is aided by muscles between the ribs. These muscles are arranged so that your chest cavity can expand and relax as you breathe in and out.

GOALS

You will study . . .
1. the structures and functions of the respiratory system.
2. three organs of excretion.

What do cells use oxygen for?

What is the function of the respiratory system?

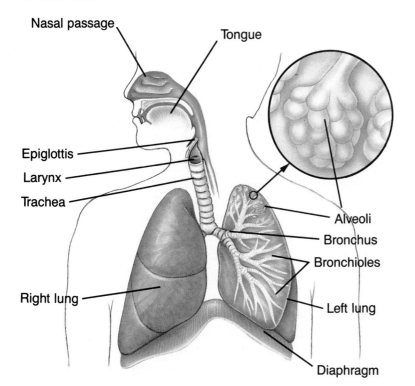

FIGURE 23–16. Parts of the human respiratory system

FIGURE 23–17. The diaphragm contracts and relaxes as you breathe.

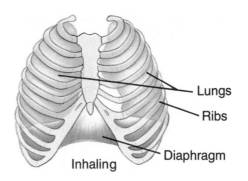
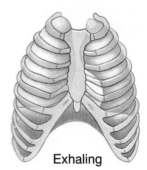

FIGURE 23–17. The diaphragm contracts and relaxes as you breathe.

Lungs
Ribs
Diaphragm
Inhaling
Exhaling

23:8 Inhaling and Exhaling

Air moves into the lungs with the help of a large flat sheet of muscle under the heart and lungs called the **diaphragm.** When you breathe in, the brain sends impulses to make the diaphragm contract and become flattened. This causes the air pressure in your chest to become less. Air from the outside, under greater pressure, pushes in and fills up the alveoli. Your rib cage opens up. This is the process of inhaling.

When you exhale, the diaphragm relaxes and is pushed up into a dome-like position. This increases the pressure inside the chest cavity and forces air up out of the alveoli. Some air is always left in the lungs. This is called residual air.

Inhaling and exhaling are not always relaxed. A cough is a high-speed blast of air that attempts to clear the respiratory passage of annoying material. It may be dust, mucus, or food that has fallen on the epiglottis. The epiglottis is a protective flap over the larynx. Normally the epiglottis closes down over the top of the larynx to keep particles of food from getting into the trachea. Once in a while when this happens, the choking reflex occurs. Usually a few coughs clear the particle, but it can be dangerous. The Heimlich maneuver makes use of residual air in the lungs to forcefully push particles out of air passages.

Hiccups result when your diaphragm contracts suddenly in a muscle spasm. Air rushes into the lungs and the epiglottis snaps noisily down over the larynx.

23:9 From Air to the Cell

Breathing seems like a fairly simple activity. Each time you breathe in or inhale, you take about 500 mL of air into your lungs. If you are exercising, the volume of

F.Y.I. Over 8000 people die from choking each year.

What is a cough?

FIGURE 23–18. Use of the Heimlich maneuver has saved many lives.

air you take in is even greater. The rate at which you inhale and exhale depends on how active you are. An adult at rest takes about 12 breaths per minute.

How does oxygen get to your cells? Air containing oxygen enters the body through the nose where it is filtered and moistened. Filtered air passes down the back of your mouth, through the flaps of your vocal cords into the larynx, and down into the trachea. The trachea is a tube supported by rings of cartilage. The air moves into tubes that carry it to your lungs. Tubes within the lungs branch off until they are only about as big around as a piece of lead in a pencil. At the end of these tiny tubes are clusters of alveoli. The lungs are made up of about 600 million alveoli. Each of the alveoli has a wall that is only one cell thick. Each cluster is surrounded by a web of capillaries. Oxygen diffuses from the alveoli into the capillaries where it is picked up by hemoglobin in red blood cells. This oxygen-rich blood is taken to the heart and then out to the body cells. There it is used in cellular respiration. On the return trip, carbon dioxide diffuses out of the cells into the plasma portion of blood. This blood is returned to the right side of the heart. It is pumped through the pulmonary arteries to the capillaries in the lungs. Carbon dioxide diffuses out of the capillaries into the alveoli. Carbon dioxide-rich air is exhaled as you breathe out.

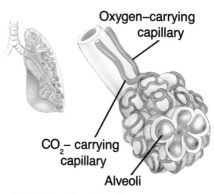

FIGURE 23–19. Oxygen enters the body through the alveoli that make up the lungs.

PROBLEM SOLVING

The Roller Coaster Ride

Kim was telling her friends about her first roller coaster ride. She said that when it stopped her heart was pounding, and she could hardly catch her breath.

Mary had never ridden a roller coaster. She wanted to know whether it was anything like having to make a speech in front of the class. Susan laughed, "A lot of things make your heart beat fast. Playing soccer makes my pulse race," she said. What did Susan mean? How can you explain why each girl's heartbeat rate increased?

23:10 The Excretory System

At some time you have probably watched a truck roll down the street collecting refuse. Communities have several methods for getting rid of wastewater, old orange peels, and household items that can't be used anymore. Your body is like a community. Trillions of cells in your body are active all the time and produce wastes. These wastes need to be removed continually if the body is to remain healthy. **Excretion** (ihk SKREE shun) is the process of removing wastes that result from metabolism in the cells of the body. The organs in the body that perform this job are the lungs, a pair of kidneys, the skin, and the digestive system.

The kidneys are the major organs of the excretory system. The kidneys are reddish-brown in color, bean-shaped, and about 12 cm long. These organs are located at the level of your waist on either side of the vertebral column. Within each kidney are about one million microscopic units called nephrons (NEF rahnz). A **nephron** is the filtering unit of the kidney. Each nephron is made up of a small cup and a series of tubes, surrounded by a network of capillaries. Blood flowing into the kidneys carries waste products from body cells. As blood flows through the kidneys, chemical wastes and excess water from the plasma filter out of the capillaries into the cup of the nephron and into a collecting tube. Some of the water is returned to the blood. The waste liquid that remains in the collecting tube is called **urine.**

Name the organs of the excretory system.

F.Y.I. All the blood in the circulatory system is filtered through the kidney about 60 times a day.

FIGURE 23–20. The nephron is the filtering unit of the kidney (a) in the human urinary system (b).

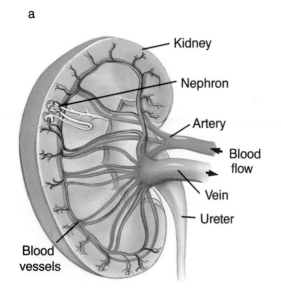

a

Kidney

Nephron

Artery

Blood flow

Vein

Ureter

Blood vessels

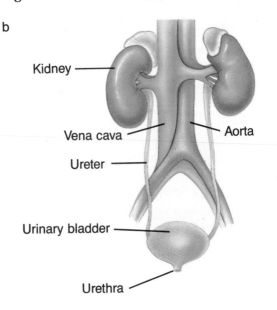

b

Kidney

Vena cava

Aorta

Ureter

Urinary bladder

Urethra

Urine leaves each kidney by a tube called the ureter. A ureter from each kidney leads to a muscular bag called the bladder, which holds urine for short periods of time. Eventually the liquid wastes are released from the bladder through a tube called the urethra.

If the kidneys stop filtering, the buildup of wastes can cause death. Persons with kidney diseases need to have their blood cleaned if they are to stay alive. A kidney machine removes wastes from the blood and returns filtered blood to the person's body. People who depend on kidney machines undergo this process three times a week. The process takes about four hours to complete each time.

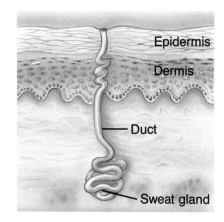

FIGURE 23–21. Sweat glands are part of the body's excretory system.

SKILL BUILDER

Using Tables

Make a table to compare alveoli and nephrons. Use the information in your table to answer the following questions. If you need help, refer to Using Tables on page 530.

Questions
1. Where are alveoli and nephrons found?
2. How many alveoli and nephrons are there?
3. What jobs do they have in common?

Your skin excretes wastes through sweat glands. Perspiration is made up of water, salts, and small amounts of urea. Your body produces about 500 mL of perspiration per day through sweat glands. In Chapter 24, you will learn that your body also excretes solid wastes from the digestive system.

REVIEW

6. What are three functions of the respiratory system?
7. Where in the respiratory system does the exchange of gases take place?
8. What happens to the diaphragm when air is inhaled and exhaled?
9. What are three organs of excretion?
10. What is the filtering unit of the kidneys?

Problem: How do skin medications affect growth of skin bacteria?

Materials 🚫 ☣️

sterile petri dishes   pen
  with nutrient agar (4)   skin medications
cotton balls (3)   (3)
cotton swabs (4)   paper towels
masking tape

Procedure

1. Use the masking tape and pen to label the cover of three petri dishes with the letter of a skin medication.
2. Rub a cotton swab once across your forehead. Remove the cover of a petri dish. Rub the swab once over the nutrient agar in the dish.
3. Moisten a cotton ball with a skin medication. Rub the cotton ball once over the nutrient agar in the dish. Replace the cover. Wash your hands.
4. Repeat steps 2 and 3 with the other skin medications.
5. Repeat step 2 with the fourth petri dish. Replace the cover and label the cover "no medication."
6. Seal the petri dishes with tape. Place the petri dishes in a warm, dark location for three days.

7. Write a hypothesis stating what you think will happen in each dish.
8. After three days, examine the four dishes. **CAUTION:** *Do not open the dishes.* Record your observations in the data table.
9. **CAUTION:** *Give the unopened petri dishes to your teacher for disposal.*

Data and Observations

Name of Medication	Observations
Medication A	
Medication B	
Medication C	
No medication	

Questions and Conclusions

1. Which petri dish showed the most growth?
2. Which petri dish showed the least growth?
3. Which skin medication affected more bacteria from the skin?
4. What was the purpose of the "no medication" dish?
5. How do skin medications affect the growth of skin bacteria?
6. Was your hypothesis supported or not supported by the test? Explain.
7. Based on your observations, explain why you might or might not purchase a particular skin medication.

SUMMARY

1. The circulatory system is made up of the cardiovascular and lymphatic systems that function to transport materials to or from body cells. 23:1
2. The heart is a muscular organ that pumps blood throughout the body. Arteries carry blood away from the heart. Veins carry blood toward the heart. 23:2
3. Blood is a tissue that consists of cells, platelets, and plasma. Blood clot formation is a function of platelets. 23:3
4. Human blood types are A, B, AB, and O. The Rh factor is a part of blood type. 23:4
5. Blood donation is safe. Blood from donors is screened for disease. 23:5
6. Antibodies are protein substances in the blood that act on specific antigens. Immunity may be acquired through a vaccine. 23:6
7. The respiratory system supplies oxygen to red blood cells and expels carbon dioxide from the body. 23:7
8. The diaphragm contracts and air is inhaled. When it relaxes, air is exhaled. 23:8
9. Gas exchange takes place in the alveoli. 23:9
10. The excretory system removes wastes from the body. The kidneys, lungs, and skin are excretory organs. 23:10

VOCABULARY

a. alveoli
b. antibodies
c. arteries
d. blood
e. capillaries
f. circulatory system
g. diaphragm
h. excretion
i. hemoglobin
j. immunity
k. nephron
l. plasma
m. platelets
n. respiratory system
o. transfusion
p. urine
q. veins

Match each description with the correct vocabulary word from the list above.

1. cell fragments in the blood
2. liquid portion of the blood
3. vessels that carry blood to the heart
4. air sacs in the lungs
5. the oxygen-carrying molecule in the red blood cells
6. filtering unit of the kidney
7. resistance to disease
8. vessels that carry blood from the heart
9. process of removing wastes from the body
10. injection of blood or plasma into the blood stream

MAIN IDEAS

A. Reviewing Concepts

Choose the word or phrase that correctly completes each of the following sentences.

1. Blood is a(n) _____ made up of liquid and solid parts.
   - **a.** organ
   - **b.** vessel
   - **c.** tissue
   - **d.** none of these
2. The lower chambers of the heart are called the _____.
   - **a.** atria
   - **b.** alveoli
   - **c.** veins
   - **d.** ventricles
3. The largest artery of the body is the _____.
   - **a.** urethra
   - **b.** coronary
   - **c.** aorta
   - **d.** vena cava
4. _____ are the smallest blood vessels of the body.
   - **a.** Arteries
   - **b.** Veins
   - **c.** Capillaries
   - **d.** Alveoli
5. The major function of red blood cells is to transport _____.
   - **a.** foods
   - **b.** oxygen
   - **c.** hormones
   - **d.** glucose
6. White blood cells destroy _____ by engulfing them.
   - **a.** microbes
   - **b.** platelets
   - **c.** fats
   - **d.** carbon dioxide
7. _____ are proteins that attach to specific antigens in the blood.
   - **a.** Antibodies
   - **b.** Vaccines
   - **c.** Minerals
   - **d.** Platelets
8. A person with type O blood can receive blood from persons with blood type _____.
   - **a.** A
   - **b.** B
   - **c.** AB
   - **d.** O
9. Air moves into the lungs when the _____ contracts.
   - **a.** diaphragm
   - **b.** alveoli
   - **c.** epiglottis
   - **d.** trachea
10. The filtration unit of the kidney is the _____.
    - **a.** nephron
    - **b.** bronchus
    - **c.** diaphragm
    - **d.** trachea
11. Masses of _____ are the air sacs that form the lungs.
    - **a.** capillaries
    - **b.** alveoli
    - **c.** platelets
    - **d.** nephrons
12. Urine leaves the body through a tube called the _____.
    - **a.** nephron
    - **b.** kidney
    - **c.** urethra
    - **d.** ureter
13. One function of the lungs is to expel _____ from the body.
    - **a.** hormones
    - **b.** salt
    - **c.** blood
    - **d.** carbon dioxide
14. The right ventricle pumps blood to the _____.
    - **a.** lungs
    - **b.** aorta
    - **c.** kidneys
    - **d.** right atrium
15. _____ help form sticky fibers that form a blood clot.
    - **a.** Red blood cells
    - **b.** Platelets
    - **c.** White blood cells
    - **d.** Nephrons

B. Understanding Concepts

Answer the following questions using complete sentences.

16. What forces blood through blood vessels?
17. Into which chamber of the heart does the blood flow when it returns from the lungs?
18. What is the function of the respiratory system?
19. How are red blood cells, hemoglobin, and oxygen related?

20. How do white blood cells destroy bacteria?
21. Compare blood on the right side of the heart with blood on the left side of the heart.
22. What happens when type A blood mixes with type B blood?
23. Where are lymphocytes found in contrast to red blood cells?
24. Explain what takes place in the alveoli.
25. What is the excretory function of sweat glands?

C. Applying Concepts

Answer the following questions using complete sentences.

26. How is the thickness of a capillary wall related to its functions?
27. Describe how a blood clot is formed in a cut.
28. Describe how air enters your lungs.
29. In what two ways are alveoli, nephrons, and sweat glands similar?
30. Why does blood need to be filtered in the kidneys?

SKILL REVIEW

If you need help, refer to the Skill Handbook, pages 526 to 537.

1. Make a data table to record your heart rate. While sitting quietly, check your pulse. Record the number of beats per minute. Perform a non-strenuous physical activity, and record your heart rate. Perform a total of three different physical activities, and record your heart rate after each.

2. Construct a bar graph. Graph your fastest heart rate from your table in Question 1 versus your sitting heart rate.
3. Identify the independent and dependent variables in the activity in Question 1.
4. A person has blood type O. She receives a successful blood transfusion at a hospital. Make an inference. What blood type was she given?
5. A person is given blood type B. He is blood type A. What effects will this have if not treated?

PROJECTS

1. Demonstrate first aid practices to stop severe bleeding. Booklets from the American Red Cross will explain approved methods such as using pressure points to prevent loss of blood.
2. Describe the effect smoking has on the respiratory system. Describe these effects to the class. Contact the local chapter of the American Lung Association for information.

READINGS

1. Asimov, Isaac. *How Did We Find Out About Blood?* New York: Walker and Co., 1986.
2. Kramer, Stephen P. *Getting Oxygen.* New York: Harper and Row, 1986.
3. Silverstein, Alvin and Silverstein, Virginia. *Heart Disease: America's Number One Killer.* New York: Harper and Row, 1985.

Career: Dietitian

Six students from the seventh and eighth grades at Monroe Middle School went to their principal with a list of ideas for improving the school lunch program. Many students wanted to have more of their favorite foods served at lunch. After talking with the students, the principal called Mrs. Franks, the school's new dietitian. Mrs. Franks was a recent graduate of the local university. She had spent a year as a dietitian for a hospital. Mrs. Franks listened to the students. She said she would be willing to work with two students from each class to develop some new menus. She also thought it would be a good way to teach the students about proper diet.

At the first meeting, two students asked whether there could be an International Day every week. On that day, lunch would be made up of food of a particular country. The location of the country could be pinpointed on a world map on the wall of the cafeteria. Posters and music of the country could be used as well. One student wanted to know what it would be like to try a vegetarian diet. Mrs. Franks agreed to plan the menus. She told the students that each menu would include foods from the four food groups.

Good nutrition is necessary for good health. In this chapter, you will study nutrients, the four food groups, and eating habits. You will also study the parts and processes of the digestive system.

F.Y.I. The American Dietetic Association, 216 West Jackson Boulevard, Chicago, IL 60606-6995

What Is a Nutrient?

GOALS
You will study. . .
1. nutrients needed by the body.
2. the role of food as the source of nutrients.

F.Y.I. The pressure of the jaw when chewing may be as much as 15kg/cm².

Why do living organisms need energy?

FIGURE 24–1. Food supplies energy for activity.

24:1 Nutrients
Some scientific discoveries have been made in unusual ways. In 1822, a young fur trapper named Alexis St. Martin was shot at close range with a musket. The shot fractured his ribs and tore a hole in his stomach. An army surgeon, William Beaumont, took care of the wound. It was severe, but Alexis St. Martin recovered. However, a hole about 6 cm² led directly into his stomach and was covered only by a flap of skin. For a number of years, the hole enabled Dr. Beaumont to observe food during digestion.

Digestion is the process that takes food and changes it into substances that can be absorbed and used by the body. There are three phases to digestion. First, food is broken up mechanically in the mouth. Second, food is changed chemically into a form that dissolves in water. Finally, food molecules are absorbed by cells and used for metabolism.

Why does your body put food through these processes? All living organisms need energy for metabolism. However, the energy that is needed is locked up in the chemical bonds of the food that you eat. Digestion breaks these bonds. Energy and materials are released and are used by your body.

The materials in food that supply needed substances are called nutrients (NEW tree unts). A **nutrient** is a substance in food that is used by the body for metabolism. There are six types of nutrients: carbohydrates, fats, proteins, minerals, vitamins, and water. Nutrition is the study of how food is used by organisms.

Carbohydrates
A carbohydrate is a compound that contains carbon, hydrogen, and oxygen. **Carbohydrates** are organic nutrients that are the main sources of energy for the body. Starch, sugars, and cellulose are carbohydrates. Foods such as beans, peas, potatoes, and cereal grains are rich in starch. Because starch is a large molecule, it is not absorbed by cells. It has to be broken apart through digestion into smaller molecules called simple sugars that cells can absorb.

FIGURE 24-2. Cereal grains are sources of carbohydrate and fiber.

Cellulose is a carbohydrate found in cell walls. Your body doesn't digest cellulose, but every time you eat fruits or vegetables, you consume a lot of cell walls. What does your body do with this material? If fruits and vegetables are cooked, the cell walls break apart and cell contents are released. Your body uses what is released from the cells. The cellulose, however, passes through your digestive system unchanged as roughage or fiber. Fiber works to help move food through your digestive system.

Fats

Fats like carbohydrates, are made up of carbon, hydrogen, and oxygen. However, they contain less oxygen than carbohydrates. A **fat** is an organic nutrient that protects internal organs, insulates to retain body heat, and is a good source of energy. Fat is found under the skin, in cell membranes, and around some neurons. Fats are obtained from meats, dairy products, nuts, seeds, and vegetable oils. Some fat is needed to maintain health. But if too many fatty foods are eaten, fat begins to fill in blood vessels and build up under the skin and in muscles. Cholesterol is a fat that attaches to the walls of the arteries. Blood flowing to the heart muscle can be cut off. A heart attack can result from cholesterol buildup in coronary arteries.

A person's body fat can be measured in several ways. One is the fatfold test. An instrument is used to estimate fat by measuring a pinch of flesh at the back of the arm. Another test estimates fat by submerging a person in water and measuring the amount of water that has been displaced. Most people take in too many fats in their diets. It is estimated that most people have a diet that is almost half fats. The American Heart Association recommends reducing this to a little less than one third of total food intake.

What results from eating too many fatty foods?

FIGURE 24-3. Body fat can be measured by the fatfold test.

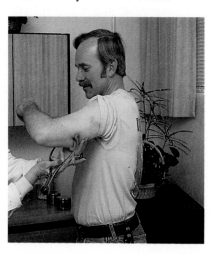

Problem: Which foods contain starch and fats?

Materials

liquid cooking oil
iodine solution
  in dropper bottle
scissors
large brown paper bag
paper towels

bread
cheese
cooked egg white
raw potato slice
cooked bacon
potato chip

Procedure

1. Open a brown bag and cut it in half. Mark one part FAT and the other part STARCH. Mark off each part into six sections. Label each section with the name of a food to be tested. **CAUTION:** *Put on an apron and goggles to protect clothing and eyes.*
2. Place a very small drop of cooking oil in a corner of the paper marked FAT. Hold the paper up to a light and observe the spot. Foods with fat leave a grease spot like this on brown paper.
3. Predict which test foods contain fat.
4. Rub each food on its labeled section on the brown paper. Let the spots dry.
5. Predict which foods contain starch. Foods that contain starch turn dark blue when iodine solution is dropped on them. **CAUTION:** *Iodine is poisonous and will stain clothing.*
6. Place foods on the labeled sections of the STARCH paper. Place a drop of iodine solution on each food on the paper. Record any color changes.
7. Record the results from the fat test. Hold the paper up to a light source.

Data and Observations

Test food	Fat		Starch	
	Predict yes/no	Result yes/no	Predict yes/no	Result yes/no
Bread				
Cheese				
Egg white				
Raw potato				
Bacon				
Potato chip				

Questions and Conclusions

1. Which test foods contain fat?
2. Whict test foods contain starch?
3. Which food contains starch and fat?
4. Which food contains neither fat nor starch?
5. How can foods be tested for fat?
6. How can you test for starch?
7. What was the control for the fat test?
8. Which of your predictions was not supported by your data?
9. Which results surprised you?

Fat or Fit?

At a yearly checkup, Harold was 183 cm tall and had a mass of 81 kg. His doctor sent him to a clinic where a test showed that 28 percent of Harold's mass was fat. His doctor said that this was too high a percentage. He advised Harold to exercise and control his diet.

A year later, Harold's mass was the same. Another test showed that his percentage of body fat was now 19 percent. The doctor told Harold that he was at his proper mass. How can Harold have the same mass but less body fat? How was the percent of fat determined?

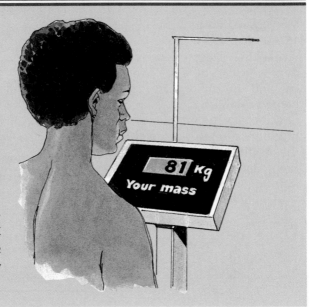

Protein

Protein is an important part of your body. Muscles, blood, enzymes, cell membranes, antibodies, hormones, tendons, and ligaments all are made of proteins. **Protein** is an organic nutrient used for growth and repair of tissues. Proteins contain carbon, hydrogen, oxygen, and nitrogen, and sometimes sulfur and phosphorus. These elements are arranged in different orders to form more than 20 different amino acids. **Amino acids** are the building blocks of proteins. Most amino acids are put together in the cells with materials supplied by digestion. However, there are eight amino acids that have to be supplied by the food you eat because the body can't make them. These are called essential amino acids. Meats, eggs, soybeans, and dairy products are high in protein. Seeds such as beans, peas, and nuts are also good sources of proteins.

People who are vegetarians do not use meat or meat products. However, they have to make sure they meet the body's daily need for essential amino acids. Combinations of foods are used to supply this need. Rice with beans or peanut butter with wheat bread supply essential amino acids.

FIGURE 24–4. These foods are rich in protein.

What Is a Nutrient? 509

FIGURE 24–5. Many foods contain mineral and vitamin supplements.

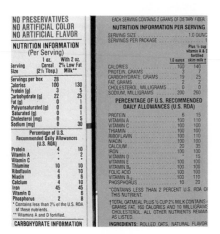

Minerals

Your body also depends on many elements other than carbon, hydrogen, and oxygen. Elements used by the body in very small amounts are nutrients called **minerals.** The body requires more of some minerals than others. For example, the body needs about 1 g of calcium per day. In contrast, a mineral such as zinc is needed only in amounts of about 0.025 g per day. Fruits, vegetables, and plant-consuming animals are the best sources of minerals in the diet. Table 24-1 lists some of the minerals needed for body functions.

Table 24–1

Minerals		
Mineral	**Function in Body**	**Food Source**
Calcium Ca	formation of bone and teeth; clotting of blood; heart and nerve action	milk, green, leafy vegetables, legumes, small bony fish
Phosphorus P	formation of bones and teeth; muscle contraction; growth	milk, eggs, all meats
Potassium K	cell growth, muscle activity; nerve impulses	meats, milk, fruits, vegetables, grains
Sulfur S	formation of proteins	all protein-containing foods
Sodium Na	regulates water balance and pressure; nerve impulses	table salt, cheese, bread, processed foods
Chloride Cl	formation of HCl acid; water balance	table salt, cheese, bread, processed foods
Magnesium Mg	enzyme activity; nerve impulses	leafy, green vegetables; legumes; grains
Iron Fe	formation of hemoglobin	red meat, dried fruit, eggs, fish, legumes, poultry,
Iodine I	prevents goiter in thyroid	iodized table salt, seafood

Vitamins

A **vitamin** is an organic nutrient needed in very small amounts for cell metabolism. Generally vitamins are supplied through food, except for vitamin D. Vitamin D is made when your skin is exposed to sunlight. Table 24-2 lists some vitamins, their functions, and some foods in which these vitamins are found.

If a vitamin or mineral is lacking in the diet, a deficiency disease results. If a person with the deficiency disease scurvy, begins to eat fruits and vegetables containing vitamin C, the symptoms of the disease go away. When the element iron is lacking in the diet, anemia (uh NEE mee uh) results. Anemia is a condition in which the blood is low in hemoglobin and a person lacks energy. Hemoglobin is the chemical in red blood cells that carries oxygen from the lungs to cells. If the supply of oxygen is limited in cells, cellular respiration is reduced. Less energy is released from food. The lack of hemoglobin causes a person to be tired and is directly related to the deficiency of iron. Daily mineral and vitamin needs can be met by eating fruits and vegetables. Using large doses of mineral and vitamin supplements may cause toxic or poisonous conditions in the body.

FIGURE 24-6. Fresh foods are an enjoyable way to meet your need for vitamins.

What is hemoglobin?

Table 24-2

Vitamins		
Vitamin	**Function**	**Food Sources**
A	maintain healthy skin, prevent night blindness	liver, whole milk, green and yellow vegetables
K	allows normal blood clotting	green leafy vegetables; egg yolk; tomatoes
B vitamins (thiamine, riboflavin, B_6, niacin)	fat and carbohydrate metabolism, protein synthesis, red blood cell production	lean meat, liver, eggs, cereal grains, vegetables, poultry, beans, milk, fruit
C	healthy teeth and gums, healing of wounds	citrus fruits; tomatoes; green, leafy vegetables

Problem: Which orange juice contains the most vitamin C?

Materials

indophenol solution
graduated cylinder
test tubes (10)
test-tube rack
masking tape
dropper bottles (4) containing (A)
  refrigerated tap water, (B) frozen
  orange juice concentrate mixed
  according to directions, (C) bottled
  orange juice, and (D) fresh-squeezed
  orange juice

goggles
apron
pen

Procedure

1. Copy the data table.
2. Label four test tubes 1 through 4.
3. Indophenol solution is an indicator. It is a blue liquid that becomes colorless when enough vitamin C is added to it. Orange juice that contains a lot of vitamin C will turn indophenol colorless with only a few drops of juice. More drops of juice with little vitamin C are needed to make the indicator colorless.
4. **CAUTION:** *Put on safety goggles and an apron.* Measure exactly 15 mL indophenol solution into each of the four test tubes.
5. Add 20 drops of water to test tube 1. Swirl the liquid carefully. The solution will stay blue. This will be your color control.
6. Add orange juice B, one drop at a time, to test tube 2, until the indicator becomes colorless. Gently swirl after each drop. Compare with your color control.

7. Record the number of drops of frozen juice it took to make the indicator colorless.
8. Repeat steps 6 and 7 for bottled orange juice (C) and fresh-squeezed orange juice (D).
9. Use the remaining test tubes to test each type of juice two more times. Record the average number of drops needed to change the indicator for each juice.
10. Give all test tubes to your teacher for proper disposal.

Data and Observation

Trial	Drops of juice needed to change indicator		
	Frozen (B)	Bottled (C)	Fresh (D)
1			
2			
3			
Average			

Questions and Conclusions

1. Did the amount of vitamin C vary in the orange juices tested? Suggest a reason.
2. Which orange juice contained the most vitamin C?
3. What was the constant in this activity?
4. Why did you test each juice three times and then average the results?
5. Hypothesize what would happen to the vitamin C content of orange juice that was not refrigerated. How would you test your hypothesis?

Water

Water is a nutrient that makes up about two-thirds of your body. Water is found in the plasma portion of your blood and in the cytoplasm of all your cells. Chemical reactions are going on constantly in your body. These reactions need water to take place. Most of this water is supplied in the foods you eat. The rest is taken in the form of liquids. Water is an essential nutrient. This means that your body needs water to stay alive. The body is able to live for a long while without most nutrients, but without water it will die.

FIGURE 24–7. Your body needs water every day.

24:2 Food: Your Source of Nutrients

You have learned that food is made up of six nutrients. Each day you need to eat a variety of foods to obtain these nutrients. A diet of potato chips provides only a few nutrients. A **balanced diet** is the food you eat during the day that gives your body all the nutrients needed to carry out all the life processes. The amount of food required to meet daily nutritional needs is called the Recommended Daily Allowance or RDA. The RDA is the amount of each nutrient a person needs each day to maintain good health, depending on height, age, activity, and sex.

What is the RDA?

A balanced diet includes eating certain amounts of foods from specific food groups. There are four basic food groups: the milk, meat, fruit-vegetable, and grain groups. Each group includes foods that provide the body with essential nutrients. Table 24-3 shows the four food groups and the nutrients they supply.

Table 24–3

Food for Good Health			
Milk group	**Meat group**	**Fruit-vegetable group**	**Grain group**
Supplies: calcium riboflavin (B₂) protein for strong bones and teeth, healthy skin, and good vision	Supplies: protein fats niacin (B₁₂) iron thiamin (B₁) for muscle, bone, and blood cells and healthy skin and nerves	Supplies: vitamin A vitamin C for night vision and to help resist infections and heal wounds	Supplies: carbohydrate thiamin (B₁) iron niacin (B₁₂) for energy and a healthy nervous system
Eat 4 servings per day	Eat 2 servings per day	Eat 4 servings per day	Eat 4 servings per day

Energy used by the body is often measured in **Calories.** A person with a mass of 45–50 kg needs between 2200 and 2700 Calories per day. If this person takes in 3000 Calories of food in a day, the food not needed is changed to fat. Taking in less food energy than is needed results in weight loss.

REVIEW

1. What are the three phases of digestion?
2. What are six types of nutrients needed by the body?
3. How is the body kept supplied with water?
4. What is fiber and what is its function?
5. Which nutrients are used in small amounts in the body?

What Happens When You Eat?

24:3 The Digestive System

The human digestive system is made up of a mouth, esophagus, stomach, small intestine, large intestine, rectum, and anus. Each part has a different function in the process of digestion. Some parts have mechanical functions. Other parts have mechanical and chemical functions.

The mechanical part of digestion begins in your mouth. Teeth bite and grind food into small pieces. Smaller pieces of food are digested more easily than larger pieces.

As food is chewed, it is mixed with saliva. **Saliva** is a watery substance in the mouth that begins the process of digestion of carbohydrates. Saliva contains an enzyme. An **enzyme** is a protein catalyst that changes the rate of a chemical reaction. All the chemical reactions in the body depend on enzymes.

Once food is thoroughly chewed and mixed, your tongue moves the moistened mass to the back of your throat. There the swallowing reflex moves the food into the esophagus, a 25-cm long muscular tube that leads to the stomach. Once in the esophagus, food is moved to the stomach in about 15 seconds by peristalsis (per uh STAHL sus). **Peristalsis** is the series of muscular contractions that moves food through the digestive system. The stomach is a saclike organ with muscular walls and many glands. The glands in the walls of the stomach make gastric juices, mucus, and enzymes. All of these are added to the food mass and it becomes more liquid. No actual digestion takes place in the stomach. However, some substances are produced that make certain nutrients such as iron, calcium, vitamin C, and vitamin B_{12} more ready to be absorbed. In the stomach, fats also float to the top of the mixture of juices. Peristalsis in the stomach helps churn the food so that it gets mixed thoroughly.

Food is released a little at a time from the stomach into the small intestine. The liver, gall bladder, and pancreas are located near the point where food enters the small intestine. Food does not pass through any of these organs. However, the liver and pancreas produce substances that help break down nutrients.

GOALS

You will study . . .
1. the parts and functions of the digestive system.
2. chemical digestion of nutrients.
3. eating disorders.

F.Y.I. Peristalsis is so strong that even if you stood on your head, food would still move toward your stomach.

FIGURE 24–8. Peristalsis moves food through the digestive system.

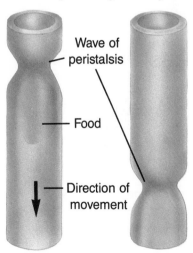

Wave of peristalsis

Food

Direction of movement

FIGURE 24—9. The human digestive system.

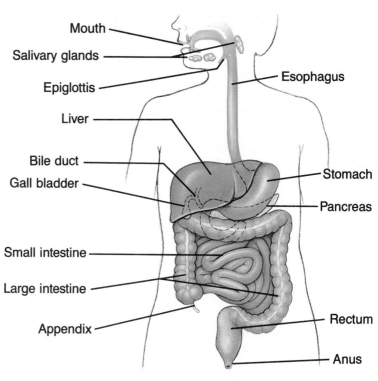

Mouth

Salivary glands

Epiglottis

Esophagus

Liver

Bile duct

Gall bladder

Stomach

Pancreas

Small intestine

Large intestine

Rectum

Appendix

Anus

Where does most digestion of food take place?

FIGURE 24—10. Food takes more than 24 hours to move through the digestive system.

The small intestine is a muscular tube about 7 m long. Most digestion takes place and nutrients are absorbed in the small intestine. The walls inside the small intestine have a velvet-like appearance. The lining of the small intestine is made up of millions of tiny parts called villi (VIHL eye). **Villi** are fingerlike structures through which nutrients are absorbed into the blood stream. Some fats enter lymph vessels in the center of each villus.

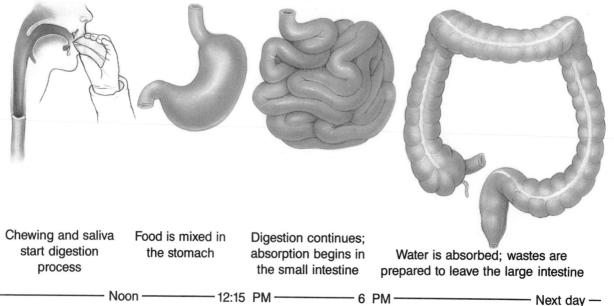

Chewing and saliva start digestion process

Food is mixed in the stomach

Digestion continues; absorption begins in the small intestine

Water is absorbed; wastes are prepared to leave the large intestine

——————— Noon ——————— 12:15 PM ——————— 6 PM ——————— Next day —

Any material that is not absorbed into the villi of the small intestine is moved by peristalsis into the large intestine. The large intestine is about 1.5 m long. Large amounts of water are absorbed into the blood stream from materials in the large intestine. The remaining solid materials are eliminated from the body through the rectum and the anus. This solid waste is called feces.

24:4 From the Table to the Cell

As it moves through the digestive system, food undergoes chemical changes. **Chemical digestion** is the changing of food into a form that the body can use.

The chemical digestion of carbohydrates begins in the mouth. An enzyme in saliva, called ptyalin (TI uh lin), acts on a complex carbohydrate such as starch and begins to break it down to simple sugars. No fats or proteins are digested in the mouth. As the mass of food moves down the esophagus, ptyalin continues to act on carbohydrates. In the stomach, proteins are broken apart by an enzyme. At the same time, hydrochloric acid made in the stomach breaks down ptyalin, and carbohydrate digestion stops. Hydrochloric acid is so strong that it should digest the stomach lining itself. However, the stomach is protected by a thick layer of mucus. Hydrochloric acid also kills bacteria that have come in with the food.

After leaving the stomach, the partially digested food enters the small intestine. Here it is mixed with secretions from the liver and pancreas. The liver produces a greenish liquid called bile. Bile is not an enzyme. It is stored near the liver in a sac called the gall bladder. Bile changes fats physically by breaking up large globs into smaller particles. It pours out over food through a small tube where the small intestine begins. Bile also stops the action of hydrochloric acid. Juices produced by the pancreas contain three enzymes. One is for the breakdown of proteins, and a second changes starch to sugar. A third breaks down fats to fatty acids and glycerol. Breakdown of fats is then complete.

The small intestine makes enzymes that finish the digestion of proteins and carbohydrates. Proteins are broken down into amino acids. Carbohydrates are broken down into simple sugars.

Where does the chemical digestion of carbohydrates begin?

F.Y.I. "Heartburn" is due to stomach acid backing up into the esophagus.

FIGURE 24–11. Nutrients are absorbed in the small intestine through thousands of villi.

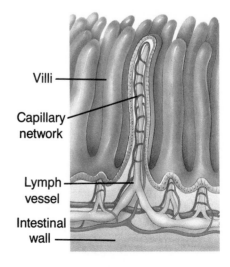

Villi

Capillary network

Lymph vessel

Intestinal wall

Table 24–4

Digestion of Nutrients			
Organ	**Protein**	**Carbohydrate**	**Fat**
Mouth	No digestion of protein	Ptyalin begins carbohydrate digestion	No digestion of fat
Stomach	Protein digestion begins	Digestion of carbohydrates is stopped by hydrochloric acid	No digestion of fat
Small Intestine	Enzymes of pancreas and intestine complete protein digestion	Enzymes of pancreas and intestine complete carbohydrate digestion	Bile physically breaks up fat Pancreatic enzymes digest fat
End products that are absorbed	Amino acids	Simple sugars	Fatty acids and glycerol

By the time chemical digestion is finished, the mass in the small intestine has become very watery. At this point, amino acids, simple sugars, fatty acids, and glycerol are absorbed through the villi. Villi contain muscle and move back and forth in the digested mass. Nutrients pass into the blood and lymph vessels in each villus and are carried to the cells of the body.

How are nutrients carried from the villi to the cells of the body?

Table 24–4 summarizes the major points of digestion of proteins, carbohydrates, and fats.

SKILL BUILDER

Outlining

Outline the functions of saliva, hydrochloric acid, bile, and enzymes produced by the pancreas. Use your outline to answer the questions below. If you need help, refer to Outlining on page 527.

Questions

1. What can you infer about the digestion of fats if the gall bladder is removed?
2. Which organ plays a part in digestion of carbohydrates, fats, and proteins?
3. What health function does hydrochloric acid have in the stomach?

TECHNOLOGY

Fake Fats?

Cholesterol in the diet contributes to heart attack by blocking blood vessels. Sticky, fatty plaque collects on the walls of arteries when too many saturated fats are a regular part of the diet. Eating cholesterol-free foods is thought to be one way to prevent the buildup of plaque. In addition, many cholesterol-free food substitutes have been invented and are used by the public. These substitutes have replaced milk, eggs, and margarine. Many look, smell, taste, and cook like "real" foods. Still, no one knows exactly what the body does with many of these fake foods.

ADVANCE

Olestra is an experimental fat substitute that tastes like fat, has no calories, and passes through the body without being digested. It is made of a molecule that can't be acted on by digestive enzymes.

SCIENCE AND SOCIETY

24:5 Eating Disorders

Signs for fast food restaurants blink and shine, advertising the foods they serve. Commercials for skin products remind you of your appearance. Ads for diet plans remind you to keep your body in shape. Sometimes it seems as if you are bombarded by ads for food, fitness, and fashion. It is easy to see why food becomes a problem for some people. But some people are willing to endanger their health to keep a certain appearance.

Anorexia nervosa is an eating disorder in which fear of becoming overweight develops into starvation. Persons with this condition say that they feel fat even when they are underweight. Approximately one out of every 100 adolescent girls has this disorder. It almost never occurs in boys.

How many adolescent girls have anorexia nervosa?

A person with anorexia may eat very little. The body slowly starves. The individual may also exercise compulsively to reduce imagined fat reserves. Both of these actions can result in serious damage to body systems. Lack of a balanced diet causes low blood pressure, slower respiratory rate, irregular heartbeat

FIGURE 24–12. Information and support services are available to people with eating disorders.

How many Calories might a person with bulimia eat in one meal?

rate, and loss of bone material. Cardiac muscle is damaged. The small intestine can no longer absorb nutrients properly. If not treated, death may occur.

Bulimia is an eating disorder in which an individual diets strictly and then eats large amounts of food at one time. This is followed by intentional vomiting or use of laxatives to get rid of food. A person with bulimia may eat more than 10 000 Calories of food at one meal. These eating binges result in swollen hands and feet, headache, tiredness, and pain. However, the person may remain very thin. Use of laxatives or the vomiting reflex removes nutrients before they can be absorbed by the digestive system. As a result, the body is starved. Fatigue, muscle cramps, and an irregular heart rhythm occur. Gastric juices from vomiting irritate the esophagus and damage teeth.

Why do some people think it is important to be thin? Do you think people with these conditions realize they are harming their body systems? What can be done to help people who show these disorders?

REVIEW

6. What is the function of teeth in digestion?
7. What is the role of an enzyme in chemical reactions?
8. What is the function of peristalsis?
9. What does bile do in the digestive system?
10. What are villi and what is their function in the small intestine?

SUMMARY

1. Carbohydrates, fats, proteins, minerals, vitamins, and water are nutrients used by the body for metabolism.   24:1
2. Food supplies nutrients and must be consumed to maintain health. A balanced diet consists of foods that provide nutrients for metabolism.   24:2
3. Nutrients are acted on mechanically and chemically in different parts of the digestive system.   24:3
4. Chemical digestion of carbohydrates, fats, and proteins is accomplished with different enzymes in different parts of the digestive tract. Absorption of all nutrients takes place in the small intestine.   24:4
5. Eating disorders affect health and may alter the digestive system or bring about death.   24:5

VOCABULARY

a. amino acids
b. anorexia nervosa
c. balanced diet
d. bulimia
e. Calories
f. carbohydrates

g. chemical digestion
h. digestion
i. enzyme
j. fat
k. minerals
l. nutrient

m. peristalsis
n. protein
o. saliva
p. villi
q. vitamin

Match each description with the correct vocabulary word from the list above.
1. complex organic nutrient made up of amino acids
2. substance found in food, required by the body for metabolism
3. nutrient group that includes sugars and starch
4. catalyst that controls reactions throughout the body
5. a rhythmic series of muscular contractions in the digestive system
6. elements that are nutrients
7. a disorder that involves eating extremely large quantities of food
8. nutrient that insulates and is found in cell membranes
9. building blocks of protein
10. finger-like projections in the small intestine where absorption of nutrients takes place

MAIN IDEAS

A. Reviewing Concepts

Choose the word or phrase that correctly completes each of the following sentences.

1. The substance produced by glands in the mouth is _____.
   - **a.** starch
   - **b.** nutrient
   - **c.** amino acid
   - **d.** saliva

2. The _____ leads from the throat to the stomach.
   - **a.** trachea
   - **b.** esophagus
   - **c.** larynx
   - **d.** villi

3. _____ is the process of converting food to molecules that can be absorbed by cells.
   - **a.** Digestion
   - **b.** Bulimia
   - **c.** Peristalsis
   - **d.** Nutrition

4. _____ is a carbohydrate in plants that humans can't digest.
   - **a.** Glycogen
   - **b.** Calcium
   - **c.** Sugar
   - **d.** Cellulose

5. Nutrients are absorbed in the _____.
   - **a.** small intestine
   - **b.** esophagus
   - **c.** liver
   - **d.** stomach

6. The stomach makes _____ acid that kills bacteria.
   - **a.** amino
   - **b.** folic
   - **c.** hydrochloric
   - **d.** citric

7. The nutrient that helps retain body heat when stored is a _____.
   - **a.** fat
   - **b.** protein
   - **c.** mineral
   - **d.** vitamin

8. The nutrient that is absorbed in large quantities in the large intestine is _____.
   - **a.** fat
   - **b.** water
   - **c.** carbohydrate
   - **d.** amino acid

9. Iron is needed for _____ molecules to form in a red blood cell.
   - **a.** vitamin
   - **b.** mineral
   - **c.** enzyme
   - **d.** hemoglobin

10. Vitamin _____ is produced when skin is exposed to sunlight.
    - **a.** A
    - **b.** B
    - **c.** D
    - **d.** C

11. The nutrient that is used to make enzymes and antibodies is _____.
    - **a.** protein
    - **b.** carbohydrate
    - **c.** fat
    - **d.** vitamin C

12. Cereals are good sources of _____ because they contain carbohydrates.
    - **a.** water
    - **b.** energy
    - **c.** minerals
    - **d.** enzymes

13. Amino acids that must be supplied by food are _____.
    - **a.** minerals
    - **b.** essential
    - **c.** glycerol
    - **d.** fatty acids

14. Carbohydrates are absorbed in the small intestine as _____.
    - **a.** amino acids
    - **b.** glycerol
    - **c.** simple sugars
    - **d.** starch

15. The _____ is an organ that produces bile for breaking up fat.
    - **a.** gall bladder
    - **b.** liver
    - **c.** pancreas
    - **d.** spleen

B. Understanding Concepts

Answer the following questions using complete sentences.

16. What are two functions of saliva?
17. Where in the digestive system does the digestion of fats begin and end?
18. What is digestion?
19. What happens to carbohydrate digestion in the stomach?
20. What is the importance of the Recommended Daily Allowance and food groups?
21. Explain the need for carbohydrates in the diet.
22. List the products of digestion of carbohydrates, proteins, and fats.

23. How is a balanced diet related to the four food groups?
24. Why is water important in the body?
25. What is anorexia nervosa and what are its physical effects?

C. Applying Concepts

Answer the following questions using complete sentences.

26. Describe the effects of a mineral deficiency, such as a lack of iron, in the diet.
27. How are teeth and bile alike? How are they different?
28. Why does a person with bulimia continue to lose weight?
29. Why does eating too many carbohydrates generally cause a person to gain weight?
30. Explain the relationship between the digestive system and the liver, gall bladder, and pancreas.

SKILL REVIEW

If you need help, refer to the Skill Handbook, pages 526 to 537.

1. List the steps of protein digestion in order.
2. Classify the food you ate for lunch by the six nutrient types.
3. Using the data in Table 24–1, determine which elements affect the health of bone.
4. You join the cross-country team at school and begin practicing every day. After a month, you observe that you have lost 5 kg. What can you infer about this mass loss? How can you avoid losing more mass?
5. What are the end products of digestion? Use Table 24–4 to find your answer.

PROJECTS

1. Using a standard Calorie chart found in the back of a cookbook, calculate the number of Calories in a meal served in the cafeteria one day. Find out how many meals were served that day and calculate the total number of Calories consumed. Figure how many kilometers a person would have to walk to use up that number of Calories.
2. Obtain food reports from fast-food restaurants. Compare the Calories in these foods with foods usually served at home.

READINGS

1. Brody, Jane. *Jane Brody's Nutrition Book.* New York: Bantam, 1987.
2. Cajacob, Thomas, and Teresa Burton. *Water for Life.* Minneapolis, MN: Carolrhoda, 1986.
3. Londer, Randi. "Meals for the Millenium." *Discover.* November, 1988. pp. 60-63.

FUN WITH

1846
Ether is used as a dental anesthetic.

Jeans are created by Oscar Levi Strauss.

1850

1881

Sphygmomanometer is invented.

Coca-Cola® is invented in Georgia.

1886

At about 6:00 P.M., a piece of meat enters your mouth. At 6:03 P.M., it passes through the esophagus, and two minutes later it is in your stomach. In about 4 hours, the meat reaches the small intestine and about 10:00 A.M. the undigested food enters the large intestine. In three to five hours, it leaves your body.

QUIZ

Blood makes one complete trip through your body in about 25 seconds. How many trips does it make in one day?

THE FAR SIDE

"Pull out, Betty! Pull out! . . . You've hit an artery!"

524

JOKE

Q. Why did the nurse put a box of bandages in the refrigerator?
A. in case the patients had cold cuts

Carla is planning to run 40 km Sunday evening. Which of the following meals should she eat for Sunday lunch? (a) cheeseburger, french fries, green beans, diet cola; (b) fried fish, mashed potatoes and gravy, cauliflower with cheese sauce, iced tea; (c) pasta with tomato sauce, green salad, wheat roll with butter, milk.

SCIENCE

1888

Aspirin is introduced in Germany.

Dry ice is used to keep ice cream cold.

1930

1963

First liver transplant is performed.

Witt and Boitano win Olympic gold medals in figure skating.

1988

How long are capillaries?

Capillaries are microscopic blood vessels that connect arteries and veins. Capillaries are only about 1 mm long. However, in an average adult human, the capillary network spans about 96 000 km.

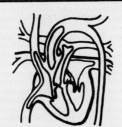

Did you know that your body has over 600 muscles?

Riddle

Q. What has no bones and no flesh but has four fingers and a thumb? **A.** a glove

QUESTION AND ANSWER

What is a biometric security system? Biometrics is being used in some types of security systems. Rather than using an entrance card or a secret password, a biometric system checks you against body measurements such as the sound of your voice, your fingerprints, the palm of your hand, or the vein patterns in your eyes. Each of these characteristics is unique. Some computers can identify and match nearly 500 fingerprints per minute! Blood vessels in an eye can be identified in about 5 seconds. Several types of biometric security systems are currently in use at Fort Knox, Kentucky.

TEASER

FUN RECIPE

BRAN MUFFINS

Combine 1 cup flour, 1/2 cup sugar, 2 1/2 teaspoons baking powder, 1/2 teaspoon baking soda, and a dash of salt in a bowl. Set aside. Mix 1 1/4 cup 100 percent bran and 1 cup milk. Let stand 5 minutes. Add 1 egg and 1/4 cup cooking oil and blend. Add the flour mixture and stir. Don't overmix. Fill muffin cups 2/3 full. Bake at 400°F for 20 minutes.

Answers
Quiz: *3456 trips/24 hours*
Teaser: *Meal c contains complex carbohydrates and is low in fats.*

525

SKILL HANDBOOK

You may think of a science class as a place you are expected to learn facts. Every chapter holds new definitions to learn and new concepts to master. However, there are many things that, once learned, can be applied over and over to new situations, both in science and in your other classes. The *SKILL HANDBOOK* has been provided to help you master some of these skills.

In each chapter of **SCIENCE CONNECTIONS,** you will find a *SKILL BUILDER* activity. The activity usually provides some background and then asks some questions. Just before the questions, you will be told to look at one of the pages in the *SKILL HANDBOOK* if you need help. These pages provide step-by-step instructions on skills such as Outlining, Measuring in SI, Using Tables, and determining Variables, Constants, and Controls. Using the information on these pages, you will be able to apply the same skills to many different situations. For example, you will see how sequencing applies to both the changes rocks undergo at Earth's surface and the changes an insect undergoes as it changes from a caterpillar to a butterfly. You will see how outlining can help you organize a lot of information into a more readable form. And you will see how presenting information in tables and graphing can help you see the relationships among data.

To help you keep in practice, a *SKILL REVIEW* section has been included at the end of each chapter. Again, use the *SKILL HANDBOOK* as a reference to help you with these problems.

CONTENTS

Outlining

You may take notes on lectures in class. Taking notes while your teacher talks helps you organize and remember important information. It also gives you a way to review material. Taking notes as you read can also help you organize, remember, and review. Many people take notes in outline form. An **outline** shows relationships among the main ideas.

Read the paragraph below.

> Natural resources are classified as either renewable or nonrenewable. Renewable resources are almost unlimited in supply, or can be replaced in less than 100 years. Examples are air, forests, and solar energy. Nonrenewable resources are limited in supply and can't be replaced in less than 100 years. Examples are soil, oil, and metals.

What is the main idea or central point of the paragraph? The main idea is the difference between renewable and nonrenewable resources. You should always be able to find a group of words that summarizes the main idea. Most of the sentences should refer to the main idea. If they don't, you may need to choose another group of words.

Next, you need to determine what is being said about the main idea. Below is an outline of the first part of the paragraph.

I. Renewable and nonrenewable resources
  A. Renewable resources
    1. Definition
      a. in unlimited supply or
      b. replaceable in less than 100 years
    2. Examples
      a. air
      b. forests
      c. solar energy

Your textbook is written in an outline format. The questions that appear in the bands of color are main ideas. These correspond to I in the outline above. The numbered sections subdivide the rest of the text into supporting ideas. These would correspond to A in the outline above. Look at Chapter 1. What would an outline of this chapter look like? An example of part of an outline of the first main idea is shown.

CHAPTER 1—The Methods of Science
I. What Is Science All About?
  A. The Nature of Science (1:1)
    1. Definition of Science
      a. knowledge of everything around you
      b. process or way you learn about the world
    2. Three Areas of Science
      a. Earth—study of planet Earth and its place in space
      b. Life—study of organisms
      c. Physical—study of structure and properties of matter and energy
    3. Description of a Scientist
      a. learned special problem-solving skills
      b. looks at problems as opportunities

The form of your outline can vary. The style outlined here uses major heads and numbered section titles as the main headings of the outline. This style makes it easy to refer to specific sections when you want to review for a test. You may want to develop another style. The important thing in an outline is to show the relationships between main ideas and the information about the main ideas.

Measuring in SI

As you work on science activities in this textbook, you will be asked to take different types of measurements. Measurements allow you to compare properties of objects and substances.

Measuring Temperature

Temperatures in SI are measured with a Celsius thermometer. In the Celsius scale, water boils at 100°C and freezes at 0°C, and normal body temperature is 37°C. To read a thermometer, suspend it in the substance being measured. Lower your eyes to the same level as the thermometer. Notice the marks along the side of the thermometer. Each of these marks represents a certain number of Celsius degrees. Inside the tube of the thermometer there is a thick red or silver bar. The temperature is read at the top of this thick bar. The temperature reading on the thermometer below is 34.5°C.

Using a Thermometer

1. Always use care when handling a glass thermometer. Glass breaks easily.
2. When measuring hot liquids, use a thermometer that is marked to measure high temperatures.
3. The bulb of the thermometer should be in the liquid or substance when measuring the temperature.
4. Never let the bulb of the thermometer touch the container.
5. Never stir with a thermometer.

Measuring Volume

The volume of a liquid can be measured in a container such as a glass cylinder. A cylinder is marked in milliliters. Each of the marks, called graduations, along the side represents 1 mL. The cylinders are called "graduated cylinders."

The curved shape of the graduated cylinder causes liquids to be drawn up a little on the insides. Thus, the level of the liquid in a cylinder appears curved. This curve is known as a meniscus.

Using a Graduated Cylinder
1. Pour the liquid into the cylinder.
2. Bend down to read the graduation at eye level. Do not tilt the cylinder.
3. Read the volume by matching the bottom of the meniscus with a graduation.

The volume of irregularly shaped objects can be measured using a graduated cylinder. Fill the cylinder with water up to the halfway mark. Record the level of the water. Then carefully lower the object to be measured into the cylinder. Record the new water level. The difference between the first and second readings will tell you the volume of the object. What is the volume of the rock shown below? If you said 10 mL, you are correct.

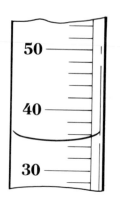
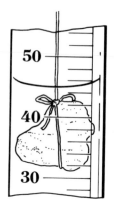

Measuring Length

The SI unit of length is the meter. A meter can be divided into 100 smaller units called centimeters. Each centimeter is made up of ten millimeters. The rulers you will use are divided into these units.

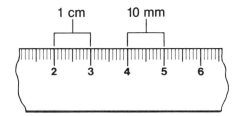

Using a Metric Ruler

1. Note the units of length marked on your ruler. Is it marked in centimeters, millimeters, or both?
2. Decide which unit you want to use. Do you want to measure something between two and three centimeters? Then you should look at the lines that represent millimeters.
3. Line up the end of the ruler with one edge of the object to be measured. Read the number of millimeters where the other edge of the object ends.
4. Record the length. Be sure to include the units of your measurement.
5. Repeat steps 3 and 4 to make sure your measurement was correct.

Measuring Mass

Balances use objects of known mass to find the unknown mass of another object. A beam balance similar to one you might use in your classroom is shown. A beam balance has a set of beams on one side where the objects of known mass are hung. These objects are known as riders. On the other side is a pan.

How to Carry a Balance
1. Set the scale to zero.
2. If there is a locking mechanism for the pan, set it on lock.
3. Grip the beam support with one hand and place the other under the balance.

How to Set a Balance to Zero
4. Slide each rider to the zero point.
5. Release the locking mechanism.
6. See if the pointer swings an equal distance above and below the zero point of the scale. If the swing is not equal, adjust it by turning the screw.

How to Mass an Object or Substance
7. Never place a hot object directly on the balance pan. Never pour chemicals directly onto the balance pan because they could corrode the metal. Set waxed paper into the pan before you place dry chemicals on it.
8. Place the object on the pan.
9. Move the riders along the beams, moving from larger to smaller masses.
10. Make sure each rider is in a notch.
11. The mass of the object equals the sum of the masses indicated by the positions of the riders on the beams.
12. Take the reading when the pointer is swinging an equal distance above and below the zero point of the scale.

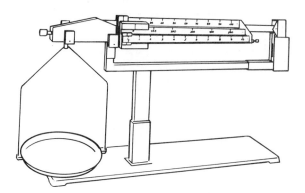

Using Tables

Tables are used to organize information so that it can be understood quickly and easily. If you look through your textbook, you will find many tables. Almost every activity contains a table for recording data. These tables will help you arrange your data for easy reference and interpretation. Other tables are found throughout the reading. They will help you summarize information presented in the text. How can you interpret these tables?

In order to use a table, you must understand its purpose. Most tables have a title that tells you what the table is about. What is the title of the table below? The title is "Number of Calories Expended by Walking (per hour)."

Tables are organized into columns and rows. The first column in a table lists the items that are going to be compared. In this table, different speeds are listed. Across the top of the table are the characteristics that are being compared. In this table, increasing mass in kilograms is being compared.

How many Calories would you burn in each hour of walking if you have a mass of 65 kg and you walk at a speed of 6 km per hour? If you answered 290 Calories, you are correct. To find this answer, you should have found the mass in kilograms (65) in the top row of the table, and the speed walked (6) in the first column. The point in the table where the row and column intersect (290 C) is the answer. If you burn 250 Calories in one hour and you have a mass of 65 kg, how fast are you walking? You should have said 5 km per hour.

Now that you understand how tables are organized, you should be able to make your own table. A class of students observed goldfish in different temperatures of water. They counted the number of times the fish "breathed" per minute. Team one collected the following data: 10°C, 20; 20°C, 38; 30°C, 65. The compiled class data looked like this: 10°C, 30; 20°C, 50; 30°C, 70. Make a table like the one shown and record this data in the table.

Number of Calories Expended by Walking (per hour)				
Walking Speed km/h	Mass in kilograms			
	45	55	65	70
3	130 C	160 C	185 C	210 C
4	155 C	185 C	220 C	250 C
5	180 C	215 C	250 C	285 C
6	205 C	248 C	290 C	330 C

Data and Observations

Temperature °C	"Breathing" rate	
	Team 1	Class

Tables are used by scientists to summarize and organize information. By using tables, you should be able to organize your data quickly and interpret it easily.

Variables, Constants, and Controls

As you take science courses, you will be asked to perform many activities. Each of these activities will use an organized process to test a hypothesis. In this textbook, your activities have been organized into a process for you. A **problem**, or question, is posed, **materials** are suggested, a step-by-step **procedure** is outlined, a sample **data table** is provided, and **questions** to help you interpret your data are asked. What other elements are important in an experiment?

Suppose you wanted to do an experiment to test whether a certain detergent cleans more greasy dishes than any other. How would you set up an experiment to test this? How can you make sure that your results will be reliable? You set up your experiment as follows. You use the same amount of water, the same temperature water, and the same amount of detergent for each detergent tested. These factors are constants. A **constant** does not change throughout the experiment. What factor will you change or vary? For each trial, you will change the brand of detergent used. Because the brand of detergent is the factor changed by you, the experimenter, brand of detergent is the **independent variable**. What will change in response to the change in detergent? The number of dishes cleaned will change.

The number of dishes cleaned is the **dependent variable**. The dependent variable changes as a result of a change in the independent variable. How can you be sure that the dependent variable is not changed by any other factor? A **control** is used to show that the result of your experiment is due only to the independent variable. A control is a standard for comparison. In this experiment, your control could be dishes washed without detergent.

Suppose your science teacher asked you to determine the effect of the length of light exposure on plant growth. You are given a light and five house plants of the same type and size. What factors will you keep constant? Temperature of the plant and amount of water and fertilizer should be kept constant for each plant. What would be the independent variable in this experiment? Because you would be changing the length of light exposure given each plant, light would be the independent variable. What is the dependent variable? The amount of plant growth is the dependent variable. What would be the control? A plant exposed to light 24 hours a day could act as a control. In every experiment you perform, you should be able to pick out factors that are variables and constants. Also, every experiment should have a control with which you can compare your experimental results.

Graphing

Often information can be communicated more easily with a picture instead of words. Graphs show data in picture form and make analyzing data easier.

A line graph is made of two axes. The variables tested by the experimenter are written along the axes. The independent variable always goes along the horizontal, or *x*-axis. The dependent variable always goes along the vertical, or *y*-axis.

Making a Line Graph

Suppose you wanted to make a line graph of your friend Deb's science grades from September through January.

Month	Grade
September	63
October	85
November	95
December	82
January	97

How would you set up the axes? Month is the independent variable and should be on the *x*-axis. Grades are the dependent variable and should be on the *y*-axis.

Next, you must label each axis with a scale. On the *x*-axis, you would simply list the months. To make a scale of the grades for the *y*-axis, you must determine the range of the data. Substract the smallest data value from the largest. The difference between 97 and 63 is 34. You will need a spread of at least 34 units along the *y*-axis. After examining the data, you might decide to start numbering the *y*-axis at 60 and number by tens to 100.

The first pair of data you want to plot is September, 63. Locate September on the

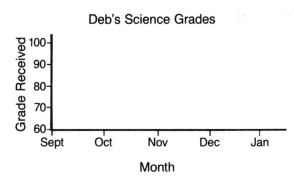

Deb's Science Grades

x-axis and 63 on the *y*-axis. Sight straight up from September and straight across from 63. The point where these two imaginary lines cross is where the data point should be plotted. After all the points are plotted, connect them with a smooth line.

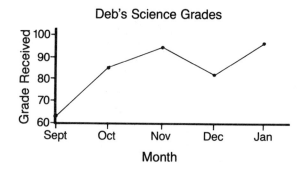

Deb's Science Grades

Sometimes you may want to plot two sets of data on the same graph. Suppose you wanted to compare Fred's grades with Deb's. The graph below shows both Fred's and Deb's grades. A key is included to tell you which set of data is which.

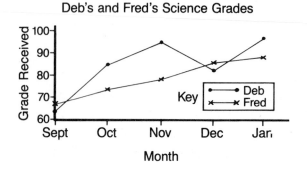

Deb's and Fred's Science Grades

Making a Bar Graph

A bar graph is set up similar to a line graph, but a bar graph has thick bars instead of data points. Bar graphs are often used to show comparisons. To make a bar graph, set up your axes in the same way as for a line graph. Plot your data by drawing bars that extend from the *x*-axis to the point where your imaginary extensions of the *x*-axis and *y*-axis intersect. Look at the bar graph below. The activity performed by a male or female is the independent variable. The number of calories used per hour for a male or a female doing the same activity is being compared.

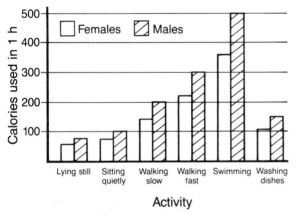

Activity

Making a Pie Graph

A pie graph uses parts of a circle to display data. A pie graph shows how each part is related to the whole. Each part of a pie graph is called a section. When all the sections of the pie are added together, they equal 100 percent.

To make a pie graph, you need to calculate how much of the pie each section should take. Suppose you wanted to make a pie graph that shows where Earth's water supply is found. Earth's total supply is 1398 million cubic kilometers. Therefore, the whole pie will represent this amount. The volume of water in Earth's oceans is 1356 million km^3. Glacial ice contains 28 million km^3. Freshwater contains 14 million km^3. Each of these three locations will be represented by a section of the pie graph. To find how much of the pie each section should take, follow this rule. Divide the amount of water in each location by the total amount of water. Multiply your answer by 360, which is the number of degrees in a circle. Round your answer to the nearest whole number. The ocean section would be determined using the following calculation.

$$\frac{1356}{1398} \times 360 = 349.18 \text{ or } 349°$$

Use the following procedure to plot this section on the graph. Use a compass to draw a circle. Use a ruler to draw a line from the edge of the circle to its center. Put your protractor on this line and use it to mark a point on the edge of the circle at 349°. Connect this point with a straight line to the center of the circle. Repeat this procedure starting from the line you just drew for each section of the circle. Label all the sections of your graph.

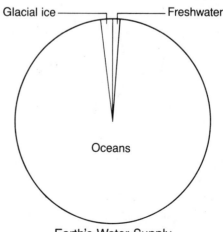

Earth's Water Supply

Classifying

In order for you to understand the large number of things in the world around you, you must impose some sort of order. You impose order by observing similarities, differences, and relationships among objects, and based on these observations, by grouping these objects. When you walk into a music store, you usually find bins containing record albums and shelves containing cassette tapes and compact discs. How are these items classified?

Items in a music store are classified first according to format, or type of recording. Record albums are all placed together, as are cassettes and compact discs. The items within each group are subdivided further into type of music. Within each category of music, the items are placed in alphabetical order based on the name of the artist or composer.

A list of the steps used to organize the items might look like this.

1. Sort items by type of recording.
2. Subgroup each type of recording according to type of music.
3. Place each subgroup into alphabetical order by artist or composer.

How are the categories for a classification system determined? It was simple for the music store manager. Most music can be placed easily into the proper category. When you begin to classify objects, you should identify some common properties. Study the items below.

What are some observable properties that can be used to group the items into two subgroups? You might list pointed end or blunt end, flat head or round head, straight shaft or spiral shaft. Note that for each property, each item is assignable to only one subgroup. After you decide on the first property that divides the items into two subgroups, you should examine each subgroup for a property or set of properties that further groups the items. The chart shows one classification.

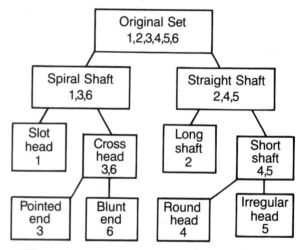

The most important requirement of any classification system is that it must be useful. In the music shop, it is possible to group together all recordings with a blue cover. How useful would this system be if you wanted to find this week's number one seller?

Classifying things is an important skill that can be done easily if you remember a few important points. Classification is putting similar objects together for a purpose. You must choose which similarities are useful for the purpose you are studying. You must then group the objects you are classifying by the similarities you have chosen.

Observing and Inferring

Information comes to you continually through your senses. You see, hear, smell, taste, and feel. Whenever you become aware of something through your senses, you are observing. You use your eyes to observe the different parts of a candle flame. You use your ears to observe two different bird calls in your backyard. You use your sense of touch when you touch the handle of a pan on the stove. You smell and taste the spaghetti in your lunch.

Many observations you make are qualitative. Qualitative observations are obtained using the senses alone. Below are some qualitative observations you might make about a part of your lunch.

Sight: round, red skin, white flesh
Smell: fruity
Taste: tart
Touch: skin is waxy and smooth
Hearing: crunches when bitten into

In science, you often will be asked to make quantitative observations. These observations involve measurements. Quantitative observations are easy to communicate to others and provide a concrete basis of comparison. Below are some quantitative observations you could make about part of your lunch. The instrument used to make the observation is also included.

Balance: Mass—50 g
Ruler: Length—4 cm
           Height—8 cm
           Width—4 cm

Now that you know what observations are, what should you do with this information? When you explain or interpret information, you make an inference. From the observations above, you might infer that you have an apple in your lunch. An inference goes beyond the strictly observable and attempts to explain the observation.

You see a neighbor raking leaves. Later in the day, you smell smoke. You might infer from your observations that your neighbor is burning leaves. A test tube gets warmer after two chemicals are added to it. What can you infer? You might infer that an energy-producing reaction is taking place. In science, you will be making inferences as a result of your observations. By making inferences, you will be able to recognize patterns and explain the world around you.

Cause and Effect

Each day you may notice many events around you and wonder how or why they happen. Each time you open a can of cat food, your cat immediately bounds into the room. Ice cubes left out in the sun on a hot summer day melt quickly. Shadows cast by a tree on a sunny day change position from morning to evening.

An event is called an **effect**. The reason an event takes place is called the **cause**. On long sea voyages, sailors often developed a disease called scurvy. In time, it was found that the cause of this condition was the lack of vitamin C in their diets. Absence of vitamin C in the diet was the cause. Scurvy was the effect.

Sometimes as you read, you will come across certain "clue" words that signal a cause and effect relationship. Some of these words are listed here.

CAUSE	EFFECT
since	therefore
because	so, thus
when	then
due to	as a result

Cause and effect are involved every time you wonder why or how something is the way it is. The relationship between cause and effect provides scientists with many of the ideas they use to formulate experiments. Scientists observe effects about which they then ask questions. An experiment is done in order to find out some of the causes for the effects that have been observed.

How can you determine the cause of the cat's speedy arrival when the food can is opened? Maybe the cat smells the food faster than you think. Maybe the cat has become conditioned to the sound of the can opener and relates the sound to eating. Do you feed the cat at the same time each day? Maybe it is the timing of the opening of the can that brings the cat. You could set up the following experiments to test these possible causes.

1. At the same time of day that you usually feed the cat, open a can of green beans. If the cat comes running, you know that the sound of the can opener or the time of day is a cause for the cat's actions

2. Open a can of green beans at a different time of day from when you usually feed the cat. This will help you decide if it is the sound of the can opener alone that causes the cat's actions.

By experimenting to eliminate one or more possibilities, you may be able to determine the cause of the cat's behavior. You may find that a combination of actions causes the cat's behavior. Sometimes there are several causes for an effect. You will need to make careful observations and logical inferences in order to determine cause and effect.

Sequencing

How do you make a peanut butter and jelly sandwich? Do you first scrape jelly onto your knife and then open the package of bread? Do you place two pieces of bread together before spreading the peanut butter? You know that to make a sandwich you must carry out a set of steps in a certain order. This order of steps is called a **sequence**.

You use sequencing every day. A typical sequence of events might be

1. shower
2. dress
3. eat breakfast
4. walk to school
5. attend classes
6. walk home
7. play with friends
8. eat dinner
9. study
10. go to bed

Simple tasks often follow a sequence. The steps below can be used to make gelatin.

1. Gather together a 1-L bowl, wooden spoon, measuring cup, package of flavored gelatin, a pan, and water.
2. Pour the contents of the package of gelatin into the bowl.
3. Pour 0.5 L of water into a pan.
4. Heat the water until it boils.
5. Pour the boiling water over the gelatin in the bowl.
6. Stir with the wooden spoon until the gelatin dissolves.
7. Add 0.5 L of cold water to the gelatin and stir.
8. Place the bowl of gelatin in a cool place overnight to gel.

When you carry out activities in this textbook, you will be asked to follow steps in a certain order. What would happen if you did step 7 before you did step 5? You might have trouble dissolving the gelatin. If any of these steps are left out, the results of the activity will be affected. What would be the result if you left out step 7 when making gelatin? The gelatin would be too concentrated.

Scientists often study the sequence of events in natural processes. How can the study of sequences be useful? If the order of steps in a sequence is known, then you can predict what will come next. The sequence of events in the life of an organism makes up its life cycle. A puppy grows up to be a dog. You know that a puppy will never become a bear. The sequence of events that lead up to a tornado often follows the same pattern. Scientists who study the weather know to look for a certain sequence of events that has led to tornadoes in the past. When this sequence is recognized, they can warn people that conditions are right for a tornado to form.

When you are asked to write a sequence of events, you need to keep in mind some important points. Always ask yourself what must happen first. Then decide what must happen second. Continue ordering steps until the sequence is complete. Check to make sure that the steps you have chosen make sense. In a sequence, each step must lead logically to the next step.

APPENDIX A

Safety in the Science Classroom

1. Always obtain your teacher's permission to begin an investigation.
2. Study the procedure. If you have questions, ask your teacher. Be sure you understand any safety symbols shown.
3. Use the safety equipment provided for you. Goggles and a safety apron should be worn when any investigation calls for using chemicals.
4. When you are heating a test tube, always slant it so the mouth points away from you and others.
5. Never eat or drink in the lab. Never inhale chemicals. Do not taste any substance or draw any material into a tube with your mouth.
6. If you spill any chemical, wash it off immediately with water. Report the spill immediately to your teacher.
7. Know the location and proper use of the fire extinguisher, safety shower, fire blanket, first aid kit, and fire alarm.
8. Keep all materials away from open flames. Tie back long hair.
9. If a fire should break out in the classroom, or if your clothing should catch fire, smother it with the fire blanket or a coat, or get under a safety shower. **NEVER RUN.**
10. Report any accident or injury, no matter how small, to your teacher.

Follow these procedures as you clean up your work area.
1. Turn off the water and gas. Disconnect electrical devices.
2. Return materials to their places.
3. Dispose of chemicals and other materials as directed by your teacher. Place broken glass and solid substances in the proper containers. Never discard materials in the sink.
4. Clean your work area.
5. Wash your hands thoroughly after working in the laboratory.

Table A–1

FIRST AID	
Injury	**Safe response**
Burns	Apply cold water. Call your teacher immediately.
Cuts and bruises	Stop any bleeding by applying direct pressure. Cover cuts with a clean dressing. Apply cold compresses to bruises. Call your teacher immediately.
Fainting	Leave the person lying down. Loosen any tight clothing and keep crowds away. Call your teacher immediately.
Foreign matter in eye	Flush with plenty of water. Use eyewash bottle or fountain.
Poisoning	Note the suspected poisoning agent and call your teacher immediately.
Any spills on skin	Flush with large amounts of water or use safety shower. Call your teacher immediately.

APPENDIX B

Safety Symbols

	DISPOSAL ALERT This symbol appears when care must be taken to dispose of materials properly.		**ANIMAL SAFETY** This symbol appears whenever live animals are studied and the safety of the animals and the students must be ensured.
	BIOLOGICAL SAFETY This symbol appears when there is danger involving bacteria, fungi, or protists.		**RADIOACTIVE SAFETY** This symbol appears when radioactive materials are used.
	OPEN FLAME ALERT This symbol appears when use of an open flame could cause a fire or an explosion.		**CLOTHING PROTECTION SAFETY** This symbol appears when substances used could stain or burn clothing.
	THERMAL SAFETY This symbol appears as a reminder to use caution when handling hot objects.		**FIRE SAFETY** This symbol appears when care should be taken around open flames.
	SHARP OBJECT SAFETY This symbol appears when a danger of cuts or punctures caused by the use of sharp objects exists.		**EXPLOSION SAFETY** This symbol appears when the misuse of chemicals could cause an explosion.
	FUME SAFETY This symbol appears when chemicals or chemical reactions could cause dangerous fumes.		**EYE SAFETY** This symbol appears when a danger to the eyes exists. Safety goggles should be worn when this symbol appears.
	ELECTRICAL SAFETY This symbol appears when care should be taken when using electrical equipment.		**POISON SAFETY** This symbol appears when poisonous substances are used.
	PLANT SAFETY This symbol appears when poisonous plants or plants with thorns are handled.		**CHEMICAL SAFETY** This symbol appears when chemicals used can cause burns or are poisonous if absorbed through the skin.

Lab Equipment

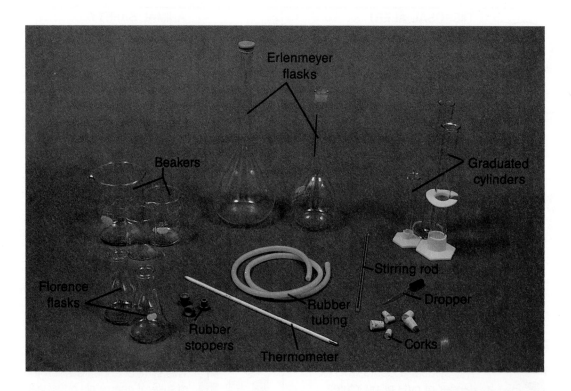

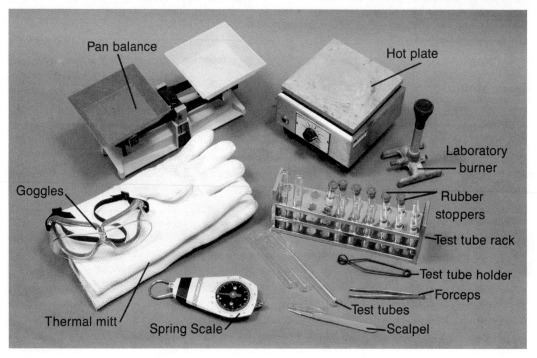

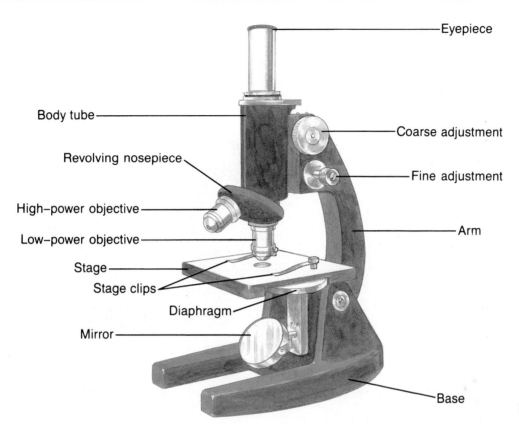

Eyepiece

Body tube

Coarse adjustment

Revolving nosepiece

Fine adjustment

High-power objective

Low-power objective

Arm

Stage

Stage clips

Diaphragm

Mirror

Base

Parts of a Microscope

1. **Eyepiece** — contains the magnifying lens through which you look

2. **Body tube** — maintains the correct distance between the eyepiece and objective lens

3. **Arm** — supports the body tube

4. **Nosepiece** — holds the high and low power objectives; can be rotated to change the magnification

5. **High power objective** — provides the most magnification, which is usually about 40 ×

6. **Low power objective** — provides the least magnification, usually 10 ×

7. **Coarse adjustment** — moves the body tube up and down for focusing

8. **Fine adjustment** — used to sharpen the image, moves body tube only slightly

9. **Stage clips** — hold the microscope slide in place

10. **Stage** — platform to support the microscope slide

11. **Diaphragm** — regulates the amount of light that enters the body tube

12. **Mirror or light** — reflects light upward through the diaphragm, the object, and the lenses

13. **Base** — usually heavy to provide support for the microscope

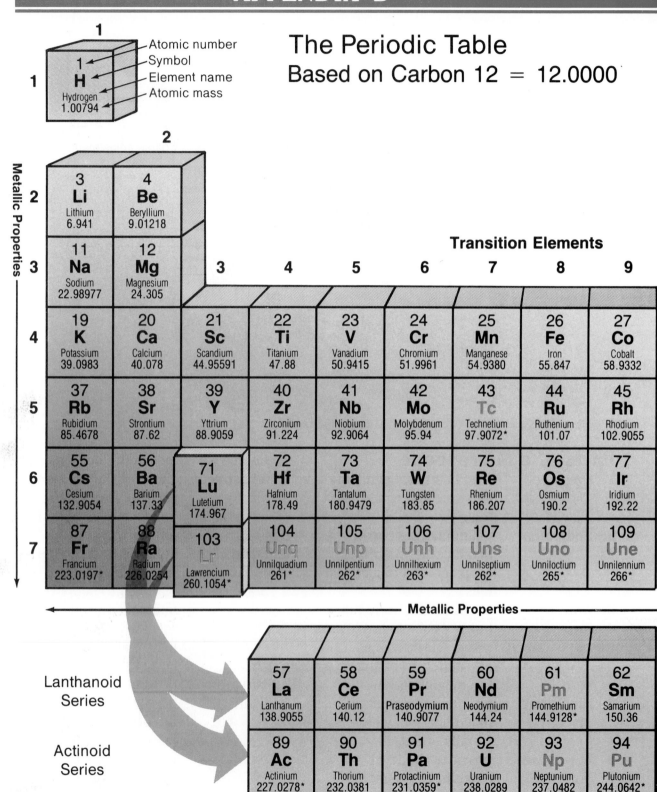

The Periodic Table
Based on Carbon 12 = 12.0000

Atomic number — 1
Symbol — H
Element name — Hydrogen
Atomic mass — 1.00794

Transition Elements

Metallic Properties

1	2	3	4	5	6	7	8	9
1 H Hydrogen 1.00794								
3 Li Lithium 6.941	4 Be Beryllium 9.01218							
11 Na Sodium 22.98977	12 Mg Magnesium 24.305							
19 K Potassium 39.0983	20 Ca Calcium 40.078	21 Sc Scandium 44.95591	22 Ti Titanium 47.88	23 V Vanadium 50.9415	24 Cr Chromium 51.9961	25 Mn Manganese 54.9380	26 Fe Iron 55.847	27 Co Cobalt 58.9332
37 Rb Rubidium 85.4678	38 Sr Strontium 87.62	39 Y Yttrium 88.9059	40 Zr Zirconium 91.224	41 Nb Niobium 92.9064	42 Mo Molybdenum 95.94	43 Tc Technetium 97.9072*	44 Ru Ruthenium 101.07	45 Rh Rhodium 102.9055
55 Cs Cesium 132.9054	56 Ba Barium 137.33	71 Lu Lutetium 174.967	72 Hf Hafnium 178.49	73 Ta Tantalum 180.9479	74 W Tungsten 183.85	75 Re Rhenium 186.207	76 Os Osmium 190.2	77 Ir Iridium 192.22
87 Fr Francium 223.0197*	88 Ra Radium 226.0254	103 Lr Lawrencium 260.1054*	104 Unq Unnilquadium 261*	105 Unp Unnilpentium 262*	106 Unh Unnilhexium 263*	107 Uns Unnilseptium 262*	108 Uno Unniloctium 265*	109 Une Unnilennium 266*

← Metallic Properties →

Lanthanoid Series

57 La Lanthanum 138.9055	58 Ce Cerium 140.12	59 Pr Praseodymium 140.9077	60 Nd Neodymium 144.24	61 Pm Promethium 144.9128*	62 Sm Samarium 150.36

Actinoid Series

89 Ac Actinium 227.0278*	90 Th Thorium 232.0381	91 Pa Protactinium 231.0359*	92 U Uranium 238.0289	93 Np Neptunium 237.0482	94 Pu Plutonium 244.0642*

* mass of isotope with longest half–life, that is, the most stable isotope of the element

Noble Gases

					18

Nonmetallic Properties →

13	14	15	16	17	18
					2 **He** Helium 4.002602
5 **B** Boron 10.811	6 **C** Carbon 12.011	7 **N** Nitrogen 14.0067	8 **O** Oxygen 15.9994	9 **F** Fluorine 18.998403	10 **Ne** Neon 20.179
13 **Al** Aluminum 26.98154	14 **Si** Silicon 28.0855	15 **P** Phosphorus 30.97376	16 **S** Sulfur 32.06	17 **Cl** Chlorine 35.453	18 **Ar** Argon 39.948

10	11	12	13	14	15	16	17	18
28 **Ni** Nickel 58.69	29 **Cu** Copper 63.546	30 **Zn** Zinc 65.39	31 **Ga** Gallium 69.723	32 **Ge** Germanium 72.59	33 **As** Arsenic 74.9216	34 **Se** Selenium 78.96	35 **Br** Bromine 79.904	36 **Kr** Krypton 83.80
46 **Pd** Palladium 106.42	47 **Ag** Silver 107.8682	48 **Cd** Cadmium 112.41	49 **In** Indium 114.82	50 **Sn** Tin 118.710	51 **Sb** Antimony 121.75	52 **Te** Tellurium 127.60	53 **I** Iodine 126.9045	54 **Xe** Xenon 131.29
78 **Pt** Platinum 195.08	79 **Au** Gold 196.9665	80 **Hg** Mercury 200.59	81 **Tl** Thallium 204.383	82 **Pb** Lead 207.2	83 **Bi** Bismuth 208.9804	84 **Po** Polonium 208.9824*	85 **At** Astatine 209.98712*	86 **Rn** Radon 222.017*

Metallic Properties
Nonmetallic Properties
Metalloids
Synthetic Elements

63 **Eu** Europium 151.96	64 **Gd** Gadolinium 157.25	65 **Tb** Terbium 158.9254	66 **Dy** Dysprosium 162.50	67 **Ho** Holmium 164.9304	68 **Er** Erbium 167.26	69 **Tm** Thulium 168.9342	70 **Yb** Ytterbium 173.04
95 **Am** Americium 243.0614*	96 **Cm** Curium 247.0703*	97 **Bk** Berkelium 247.0703*	98 **Cf** Californium 251.0796*	99 **Es** Einsteinium 252.0828*	100 **Fm** Fermium 257.0951*	101 **Md** Mendelevium 258.986*	102 **No** Nobelium 259.1009*

GLOSSARY

The glossary contains all of the major science terms of the text and their definitions. Below is a pronunciation key to help you use these terms. The word or term will be given in boldface type. If necessary, the pronunciation will follow the term in parentheses.

a . . . **b**a**ck** (bak)
ay . . . **day** (day)
ah . . . **fa**ther (fahth ur)
ow . . . fl**ow**er (flow ur)
ar . . . **car** (car)
e . . . l**e**ss (les)
ee . . . l**ea**f (leef)
ih . . . tr**i**p (trihp)
i (i + con + e) . . . **i**dea (i dee uh), l**i**fe, (life)
oh . . . g**o** (goh)
aw . . . s**o**ft (sawft)
or . . . **or**bit (or but)
oy . . . c**oi**n (coyn)
oo . . . f**oo**t (foot)

ew . . . f**oo**d (fewd)
yoo . . . **pu**re (pyoor)
yew . . . f**ew** (fyew)
uh . . . comm**a** (cahm uh)
u (+ con) . . . fl**ow**er (flow ur)
sh . . . **sh**elf (shelf)
ch . . . na**t**ure (nay chur)
g . . . **g**ift (gihft)
j . . . **g**em (jem)
ing . . . s**ing** (sing)
zh . . . vi**s**ion (vihzh un)
k . . . **c**a**k**e (kayk)
s . . . **s**eed, **c**ent (seed, sent)
z . . . **z**one, rai**s**e (zohn, rayz)

A

abdomen: the last body segment of an insect that has organs of reproduction

abrasion: the scouring action of particles carried by the wind

absolute zero: the point at which almost all movement of the atoms in a material stops 38

abyssal (uh BIHS ul) **plains:** the flat, level parts of the ocean floor 324

acceleration: the rate at which velocity changes 136

accuracy: degree of conformity of a measure to a standard or a true value

acid: a substance that forms hydrogen ions as it dissolves in water

acid precipitation: rain or snow containing nitric acid, sulfuric acid, and other pollutants 283

action-reaction forces: force pairs that are equal and opposite and that act on different objects

active transport: the movement of materials across a membrane in living cells from areas of lower concentration to areas of higher concentration

adaptation: a trait that increases the chances of an organism surviving in its environment 345

addict: a person who can no longer control the use of a drug and may even be unaware that he or she is dependent on the use of the drug 476

air mass: a large body of air in which the temperature and moisture content stay about the same 285

air resistance: the force exerted by air on a moving object 138

algae: seaweeds or monerans and protists that contain chlorophyll and live in water

alpine glaciers: glaciers formed at high elevations that move down mountain slopes due to the force of gravity

alveoli: large, spongy masses of tiny sacs in the lungs 495

amino acids: the building blocks of proteins 509

amoeba (uh MEE buh): a protozoan that moves by means of pseudopods

amphibians: cold-blooded vertebrates that have a moist skin with no scales and live part of their lives in water and part on land

anemometer: an instrument that measures wind speed

angiosperm (AN jee uh spurm): vascular seed plants that produce flowers and seeds protected by a fruit

animal-like protists: protozoans

annuals: plants that grow from seeds, produce seeds, and die in one year

anorexia nervosa: an eating disorder in which fear of becoming overweight develops into starvation 519

anthracite: the final stage in coal formation

antibodies: proteins that are produced on lymphocytes 494

anticyclone: high pressure area containing cold, dry air, with winds that spiral around and out from the center

antigens: substances that cause the formation of antibodies

aorta (ay ORT uh): the largest artery in your body

appendages: any structures that grow out from the main part of the body

appendicular (a pan DIH khew lur) **skeleton:** the limbs and any bones that attach these limbs to the axial skeleton 445

aquifers: permeable rock layers filled with water 241

Archimedes' principle: the buoyant force on an object in a fluid is equal to the weight displaced by the object 155

area: the amount of space on the surface of an object 32

artery (ART uh ree): a blood vessel that carries blood away from the heart 485

arthropods: invertebrates that have jointed legs, an exoskeleton, and a segmented body

astronomy: the study of the universe

atmosphere: the blanket of air that surrounds Earth 258

atmospheric pressure: the measure of the weight of air molecules pressing down on a specific point on Earth 262

atomic number: the number of protons in an atom 53

atom: the smallest unit of an element that still keeps the properties of the element 51

atrium (AY tree um): the heart chamber that receives blood from veins in vertebrates

average speed: the total distance traveled divided by the total time of travel 131

axial (AK see ul) **skeleton:** bones and cartilage that support and protect the head, neck, heart, and lungs 445

axis: an imaginary line around which Earth spins 174

axon (AK sahn): a long nerve fiber that carries impulses from the cell body of one neuron to the next

B

bacteria: a one-celled organism with no nucleus and usually no chlorophyll

balanced diet: the food you eat during the day that gives your body all the nutrients needed to carry out all life processes

balanced forces: forces, acting on the same object, equal in size but opposite in direction 96

ball-and-socket joint: a joint that allows circular movement

barometer: an instrument used to measure air pressure

barrier island: a sand bar that forms offshore and parallel to the coast

bars: long ridges of sand and gravel that are deposited in a stream's channel 237

base: a substance that dissolves in water to form hydroxide ions

benthos (BEN thahs): organisms that live on the ocean floor 327

Bernoulli's principle: the pressure in a fluid decreases as the speed of the fluid increases 159

biennials: plants that complete their life cycle in two years

bile: a greenish-liquid produced in the liver that breaks down fats into tiny particles

bituminous coal: a type of coal in the third stage of coal formation

bivalves: mollusks that have two shells hinged together

bladders: air-filled sacs that help seaweed float

blood: a tissue made up of liquid and solid parts 489

boiling point: the temperature at which a substance changes rapidly from a liquid to a gas 74

bony fish: a type of fish with a skeleton made of bone and scales that are smooth

Boyle's law: increasing the volume of a gas will increase the pressure the gas exerts if the temperature remains constant 162

brain: the major control center of all body activity 462

breaker: a wave that forms a sharp peak and then falls forward when it reaches shore 313

bronchioles: tiny branches of the bronchi in the lungs

budding: a form of reproduction in which a new organism is formed by an outgrowth of a parent organism 374

bulb: an underground storage organ that is a short stem surrounded by swollen leaf bases

bulimia: an eating disorder in which an individual diets strictly and then eats large amounts of food at one time 520

buoyant force: the upward force of a fluid on an object in it 155

C

caffeine: a stimulant found in many soft drink beverages, coffee, tea, diet pills, and some cold medicines, candy, and pain relievers

calcium: a mineral that makes bone hard

Calorie: a measure of the energy in food 514

camouflage (KAM uh flahj): the natural disguise that hides an animal from its predators or its prey 415

capillaries: the smallest blood vessels in the body 486

carbohydrates: organic nutrients that are the main sources of energy for the body 506

cardiac muscle: muscle tissue found only in the walls of the heart 451

cardiovascular system: the heart, blood, and blood vessels

carnivores: animals that feed on other animals

cartilage: a tough, flexible tissue in the bodies of vertebrates 427

cartilage fish: a type of fish with a skeleton made of cartilage and scales that are toothlike

cell: the basic unit of all living things 344

cell membrane: a thin layer that surrounds and holds the parts of a cell together 350

cellulose (SEL yuh lohs): the substance that makes up most of the cell walls of plants; carbohydrate found in cell walls 384

cell wall: a rigid layer that provides support for a plant

centi-: a prefix meaning one-hundredth

central nervous system: a major part of the nervous system composed of the brain and spinal cord 462

centripetal (sen TRIHP ut ul) **force:** the force that acts toward the center of a circle 141

cerebellum (ser uh BEL um): the part of the brain that controls the body's balance and voluntary muscle action

cerebrum (suh REE brum): the largest part of the human brain that controls thinking and awareness

Charles's law: the volume of a gas increases as its temperature increases if the pressure remains constant 162

chemical change: any change or reaction in which a new substance is formed 78

chemical digestion: the changing of food into a form that the body can use 517

chemical energy: potential energy that is stored in bonds between atoms 101

chemical equation: a shorthand way of writing the changes that occur during a chemical reaction 79

chemical property: determines how a substance reacts to form other substances 50

chemical reaction: a chemical change

chlorofluorocarbons (CFCs): chemicals that contain chlorine, fluorine, and carbon 164

chlorophyll: a substance that makes a plant green and that traps light energy to make food

chloroplasts (KLOR uh plastz): small, oval-shaped bodies that contain a molecule called chlorophyll 350

cholesterol: a fat that attaches to the walls of the arteries

chromosomes (KROH muh sohmz): threadlike structures in a cell's nucleus that carry the code for the life processes of an organism 351

cilia: short hair-like structures 370

ciliate (SIHL ee ayt): a protozoan that moves by means of cilia

circular motion: motion in a circle

circulatory system: a transport system made up of the heart, blood and lymph, and vessels that link all the systems in the body 484

cirrus: a high, white, feathery cloud composed of ice crystals or supercooled water and associated with fair weather

class: the category of organisms that groups similar orders

classifying: the placing of items into groups

clastic: sedimentary rock made of rock fragments, minerals, and broken shells

cleavage: the name given to breakage of a mineral along smooth, flat planes

climate: the average of all weather conditions of an area over a period of about 30 years 292

clouds: collections of tiny droplets of water suspended in air 279

club fungi: fungi whose spores are formed on the underside of an umbrella-like cap

club mosses: vascular spore plants that produce spores in cones

coal: a fossil fuel composed of plant remains that have been compacted to form a rock 209

cocaine: a fast-acting addictive stimulant drug made from the coca plant 477

cold-blooded vertebrates: vertebrates having body temperatures that change with the surrounding temperature

cold front: a boundary that develops when a cold air mass meets a warm air mass 286

communication: the exchange of signals or messages such as flashing lights, odors, bright colors, or sound

communication satellites: satellites that receive, amplify, and relay telephone, TV, and radio signals 144

compact bone: a very hard layer of bone containing cells and blood vessels

compound: a substance made of two or more elements whose atoms are chemically combined 57

compound fracture: a break in a bone where the broken ends of a bone push through the muscle and skin

compound machine: two or more simple machines working together 121

conclusion: a logical answer to a problem question based on data 9

condensation: the process in which a gas changes to a liquid 74

conduction: the transfer of heat through matter by actual contact of molecules 264

conductivity: the ability of a material to transmit heat or electricity

conic map projection: a type of map projection whereby points and locations are projected onto a piece of paper that has been rolled into a cone

conifer: a group of seed plants that produce seeds in cones 398

constant: a factor that does not change during an experiment 12

consumers: plants or animals that are unable to manufacture their own food and must feed on other organisms 388

continental glaciers: large sheets of ice whose movements are outward due to pressure from overlying ice and snow

continental shelf: the gently sloping part of the continent that is covered with water 324

continental slope: the steeply sloping area that connects the continental shelf and the ocean floor 324

contour plowing: a farming method in which fields are plowed and planted across a slope

control: a standard for comparison 11

convection: the transfer of heat due to density differences 264

Coriolis (kor ee OH lus) **effect:** the deflection of moving objects to the right in the Northern Hemisphere and to the left in the Southern Hemisphere; brought about by Earth's rotation 269

corm: an underground storage organ that is a short stem

coronary (KOR uh nair ee) **circulation:** the pathway that blood takes to service the heart muscle

corrosion: the result of the reactivity of some metals

cotyledons (kaht ul EED unz): the seed leaves in the embryo of a seed

crack: cocaine in the form of small white or brown chunks 478

creep: a slow downhill movement of material 220

crest: the highest point of a wave

crystal: the same repeating pattern 70

cubic meter: standard SI unit for volume 32

cumulus: a thick, puffy cloud that develops when rising columns of air are cooled to the dew point

cyanobacteria (si uh noh bak TIHR ee uh): one-celled organisms with no nucleus but containing chlorophyll

cyclone: a low pressure area containing warm air, with winds that spiral around and into the center

cytoplasm (SITE uh plaz um): a thick liquid-like substance 350

D

data: the recorded facts or measurements from an experiment 9

daylight saving time: a system in which clocks are set one hour ahead of standard time between the months of April and October 188

deci-: a prefix meaning one-tenth

deciduous: a type of plant that loses its leaves each year

declination: the angle of difference between geographic north and magnetic north 178

decomposer: an organism that breaks down complex organic compounds into simpler compounds 377

decomposition reaction: a chemical change in which a substance breaks down or decomposes into other substances 81

deflation: wind erosion that removes loose material from the ground surface

delta: sediment deposited in a fan-shaped body 238

dendrites (DEN drites): branches of a neuron that receive stimuli

density: the amount of mass a material has for its volume 35

density currents: currents that flow because of a difference in the density of ocean water 306

dependent variable: the change that occurs as a result of the independent variable

depressant: a drug that slows or blocks impulses at the synapse 473

desalination: the removal of salts and other dissolved solids from ocean water 303

dew point: the temperature at which condensation occurs 279

diameter: the length of a straight line passing through the center of a circle or sphere from one side to the other

diaphragm: a large flat sheet of muscle under the heart and lungs 496

dicotyledons: flowering plants with two seed leaves and flower parts in fours or fives 403

diffusion (dihf YEW zhun): the movement of particles from where they are more concentrated to where they are less concentrated 351

digestion: the process that takes food and changes it into substances that can be absorbed and used by the body 506

dinosaurs: an ancient group of reptiles that died out about 70 million years ago

disease: a change in the life processes of cells caused by a micro-organism

distillation: a method of desalination where salt water is evaporated and the salt is left behind

division: the largest category in the plant kingdom

doldrums: a nearly windless zone near the equator 270

double displacement reaction: reaction in which the atoms or groups of atoms in two compounds switch places 83

drainage system: a system of water channels that drains an area

drug: any chemical which, when taken into the body, changes the way the body works 472

drug abuse: incorrect or improper use of a drug 476

ductility (duk TIHL ut ee): the ability of a material to be drawn into thin wires

E

earth science: the study of Earth and its place in space

echo sounding: a method of measuring ocean depth using reflected sound waves 322

efficiency: a measurement of the work put into a machine (input) compared with the work the machine does (output) 122

effort force: the force you apply to a machine

egg: female sex cell

electrical energy: the kinetic energy of moving electrons 100

electric force: force between two objects due to their charges

electron: a particle that has a negative electric charge and a very small mass 51

electron cloud: the space around the nucleus of an atom that is occupied by electrons

element: a substance made of just one type of atom 53

embryo: the new plant inside a seed

emergent shoreline: a shoreline formed when sea level falls or the land rises 331

endangered species: species in danger of becoming extinct 416

endocrine gland: ductless gland that produces hormones that go directly into the blood stream

endocrine system: a system made up of ductless glands that produce hormones

endoskeleton (EN doh skel uht uhn): a skeleton on the inside of the body 411

endosperm: tissue in seeds of monocots in which food is stored

energy: the ability to do work

energy transfer: any flow of energy from one object to another 102

enzyme: a protein catalyst that changes the rate of a chemical reaction 515

epidermis: an upper and lower layer of covering cells

equator: an imaginary line circling the globe equally distant at all points from the poles 174

equinox: either of two times each year when the sun is directly above Earth's equator and day and night are of equal length 184

erosion: the transportation of weathered particles by water, wind, ice, or gravity 219

esophagus: a 25 cm long muscular tube that connects the mouth to the stomach

essential amino acids: eight amino acids that have to be supplied by the food you eat because the body cannot make them

estimate: to make a general but careful guess

evaporation: the change from the liquid to the gaseous state at the liquid's surface 73, 235

evergreen: a plant that retains its green leaves all year round

excretion (ihk SKREE shun): the process of removing wastes that result from metabolism in the cells of the body 498

exercise: a situation in which all the information needed to solve a problem is provided 17

exoskeleton (EK soh skel uht uhn): a hard outer covering such as the shell of a crab or a beetle 411

exosphere: the upper zone of the thermosphere that begins at about 500 kilometers above Earth and extends into space

experiment: a series of carefully planned steps that tests a hypothesis 9

external fertilization: the uniting of an egg and sperm outside of the body 413

extrusive: rock formed at Earth's surface

F

fall equinox: the first day of fall when the sun crosses the equator and night and day are equal in length

family: the category of organisms that groups similar genera

fat: an organic nutrient that protects internal organs, insulates to retain body heat, and is a good source of energy 507

feathers: the body covering of birds

ferns: vascular plants that form large numbers of spores

fertilization (furt ul uh ZAY shun): the union of an egg cell with a sperm 393

fiber: roughage that works to help move food through your digestive system

fibrous root: a root made up of many thin roots that branch and spread out

fission: the equal division of an organism into two 366

flagella (fluh JEL uh): long, thin hair-like structures 366

flagellate (FLAJ uh layt): a protozoan that moves by means of flagella

flatworms: wormlike invertebrates with a flattened, solid body and only one body opening

floodplain: an area of fertile soil composed of fine sediment deposited during floods

fluid: a material that can flow 150

food groups: four basic groups of food (milk, meat, fruit-vegetable, and grain) that provide the body with essential nutrients

force: the push or pull that one object exerts on another 94

formula: a list of elements in their exact ratios that make up a compound 58

fossil fuels: compounds of hydrogen and carbon 209

fossils: the remains or evidence of prehistoric life preserved in Earth's crust 205

fracture: a physical property that describes the breaks along irregular surfaces of a mineral; a break in a bone 444

freezing point: the temperature at which a material changes from a liquid to a solid 73

friction: a force that opposes motion 95

frond (FRAHND): the leaf of a fern 395

fruit: the ovary with the fully grown seeds inside 400

fulcrum: the point around which the arm of a lever rotates or pivots 118

fungus: an organism that has tissues made up of long, threadlike structures 373

funguslike protists: slime molds

G

gas: matter that has no definite shape or volume 71

gene: a small part of a chromosome that controls a characteristic of an organism 378

gene splicing: a technique that replaces a section of genes in one cell with a section of genes from a different cell 378

genus (JEE nus): the category of organisms that groups similar species

geology: the study of Earth

germination: the growth of a seed to form a new plant 397

gills: flaplike organs with many tubes that obtain oxygen from water in animals such as fish

glaciers: large masses of ice in motion 244

gliding joint: a movable joint that allows bones to glide back and forth over each other

global: worldwide

glycogen (GLI kuh jun): a high-energy chemical stored in skeletal muscles 454

grains: mineral particles in a rock

gravitational (grav uh TAY shun ul) **force:** the force every object exerts on every other object 94

gravitropism: the response of stems and roots to gravity

gravity: a force that every object exerts on every other object

greenhouse effect: the process by which heat is trapped by gases in Earth's atmosphere 267

ground moraine: a sheetlike deposit of till dropped from the bottom of a glacier

groundwater: precipitation that soaks into the ground through small pores or openings 240

gymnosperm (JIHM nuh spurm): vascular seed plants with naked seeds produced in cones

H

habitat: the place in the environment where an organism lives 416

hail: droplets of water that freeze in layers around a small nucleus of ice

hallucinogen: a substance that distorts the senses and causes the user to see and hear things that do not exist 478

hardness: a measure of how easily a mineral can be scratched 199

heft: a physical property that describes the heaviness of a mineral

hemisphere: half of a sphere or globe

hemoglobin (HEE muh gloh bun): the oxygen-carrying molecule in red blood cells 489

herbaceous (hur BAY shus) **stem:** a type of stem that is soft and green

heterogeneous (het uh ruh JEE nee us) **mixture:** a mixture in which the substances are not evenly distributed

hinge joint: a movable joint that allows bones to move back and forth

homeostasis (hoh mee oh STAY sus): the series of continuous processes an organism uses to keep itself in a balanced state 462

homogeneous (hoh muh JEE nee us) **mixture:** a mixture in which the particles of substances are spread evenly throughout the mixture

hormone: a chemical made by an endocrine gland in one part of the body that brings about an effect in another part of the body 468

horsetails: vascular spore plants that produce spores in cones

humidity: moisture in the atmosphere 278

hurricanes: tropical storms that form over oceans 287

hydroelectric power: the electricity generated by the use of moving water 105

hydrogen ions: charged hydrogen atoms

hydrosphere: all water that exists in Earth's streams, swamps, lakes, oceans, ground, and atmosphere 234

hydroxide (hi DRAHK side) **ion:** a unit of hydrogen and oxygen

hyphae: thin, often branching threads of fungi 373

hypothesis: a statement that suggests or predicts an answer to a question 9

I

ice age: a period of time when glaciers cover a large portion of Earth's surface 247

ice wedging: a type of physical weathering in which rocks are broken into smaller fragments

igneous (IHG nee us) **rocks:** rocks formed from molten Earth materials 202

immovable joint: a joint that allows no movement 449

immunity (ihm YEW nut ee): the body's ability to resist and overcome microbes that invade the body 494

impulse: a message or signal that travels the length of the neuron

inclined plane: a simple machine that is a slanted surface used to raise or lower objects

independent variable: a variable that an experimenter changes

inertia (ihn UR shuh): the property of an object that resists any change in velocity 135

inorganic compound: generally, a compound that does not contain carbon

insecticides (ihn SEK tuh sidez): chemicals used to kill insects

insects: arthropods whose bodies are divided into a head, thorax, and abdomen; the most abundant animals on Earth

insulators: materials through which heat and electricity cannot flow readily 76

internal fertilization: the uniting of egg and sperm inside the body of the female 414

International Date Line: the 180° meridian that is directly opposite the prime meridian 188

International System of Units: a modern form of the metric system used by scientists and other people in most countries of the world

interneurons: small neurons that connect sensory neurons with motor neurons

intrusive: rocks formed beneath Earth's surface

invertebrate (in VERT uh brayt): an animal without a backbone 410

involuntary muscle action: a movement that cannot be controlled 450

ion (I ahn): an atom or group of atoms that has gained or lost an electron 57

ionosphere (i AHN uh sfihr): the lower zone of the thermosphere that contains ions and free electrons

J

jawless fish: a type of fish with a smooth skin, no scales, and no jaws

jetties: long structures built near harbors or bays to control the effects of longshore currents 332

joint: any place where two or more bones come together 448

joule (J): the SI unit of work 113

K

kelvin: a unit of measurement for temperature in the International System of Units equal in size to a degree Celsius

kidneys: the main organs of excretion in vertebrates

kilo-: prefix meaning thousand

kilogram: standard SI unit used in mass measurement 35

kilowatt (KW): a unit of power that equals 1000 watts

kinetic energy: energy of motion 99

kingdom: the largest category of organisms 356

L

lagoon: a calm, shallow area of water between a beach and a barrier island

landslides: rapid downhill movements of large amounts of rock and soil 220

large intestine: a 1.5 m long organ that removes excess water from undigested food

larva: an early undeveloped and active stage of some animals 418

laterites: red-orange soils rich in iron and aluminum oxides 225

latitude: distance in degrees north or south of the equator as indicated by latitude lines 186

lava: molten material on Earth

law: a statement that describes nature 10

law of conservation of energy: states that energy can change from one form to another but can never be created or destroyed 104

law of conservation of mass: states that matter is neither created nor destroyed in a chemical reaction 79

leaching: a process by which some soil components in upper layers are carried to lower layers by water 223

leaf: a green plant organ that grows from the stem and makes food

levees (LEV eez): ridgelike deposits that are built up along the sides of a stream 237

lever: an arm that turns around a fixed point 118

lichen: a fungus that has green algae or cyanobacteria that live among its hyphae 375

life science: the study of living things called organisms and how they relate to each other and to everything around them

ligament: a band of strong tissue that connects bones to each other at joints 448

lignite: a type of coal in the second stage of coal formation

liquid: matter that has a definite volume and takes the shape of its container 71

liver: an organ that produces bile, removes toxic materials from the body, and stores glycogen

liverworts: a group of nonvascular spore plants that has a flat, formless body or three rows of thin leaves on a creeping stem

longitude: a term used to describe distances in degrees east or west of the prime meridian 186

longshore current: a current of water flowing parallel to the shore 329

lungs: internal saclike organs in animals that take in oxygen from the air; spongelike organs of the respiratory system where oxygen and carbon dioxide are exchanged

luster: a physical property that describes the way light is reflected from a mineral's surface 198

lymph (LIHMF): tissue fluid that circulates in the lymphatic vessels

lymph system: the network of lymph vessels and lymph nodes

M

machine: a device that makes work easier, faster, more convenient, or better suited to human body structure by changing the speed an object moves, the direction, or amount of force

magma: molten material beneath Earth's surface 196

magnet: any object that produces a magnetic field around itself

magnetic field: space around a magnet in which magnetic forces can be detected

magnetism: the power to attract another magnet or certain types of metal

malleability (mal yuh BIHL ut ee): the ability of a material to be hammered, pressed, or rolled into a thin sheet

mammary (MAM uh ree) **glands:** milk-producing organs of female mammals 431

map projection: a method that is used to project latitude and longitude lines, points, and locations from a curved surface to a flat piece of paper 189

marijuana: a drug that is present in the plant *Cannabis sativa* and is both a stimulant and a depressant

marrow (MER oh): a soft tissue found in the cavities of bones 444

marsupials: mammals that give birth to very immature young, which continue their development in a pouch on the female's body

mass: the amount of matter in an object 35

mass movement: downhill movement of weathered materials due to gravity

mass number: the number of protons plus the number of neutrons in an atom 53

matter: anything that has mass and takes up space

meanders: the curves that are formed in a stream 237

mechanical (mih KAN ih kul) **advantage** (MA): the amount a machine can increase an effort force 121

mechanical energy: the kinetic energy and potential energy that cause objects to move 100

medulla (muh DUL uh): the part of the brain at the base of the skull that controls involuntary muscle activities

melting point: the temperature at which a material changes from a solid state to a liquid state 73

membrane: a thin plastic sheet that acts as a filter in one desalination process

menageries (muh NAJ uh ruhz): collections of animals for show

Mercator map projection: a map projection whereby polar areas appear larger than they actually are

meridians: lines drawn north and south at right angles to the equator

mesosphere (MEZ uh sfihr): the coldest layer of the atmosphere that extends from 50 to 85 km above Earth's surface 261

metabolism (muh TAB uh lihz um): the use of energy for all life processes 351

metals: chemical elements that are shiny, can be hammered, and can easily conduct electricity or thermal energy

metamorphic rocks: rocks that change in form due to increases in pressure and temperature 204

metamorphosis: a series of changes in the appearance and structures of an organism as it develops from an egg to an adult 426

meteorologist: a scientist who studies the weather 289

meteorology: the study of weather and the forces and processes that cause it

meter: the SI unit used for measuring length 31

microclimates: climates that involve small areas of Earth's surface 293

mid-ocean ridges: undersea mountain chains that are found near the middle of some oceans 324

***milli-*:** a prefix meaning one-thousandth

mineral: a natural, nonliving solid with a definite chemical makeup and crystal structure; a nutrient element used by the body in very small amounts 196

mitochondria (mite uh KAHN dree uh): rod-like cell parts that release energy for cell processes 350

mixed layer: the warm surface layer where wind and waves mix the water 302

mixture: a combination of substances that is formed without a chemical reaction 61

model: anything that helps you understand how a real object looks or works 8

molecule: a particle that forms when atoms of some elements share electrons 57

mollusks: invertebrates that have soft bodies, a strong muscle called a foot, and usually have a shell

moneran (muh NIHR un): a simple, one-celled organism that has no nucleus 357

monocotyledons: plants that have only one seed leaf 403

monotremes: mammals that produce shelled eggs

mosses: a group of nonvascular spore plants with thin leaves that grow from all around an upright or creeping stem

motion: the changing of position 130

motor neurons: neurons that carry impulses away from the central nervous system to effectors

movable joint: a joint that allows movement 448

mudflow: rapid downhill movement of materials occurring after heavy rains

muscle: a tissue that contracts or shortens, resulting in the movement of body parts 450

muscle fatigue: the result of the buildup of chemical wastes in a muscle

muscle tone: a continuous state of partial contraction 453

mushroom: the reproductive structure of a club fungus

mutualism (MYEW chuh lihz um): a relationship in which two organisms live together for mutual benefit 375

N

nekton (NEK tun): all forms of ocean life that swim 326

nephron: the filtering unit of the kidney 498

net force: force that results from unbalanced forces acting on an object; force that must be present if motion is to occur 97

neuron: a single nerve cell and the basic unit of the nervous system 464

neutral shoreline: a shoreline with a flat, broad beach that doesn't show features of a submerged or emergent shoreline

neutron: a particle that has no electric charge and that is located in the nucleus of an atom 51

newton: SI unit of force 36

Newton's first law of motion: states that an object at rest stays at rest, and an object in motion keeps moving at a constant velocity unless acted on by a net force 135

Newton's second law of motion: states that the acceleration of an object depends on the mass of the object and the net force acting on it 136

Newton's third law of motion: states that when one object exerts a force on a second object, the second object exerts an equal and opposite force on the first 140

nimbus: a dark grey cloud with ragged edges from which rain or snow continually falls

nodules: small swellings filled with nitrogen-fixing bacteria on the roots of legumes

nonclastic: sedimentary rock that is deposited from solution or by organic processes

nonmetals: chemical elements that are brittle, have dull surfaces, and are poor conductors

nonvascular plants: plants without xylem or phloem tissues

nuclear energy: energy released by changes within the nucleus of the atom

nuclear (NEW klee ur) **force:** force that holds protons and neutrons together in an atomic nucleus

nucleus (NEW klee us): central structure in an atom that contains protons and neutrons; a dense, rounded structure that controls the activities of the cell, 51, 351

nutrient: a substance in food that is used by the body for metabolism 506

nutrition: the study of how food is used by organisms

nymph: a stage in incomplete metamorphosis in which an immature insect resembles the adult

O

observation: the act of gathering information using the senses 8

occluded front: a boundary that forms when two cool air masses merge, forcing the warmer air between them to rise

oceanographers: scientists who study Earth's oceans

oceanography: the study of the oceans

ocean pollution: the introduction into the oceans of substances that produce a harmful change 333

ocean trench: a long, narrow trough formed where ocean floor collides with another section of ocean floor or a continent

orbit: the path of a revolving object 180

order: the category of organisms that groups similar families

organ: a structure composed of groups of tissues that work together 355

organic compound: a compound that contains carbon

organism (OR guh nihz um): a living thing 344

osmosis (ahs MOH sus): the process of diffusion of water molecules through a cell membrane 351

outwash: material deposited by glacial meltwater 245

ovary: the part of the female reproductive organ that contains ovules

overdose: the result of too much of a drug in the body 476

over-the-counter drugs (OTC): medications that can be bought without a doctor's prescription

ovule: a small structure that contains the egg of a seed plant 397

oxide: oxygen combined with one other element

ozone (OH zohn): a form of oxygen that absorbs most of the ultraviolet radiation that enters the atmosphere 164

P

parallels: lines of latitude

parasite: an organism that lives and feeds in or on another organism 372

Pascal's principle: pressure applied to an enclosed fluid will be felt equally throughout the fluid 158

peat: the first stage in coal formation

pedalfers: soils that contain large amounts of iron oxide and aluminum-rich clays 224

pedocals: soils rich in calcium carbonate 224

pendulum: a heavy object suspended so it can swing freely

penicillin (pen uh SIHL un): an antibiotic drug extracted from the hyphae of the fungus *Penicillium*

perennials: plants that live for many years

periodic table: an arrangement of the chemical elements in rows according to increasing atomic numbers 53

periosteum (per ee AHS tee um): a tough membrane that fits tightly over the outside of bone 443

peripheral nervous system: the part of the nervous system made up of all the nerves outside the brain and spinal cord 462

peristalsis: the series of muscular contractions that moves food through the digestive system 515

permeability: the ability of a soil to allow water to flow through it 225

perpendicular: a line that is at right angles to the horizon or to another line or plane

perpetual motion machine: a mechanical device that can produce work constantly with no net energy input 124

petals: leaflike structures that are often colorful and sweet smelling

phloem (FLOH em): vascular tissues that move food materials from the leaves to all parts of the plant 385

photosynthesis (foht oh SIHN thuh sus): the process in which the energy of sunlight is trapped by chlorophyll and used to make food 352

phylum (FI lum): the largest category in a kingdom

physical property: a characteristic that may be observed without changing the chemical composition of the material 50

physical science: the study of matter, forces, and energy

pistil: the female reproductive organ of a plant 400

pivot joint: a movable joint in which the round surface of one bone rotates in a ring of a second bone

placentals: mammals that give birth to young that have developed inside the female's body

plankton: microscopic organisms that drift in the oceans 326

plantlike protists: protists with cell walls and chloroplasts that enable them to make their own food

plasma: matter that consists of charged particles; the liquid portion of blood in which cells and platelets move 72, 490

platelets: cell fragments in blood that help blood to clot 490

polar easterlies: cold, dry, dense air currents located between about 60° and 90° north and south latitudes 270

polar map projections: a representation of Earth's surface made by placing a flat sheet of paper over Earth's pole and projecting points out from the surface of the globe

polar zone: a cold climate zone that extends from the poles to 66.5° north and south latitudes

pollen: a small grainlike structure that contains the sperm of a seed plant 397

pollination: the transfer of pollen from the male organ to the female organ of a seed plant 398

pollution (puh LEW shun): the effect caused by adding substances to the environment that are harmful to living organisms 368

polydrug use: the abuse of more than one drug at a time 476

porosity: a measure of the amount of a soil's volume that is composed of pores 225

position: the place or location where an object is in relation to a reference point 130

potential energy: the energy that an object has due to its position or condition 99

power: the work done during a given unit of time 114

precipitation: rain, snow, sleet, or hail that falls from the atmosphere to Earth 282

precision: the degrees of exactness with which the object is measured 42

predator (PRED ut ur): an animal that captures other animals for food 415

prescription drug: a drug that can be obtained only with a written instruction from a doctor

preserves: large natural areas of protected land

pressure: the force applied per unit of area 151

prevailing westerlies: winds located between about 30° and 60° latitude 270

prey: animals that are eaten by a predator 415

primates: placental mammals that use their hands and sometimes their feet for grasping and holding things

prime meridian: the 0° meridian that passes through Greenwich, England 186

problem: a situation that needs thought, planning, and skills to solve 17

problem-solving skills: methods used to solve problems

procedure: describes how an experiment will be done 9

producer: an organism that makes its own food 387

property: a quality or characteristic of matter

protein: an organic nutrient used for growth and repair of tissues 509

protist: a one-celled organism that has a nucleus 357

proton: a particle that has a positive electric charge and is located in the nucleus of an atom 51

protozoan (proht uh ZOH un): a protist that can move, has no cell wall, and cannot make its own food 369

pseudopod (SEWD uh pahd): the extension of cytoplasm in an amoeba 369

ptyalin (TI uh lin): an enzyme in saliva that acts on a complex carbohydrate such as starch and begins to break it down to simple sugars

pulley: a simple machine that can change the direction of and/or the amount of applied force

pulmonary circulation: the pathway that blood takes going from the heart to the lungs and back to the heart

pupa: the stage of complete metamorphosis in which an insect develops and changes from a larva to an adult

Q

quartz: a mineral composed of oxygen and silicon

R

radiant energy: a form of energy that travels in waves

radiation: the transfer of energy by waves 264

rain: small and large drops of water that collide and join to form raindrops large enough to fall to Earth

receptors: those parts of the nervous system that detect stimuli

red blood cells: disc-shaped cells in plasma that carry oxygen

reflex action: an involuntary action in response to a stimulus 465

regeneration (rih jen uh RAY shun): the repair and regrowth of a missing part of the body 425

relative humidity: amount of water vapor in a certain volume of air compared to the maximum amount of water vapor this air could hold at a given temperature 278

reproduction: the process by which organisms produce more organisms of the same kind

reptiles: cold-blooded vertebrates with scales, internal fertilization, and shelled eggs

resistance force: the force exerted on a machine in opposition to the effort force

respiration: the process by which food is broken down and energy is released 352

respiratory system: the system that brings oxygen into the body and expels carbon dioxide from the body 495

response: a change in the behavior of an organism as a result of a stimulus 345

revolution: the movement of one object around another 180

rhizome (RI zohm): an underground storage stem

risk: any situation that might be a threat to health or well-being 21

rock cycle: the way one rock changes to another and the processes by which these changes take place 208

rockfalls: downhill movements of rock caused by gravity 220

rocks: combinations of one or more minerals 202

rodents: the largest group of placental mammals

root: a plant structure that anchors the plant and takes in water and nutrients from the ground

rotation: the spinning of Earth about its axis 179

roundworms: an invertebrate that has a round, tubelike body that tapers to a point at each end

runoff: precipitation that flows along Earth's surface 235

rusts: parasitic club fungi that produce orange spores on plants

S

sac fungi: fungi that produce spores in a sac

safety symbol: a sign that alerts you to a particular danger within an activity 14

salinity: a measure of the dissolved solids in ocean water 300

saliva: a watery substance in the mouth that begins the process of digestion of carbohydrates 515

sand bar: a ridge of sand below the surface of the water

saprophyte (SAP ruh fite): an organism that lives and feeds in or on a dead organism 373

saturated: a solution that contains the maximum amount of solute for a given temperature

scales: small, hard, overlapping structures that cover and protect the skin of fish and reptiles

science: the knowledge of all the facts that are known about the world and the methods or processes used to learn or explain these facts 6

scientific notation: a system in which a number is expressed as the product of a factor and a power of ten 43

screw: a simple machine consisting of an inclined plane wound around a cylinder

sea cliff: a wall of rock along a coastline; produced by wave erosion

seamount: an undersea volcano

seawall: a barrier, usually made of rock, constructed to protect beaches from wave erosion 332

second: the SI unit for time measurement 38

sediment: loose Earth material or debris resulting from weathering

sedimentary rocks: rocks made of loose materials that have been cemented together 205

seed: a plant structure that contains and protects an undeveloped plant 386

segmented worms: invertebrates that have a tubelike body arranged in segments and complex digestive, circulatory, and nervous systems

seismic sea wave: ocean wave formed by an earthquake 310

selective breeding: the selection and mating of organisms that have desirable characteristics 391

sense organs: the eyes, ears, nose, mouth, and skin 466

sensory neurons: neurons that carry impulses from receptors to the central nervous system

sepals: leaflike organs that protect the flower when it is still a bud

sheeting: physical weathering in which outer layers of exposed rock expand and peel off

side effect: an unexpected and unwanted reaction to a drug 472

silicates: a group of minerals composed of silicon, oxygen, and one or more other elements

simple fracture: a break in a bone where the two pieces remain near each other

simple machines: devices (levers, pulleys, wheels and axles, inclined planes, wedges, and screws) that make work easier by changing the speed, direction, or amount of force

single displacement reaction: reaction in which one element from a compound displaces another 81

skeletal muscle: a muscle that moves the bones of the body 451

skeletal system: body system of bones and joints that provides support and protection to the body and allows the body to move 442

skeleton: a frame that shapes, supports, and protects internal organs

sleet: raindrops that freeze as they fall through a layer of air that has a temperature below −3°C

slime mold: a funguslike protist that resembles a different organism at each stage of its life cycle

small intestine: a 7 m long muscular tube where most digestion takes place and where nutrients are absorbed into the body

smooth muscle: an involuntary muscle found in the walls of the stomach, intestines, and blood vessels 451

smuts: parasitic club fungi that produce black spores on plants

snow: water vapor that changes directly to a solid and falls as single ice crystals or ice crystal combinations called snowflakes

soil: a mixture of weathered rock and organic matter 222

soil profile: a description of the layers that make up a soil 223

solar energy: radiant energy from the sun that travels in waves through space 101

solid: matter that is a crystalline material with a definite volume and shape 70

solstice: either of two points where the sun reaches its greatest distance north or south of the equator 184

solubility: the amount of solute a solvent can dissolve at a given temperature

solute (SAHL yewt): in a solution, the substance being dissolved 62

solution: a homogeneous mixture 62

solvent (SAHL vunt): in a solution, the substance in which a solute is dissolved 62

species (SPEE sheez): a group of similar organisms that can mate and produce young like themselves 359

speed: a measure of how far an object moves in a given period of time 131

sperm: a male sex cell

sphere: a round, three-dimensional object whose surface at all points is the same distance from its center 174

spinal cord: a narrow bundle of nerve fibers that extends down through the bony vertebral column 463

spiny-bodied animals: invertebrates with a skeleton of hard plates with spines inside the wall of the body

spits: long, narrow ridges of sand deposited at the mouth of an inlet or a bay by a longshore current 329

sponges: simple invertebrates that live at the bottom of oceans, rivers, or streams

spongy bone: bone material with open spaces

sporangium (spuh RAN jee um) **fungi:** fungi that produce spores in sporangia

spore: a reproductive structure that can develop into a new organism 370

sporozoan (spor uh ZOH un): a parasitic protozoan that has no means of movement

spring equinox: the first day of spring when the sun crosses the equator and night and day are equal in length

square meter: the standard SI unit for area 32

SSC: Superconducting Super Collider, a new type of particle accelerator

stack: an island of rock that can form if the top of a sea arch falls 329

stamens: male reproductive organs of a seed plant 400

standard: an exact quantity against which comparisons can be made 28

starch: a carbohydrate found in beans, peas, potatoes, and cereal grains that is not absorbed by cells

stationary front: a boundary that forms when either a warm front or a cold front stops moving forward

stem: a plant structure that supports the leaves and conducts materials between the roots and other parts of the plant

stimulant: a drug that speeds up the activity of the central nervous system and causes prolonged and increased activity at a synapse 473

stimulus (STIHM yuh lus): a change in the environment that affects an organism 345

stinging-celled animals: simple invertebrates that live in oceans, rivers, or streams

stomach: a saclike organ with muscular walls and many glands

stratosphere (STRAT uh sfihr): the second layer of the atmosphere 260

stratus: a layered cloud, often covering the whole sky, associated with light drizzle

streak: the color of a mineral in powdered form 198

stream: a body of flowing water 236

striations (stri AY shunz): scratches or grooves made by rocks embedded in glaciers; bands or stripes visible in muscle

sublimation: the change from a solid to a gas or a gas to a solid without becoming a liquid 74

submerged shoreline: a shoreline formed when sea level rises or the land sinks 331

submersible: a small, deep-diving submarine 321

substance: a kind of matter that is always the same in composition 50

sugars: simple carbohydrates that the body can absorb; sources of energy

summer solstice: the time of year when the Northern Hemisphere has its longest day and the Southern Hemisphere has its shortest day

surface currents: parts of the upper layer of the ocean that move continuously in a certain direction 305

suspension (suh SPEN chun): a heterogeneous mixture in which the particles of one material are supported in a liquid 61

synapse (SIHN aps): the small space between neurons

synthesis (SIHN thuh sus) **reaction:** a chemical change in which two or more elements or compounds combine to form one compound 80

system: a group of organs that function together 355

systemic (sihs TEM ihk) **circulation:** the pathway blood takes from the aorta to the body organs and back to the heart

T

tadpole: a larva that hatches from a frog's egg

taproot: a long, thick root in which food is stored

target tissue: tissue affected by a specific hormone 468

technology: the application of scientific discoveries 20

temperate zone: a climate zone between the tropics and the polar zones where weather changes with the seasons

temperature inversion: an upper level of warm air overlies cooler air and prevents upward movement

tendon: a tough band of tissue that connects muscles to bones 451

tentacles: armlike structures in stinging-celled animals and mollusks that surround the mouth opening and are used to capture prey

terminal moraines: ridges of till deposited at the front edge of a glacier

terminal velocity: the constant velocity reached by a falling object 139

theory: an explanation of how nature works 10

thermal energy: the total kinetic energy of the moving particles that make up an object 100

thermocline: the second layer of ocean water 302

thermosphere (THUR muh sfihr): the outer layer of the atmosphere that extends from about 85 kilometers above Earth's surface 261

thorax: the middle section of an insect body that has legs and wings

thunderstorms: storms that occur with thunder and lightning when warm, moist air masses move rapidly into colder, dryer layers of air 286

till: material deposited directly by the ice of a melting glacier 245

time zones: geographic areas having the same time

tissue: a group of cells of a similar type and function 355

tornado: a violent, whirling wind that moves in a narrow path over land 287

trachea: the windpipe; a tube leading from the mouth to the bronchi

trade winds: winds that blow toward the equator from about 30° north and south of the equator 270

transfusion: the transfer of blood belonging to one person into the blood stream of another person 490

transpiration: the movement of water out of a plant 389

tropical zone: a climate zone lying between 23.5° north and south latitude that receives the greatest amount of sunlight

tropism: movement or response of a plant to a stimulus

tropopause: the boundary that separates the troposphere from the next layer in the atmosphere 260

troposphere (TROP uh sfihr): the lowest layer of Earth's atmosphere 260

trough: the lowest point of a wave 311

tuber: an underground stem that stores food

U

undertow: a current formed when the water from breaking waves flows back into the ocean under incoming waves 313

unit: donated blood collected in a plastic sack that holds 450 mL

upwellings: dense, cold polar water that moves to the surface 310

ureter: one of the two tubes that connect the kidneys to the urinary bladder

urethra: a tube that leads from the urinary bladder to outside the body

urine: the waste liquid that remains in the collecting tube 498

V

vaccine: a solution of dead or weakened microbes that is injected into the body 348

variable: anything that changes in an experiment 12

vascular tissue: a tissue that conducts water and food to all parts of the plant 384

vein (VAYN): a blood vessel that carries blood toward the heart 485

velocity (vuh LAHS ut ee): the speed and direction of a moving object 132

vena cava (VEE nuh • CAY vah): the largest vein in the body

venom (VEH num): a poisonous chemical that affects the nervous system

ventricle: the chamber that pumps blood away from the heart

vertebrate (VERT uh brayt): an animal with a backbone 411

villi: fingerlike structures through which nutrients are absorbed into the blood stream 516

virus (VI rus): a complex particle that has features of both living and nonliving things 347

viscosity: the resistance of a liquid to flow 71

vitamin: an organic nutrient needed in very small amounts for cell metabolism 511

volcano: a mountain formed by the accumulation of material that has been forced out of Earth's interior onto its surface

volume: the amount of space occupied by an object 32

voluntary muscle action: a movement that can be controlled 450

W

warm-blooded vertebrate: a vertebrate that maintains a nearly constant body temperature even in cold or hot temperatures of the environment

warm front: a boundary that develops when a less dense, warm air mass meets a denser, colder air mass 286

warning: a weather advisory issued when severe weather conditions exist 287

warning colors: bright, bold color patterns on an animal that warn predators away 415

watch: a weather advisory issued when severe weather conditions are expected to occur soon 287

water: an essential nutrient for all body processes

water cycle: the continual movement of water from one place to another 235

water molds: a group of fungi that have spores with flagella for swimming through the water

water table: the upper surface of the zone saturated with groundwater 240

watt (W): work being done at the rate of one joule per second; the SI unit of power 115

wave height: the vertical distance between the crest and the trough 311

wavelength: the distance between the crests of two successive waves 311

wave period: the time between the passing of two successive wave crests 311

weather: the condition of the atmosphere over a short period of time 278

weathering: the physical and chemical processes that break down rocks at Earth's surface 216

weather satellites: satellites that monitor weather conditions 144

wedge: a simple machine made of two inclined planes placed back to back

weight: the measure of the force of gravity acting on an object 36

wheel and axle: a simple machine consisting of a large wheel fixed to a smaller axle that rotate together

white blood cells: cells produced in bone marrow, lymph nodes, and the spleen that fight infection

wind: the movement of air from one area to another 268

windbreaks: rows of trees planted between fields of crops to prevent wind erosion of soil

wind farms: windy areas where large numbers of wind turbines are clustered 271

wind turbine: modern windmills

wind vane: an instrument used to measure wind direction

winter solstice: the shortest day of the year

withdrawal: the reaction the body undergoes when use of a drug is stopped 476

woody stem: a type of stem that is hard and rigid

work: the result of a force moving an object through a distance 112

X

xylem (zī lum): vascular tissue that conducts water and nutrients from the roots to the rest of the plant 385

Y

yeasts: one-celled sac fungi

INDEX

2-3, Courtesy The Columbus Dispatch/Chris Russell; **2**(insert) R. Keeling/FPG; **4,** Doug Martin; **6,** Hickson-Bender Photography; **7,** Tom McGuire; **8**(tr) James Westwater, (bl) ICOM, (br) Subaru of America/*Discover Magazine*, Family Media, Inc.; **13**(t) Ted Rice, (b) Doug Martin; **15,** Ted Rice; **17,** Oeder/Bavaria/H. Armstrong Roberts; **18**(l) Bob Daemmrich Photography, (r) Ted Rice; **20,** Image Workshop; **21**(l) Courtesy, The Nutrasweet Company, (r) First Image; **22,** Paul Brown; **26,** Bob Daemmrich Photography; **28,** Ted Rice; **29,** First Image; **30,** Doug Martin; **33,** Ted Rice; **35, 36**(l) First Image, (r) Doug Martin; **38,** First Image; **39,** National Bureau of Standards; **40**(l) First Image, (r) Doug Martin; **41,** Ted Rice; **43,** First Image; **48,** Doug Martin/Bron-Shoe Company; **50,** John Barger; **52,** Historical Pictures Service, Chicago; **53, 57,** Doug Martin; **58,** First Image; **59**(tl) George H. Matchneer, (tr)(bl) Doug Martin, (br) Pictures Unlimited; **60,** First Image; **61,** Doug Martin; **62**(l) Ted Rice, (r) Aaron Haupt/Merrill; **63,** Doug Martin; **68,** Ted Rice; **70**(l) Debbie Dean, (r) First Image; **71,** First Image; **76,** Pictures Unlimited; **77,** Roger K. Burnard; **78,** FPG; **79,** First Image; **80,** E. R. Degginger; **81,** Tom Stack/Tom Stack & Assoc.; **83,** Jon Feingersh/Tom Stack & Assoc.; **84,** First Image; **89,** THE FAR SIDE © 1986 Universal Press Syndicate, reprinted with permission, all rights reserved; **90-91,** Frink/Waterhouse/H. Armstrong Roberts; **90**(insert) Edward A Robinson/Tom Stack & Assoc.; **92,** Ted Rice; **94**(l) H. Armstrong Roberts, (r) Image Workshop; **95**(tl) Tim Courlas, (tr) Ted Rice, (b) Aaron Haupt/Merrill; **97, 99,** First Image; **100,** Steve Lissau; **101,** Eric Neurath/Stock-Boston; **105,** D. G. Arnold/Light Images; **106,** Larry Burton Photography; **110,** Ted Rice; **112,** Latent Image; **115,** Pictures Unlimited; **118, 119, 120**(t) First Image, (b) Tim Courlas Photography; **122,** Paul Brown; **121,** Aaron Haupt/Merrill; **128,** Image Workshop; **130,** Richard Hutchings/Photo Edit; **134**(t) Insurance Institute For Highway Safety, (b) Richard Laird/FPG; **136,** Bill Everett/Tom Stack & Assoc.; **137,** Aaron Haupt/Merrill; **138,** Image Workshop; **139,** Hank Morgan/Science Source/Photo Researchers; **140,** NASA; **143**(l) Doug Martin, (r) Courtesy Daytona International; **144,** NASA; **148,** Doug Martin; **150, 151,** First Image; **155,** Joe Whitley/Taurus Photos; **157,** David Frazier; **159,** Roger K. Burnard; **160,** Doug Martin; **163,** EPA/Documerica; **164,** First Image; **168,** THE FAR SIDE © 1986 Universal Press Syndicate, reprinted with permission, all rights reserved; **170-171,** J. Robbins/FPG; **170**(insert) NASA/Grant Heilman; **172,** Ted Rice; **175**(t) Tersch, (b) Phil Degginger; **177**(t) Doug Martin, (b) Latent Image; **179,** David Frazier; **180,** R. J. Bennett/H. Armstrong Roberts; **184**(l) Doug Martin, (r) Frank Balthis; **189,** NASA; **194,** Linda Dufuerena from Grant Heilman; **196**(a,b,c) Ted Rice, (d) Salt Institute; **197,** Ted Rice; **198**(l) Doug Martin, (r) Ted Rice; **200,** Ted Rice; **202,** Collier/Condit; **203,** Ted Rice; **204**(a,b) Elaine Comer-Shay, (c) University of Houston, (d,e,f) Doug Martin; **205**(a) Craig Kramer, (b) University of Houston (c,d) Elaine Comer-Shay; **206**(l) University of Houston, (r) Nick Anspach; **210,** Elaine Comer-Shay; **214,** Ted Rice; **216**(l) First Image, (r) E. R. Degginger; **217**(tl) David M. Dennis, (tr) Pictures Unlimited, (b) Aaron Haupt/Merrill; **219**(l) Aaron Haupt/Merrill, (r) First Image; **220**(l) James Westwater, (tr) Grant Heilman, (br) Patricia Woeber/Light Image; **222,** First Image; **223,** Dr. George Hall/OSU; **227,**

Gene Alexander/Soil Conservation Service; **228,** Courtesy Ohio Disaster Services Agency; **232,** Ted Rice; **238,** K. Scholz/H. Armstrong Roberts; **243,** M. Timothy O'Keefe/Tom Stack & Assoc.; **244,** K. Reinhard/FPG; **245,** Richard Martin; **248,** Buck Campbell/FPG; **253,** Calvin & Hobbes © 1988 Universal Press Syndicate, reprinted with permission, all rights reserved; **254-255,** Ted Rice; **254** (insert) James Aimsworth; **256,** Doug Martin; **258,** file photo; **260,** Frank Balthis; **264**(tr) Latent Image, (l) Steve Vidler/Nawrocki Stock Photo, (br) Pictures Unlimited; **268**(l) Larry Hamill, (r) Aaron Haupt; **269,** First Image; **271**(l) David Frazier, (r) Robert Frerck/TSW-Click/Chicago; **272,** Bryan Roberts, John Blackler, Alan Fein, University of Sydney; **276,** Ted Rice; **278**(l) Roger K. Burnard, (c) Doug Martin, (r) Image Brokers; **279**(tr)(br) David M. Dennis, (bl) David Frazier; **280,** Aaron Haupt/Merrill; **282**(l) L&M Photo/FPG, (r) Thomas Hovland from Grant Heilman; **283,** James Westwater; **284,** Tom Algire/Tom Stack & Assoc.; **286,** Tracy Borland; **287**(t) Edi Ann Otto, (b) file photo; **290,** Courtesy, Don Burgess, National Severe Storm Center; **298,** Maurice Landre/National Audubon Society/Photo Researchers; **300,** Aaron Haupt/Merrill; **301,** S. Wuelpern, Leslie Salt Company; **302**(t) Anna Zuckerman/Photo Edit, (b) Frink/Waterhouse/H. Armstrong Roberts; **303,** George Dritsas/Light Images; **306,** Courtesy NOAA; **307,** Ted Rice; **310**(t) Zefa/H. Armstrong Roberts, (b) Musklin/FPG; **311,** Dr. William Haxby/Lamont-Doherty Geological Observatory; **312,** Runk/Schoenberger from Grant Heilman; **313,** Steve Lissau/H. Armstrong Roberts; **318,** Geoffrey Orth/Light Images; **320**(l) Historical Pictures Service, Chicago, (r) Victor S. Sotelo/DSDP/Scripps Institution of Oceanography; **321, 322,** Woods Hole Oceanographic Institution; **323,** from a painting by Heinrich Berann, Courtesy of Aluminum Company of America; **326**(t) E.R. Degginger, (b) Sharon Kurgis; **327,** Chris McLaughlin; **329**(t) Robert Perron, (b) Terraphotographics/BPS; **331**(t) NASA, (b) Tom Benoit/Light Images; **332**(t) Image Brokers, (b) Sylvia Schlender/Nawrocki Stock Photos; **334,** Ken Sakamoto/Black Star; **338,** THE FAR SIDE cartoon by Gary Larson is reprinted by permission of Chronicle Features, San Fransisco; **340-341,** Ted Rice; **340**(insert) Douglas Faulkner/Photo Researchers; **342,** Doug Martin; **344**(l) Lynn Stone, (r) Russ Lappa; **345**(l) Tom Branch/Photo Researchers, (r) Rich Brommer; **348,** Dombrowsk/Zefa/H. Armstrong Roberts; **355**(l) Paul Brown, (r) Kodansha; **356,** Latent Image; **357**(l) Biophoto Associates/ Photo Researchers, (r) Larry Hamill; **358,** Lynn Stone; **359,** Roger K. Burnard; **364,** Ted Rice; **366**(l) Runk/Schoenberger from Grant Heilman, (r) Animals Animals/G.I. Bernard; **367**(t) William E. Ferguson, (b) Pictures Unlimited; **368,** Animals Animals/Zig Leszczynski; **369,** Roger K. Burnard; **370,** Stephen J. Krasemann/DRK; **374**(l) Dwight R. Kuhn, (r) Stephen J. Krasemann/DRK; **377**(l) First Image, (r) Biophoto Associates/Photo Researchers; **382,** Doug Martin; **384**(l) Runk/Schoenberger from Grant Heilman, (r) First Image; **385**(l) William D. Popejoy, (r) A. Jungen/FPG; **386,** Pasieka/Zefa/H. Armstrong Roberts; **387,** First Image; **389,** Erika Klass/Light Images; **391,** USDA; **392,** Larry Roberts; **393,** Al Lowry/Photo Researchers; **395,** Pictures Unlimited; **396**(l) Roger K. Burnard, (r) Dwight R. Kuhn; **398**(l) Grant Heilman, (r) Michael P. Gadomski/Photo Researchers; **399,** First Image; **403**(l) USDA,